PRENTICE HALL

SCIENCE EXPLORER

Teacher's Edition

Chemical Interactions

Prentice Hall

Needham, Massachusetts
Upper Saddle River, New Jersey
Glenview, Illinois

ISBN 0-13-054095-1

2 3 4 5 6 7 8 9 10   05 04 03 02 01

Chart your own course.

15 motivational hardcover books make it easy for you to create your own curriculum; meet local, state, and national guidelines; and teach your favorite topics in depth.

Prepare your students with rich, motivating content...

Science Explorer is crafted for today's middle grades student, with accessible content and in-depth coverage of all the important concepts.

...and a wide variety of inquiry activities.

Motivational student- and teacher-tested activities reinforce key concepts and allow students to explore science concepts for themselves.

Check your compass regularly.

Science Explorer gives you more ways to regularly check student performance than any other program available.

Utilize a variety of tools.

Integrated science sections in every chapter and Interdisciplinary Explorations in every book allow you to make in-depth connections to other sciences and disciplines. Plus, you will find a wealth of additional tools to set your students on a successful course.

h rt th ours ou t ith 15 motivating books that easily match your curriculum.

Each book in the series contains:

- Integrated Science sections in every chapter
- Interdisciplinary Explorations for team teaching at the end of each book
- Comprehensive skills practice and application—assuring that you meet the National Science Education Standards and your local and state standards

EXPLORATION TOOLS: BASIC PROCESS SKILLS

Observing

Measuring

Calculating

Classifying

Predicting

Inferring

Graphing

Creating data tables

Communicating

LIFE SCIENCE TITLES

From Bacteria to Plants
1 Living Things
2 Viruses and Bacteria
3 Protists and Fungi
4 Introduction to Plants
5 Seed Plants

Animals
1 Sponges, Cnidarians, and Worms
2 Mollusks, Arthropods, and Echinoderms
3 Fishes, Amphibians, and Reptiles
4 Birds and Mammals
5 Animal Behavior

Cells and Heredity
1 Cell Structure and Function
2 Cell Processes and Energy
3 Genetics: The Science of Heredity
4 Modern Genetics
5 Changes Over Time

Human Biology and Health
1 Healthy Body Systems
2 Bones, Muscles, and Skin
3 Food and Digestion
4 Circulation
5 Respiration and Excretion
6 Fighting Disease
7 The Nervous System
8 The Endocrine System and Reproduction

Environmental Science
1 Populations and Communities
2 Ecosystems and Biomes
3 Living Resources
4 Land and Soil Resources
5 Air and Water Resources
6 Energy Resources

 Integrated Science sections in every chapter

Posing questions

Forming operational definitions

Developing hypotheses

Controlling variables

Interpreting data

Interpreting graphs

Making models

Drawing conclusions

Designing experiments

EARTH SCIENCE TITLES

Inside Earth
1 Plate Tectonics
2 Earthquakes
3 Volcanoes
4 Minerals
5 Rocks

Earth's Changing Surface
1 Mapping Earth's Surface
2 Weathering and Soil Formation
3 Erosion and Deposition
4 A Trip Through Geologic Time

Earth's Waters
1 Earth: The Water Planet
2 Fresh Water
3 Freshwater Resources
4 Ocean Motions
5 Ocean Zones

Weather and Climate
1 The Atmosphere
2 Weather Factors
3 Weather Patterns
4 Climate and Climate Change

Astronomy
1 Earth, Moon, and Sun
2 The Solar System
3 Stars, Galaxies, and the Universe

PHYSICAL SCIENCE TITLES

Chemical Building Blocks
1 An Introduction to Matter
2 Changes in Matter
3 Elements and the Periodic Table
4 Carbon Chemistry

Chemical Interactions
1 Chemical Reactions
2 Atoms and Bonding
3 Acids, Bases, and Solutions
4 Exploring Materials

Motion, Forces, and Energy
1 Motion
2 Forces
3 Forces in Fluids
4 Work and Machines
5 Energy and Power
6 Thermal Energy and Heat

Electricity and Magnetism
1 Magnetism and Electromagnetism
2 Electric Charges and Current
3 Electricity and Magnetism at Work
4 Electronics

Sound and Light
1 Characteristics of Waves
2 Sound
3 The Electromagnetic Spectrum
4 Light

Integrated Science sections in every chapter

Turn your students into science explorers with a variety of inquiry activities.

Motivational student- and teacher-tested activities reinforce key concepts and allow students to explore science concepts for themselves. More than 350 activities are provided for each book in the Student Edition, Teacher's Edition, Teaching Resources, Integrated Science Lab Manual, Inquiry Skills Activity Book, Interactive Student Tutorial CD-ROM, and *Science Explorer* Web Site.

STUDENT EDITION ACTIVITIES

Time

Long-term · 1 Class Period · 10–25 Minutes

Chapter Project
Opportunities for long-term inquiry—start of each chapter

Real-World Lab
Everyday application of science concepts—one per chapter

Skills Lab
In-depth practice of an inquiry skill—one per chapter

Sharpen Your Skills
Practice of a specific inquiry skill—two per chapter

Discover
Exploration and inquiry before reading—start of every lesson

Try This
Reinforcement of key concepts—two per chapter

Directed · Guided · Open-ended

Inquiry

Check your compass regularly with integrated assessment tools.

Prepare for state exams with traditional and performance-based assessment.

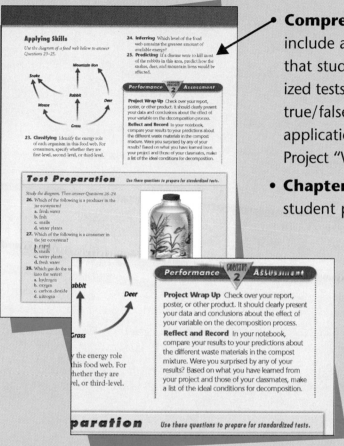

- **Comprehensive Chapter Reviews** include a wide range of question types that students will encounter on standardized tests. Types include multiple choice, enhanced true/false, concept mastery, visual thinking, skill application, and critical thinking. Also includes Chapter Project "Wrap Up."

- **Chapter Projects** contain rubrics that allow you to easily assess student progress.

- **Section Reviews** provide "Check your Progress" opportunities for the Chapter Project, as well as review questions for the section.

Additional *Science Explorer* assessment resources:
- **Computer Test Bank with CD-ROM**
- **Resource Pro® with Planning Express® CD-ROM**
- **Standardized Test Practice Book**
- **Interactive Student Tutorial CD-ROM**
- **On-line review activities** at www.phschool.com
  See pages T8 & T9 for complete product descriptions.

Self-assessment opportunities help students keep themselves on course.

- **Caption Questions** throughout the text assess critical thinking skills.

- **Checkpoint Questions** give students an immediate content check as new concepts are presented.

- **Interactive Student Tutorial CD-ROM** provides students with electronic self-tests, review activities, and Exploration activities.

- **www.phschool.com** provides additional support and on-line test prep.

Utilize a wide variety of tools.

Comprehensive print components

Easy-to-manage, book-specific teaching resources

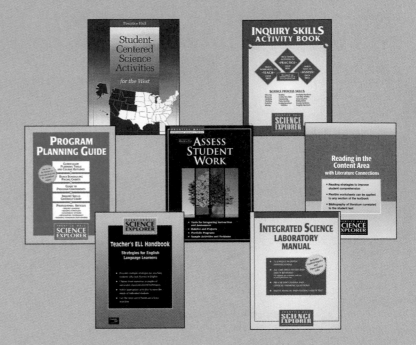

15 Teaching Resource Packages, each containing a Student Edition, Teacher's Edition, Teaching Resources with Color Transparencies, Interactive Student Tutorial CD-ROM, Guided Study Workbook, Guided Reading Audio CD, and correlation to the National Science Education Standards.

15 Teacher's Editions with a three-step lesson plan–Engage/Explore, Facilitate and Assess–that is ideal for reaching all students. Chapter planning charts make it easy to find resources, as well as to plan for block scheduling and team teaching.

15 Teaching Resource Books with Color Transparencies offer complete teacher support organized by chapter to make it easy for you to find what you need–when you need it.

15 Guided Reading Audio CD's and Audiotapes provide section summaries for students who need additional support. Available in English and Spanish.

15 Guided Study Workbooks containing blackline master worksheets for assessing, understanding, and developing study skills. Teacher's Edition available for each workbook.

Integrated Science Lab Manual SE & TE—74 in-depth labs covering the entire curriculum, with complete teaching support.

Inquiry Skills Activity Book—additional activities that introduce basic and advanced inquiry skills and reinforce skills on an as-needed basis.

Program Planning Guide—course outlines, block scheduling pacing charts, correlations, and more.

Reading in the Content Area with Literature Connections—provides students with additional strategies for successful reading.

Standardized Test Preparation Book—provides students with hints, tips, strategies, and practice to help them prepare for state and local exams.

How to Assess Student Work—professional articles and example activities that help you design assessments, use rubrics effectively, and develop a portfolio assessment program.

Student-Centered Science Activities—five regional activity books, for the Northeast, Southeast, Midwest, Southwest, and West.

How to Manage Instruction in the Block—comprehensive collection of block scheduling resources, from managing classroom routines to checklists for monitoring and assessing small group learning.

Teacher's ELL Handbook—provides multiple strategies for reaching English language learners. Select appropriate activities to meet the needs of individual students.

Program-wide technology resources

Interactive Student Tutorial CD-ROMs—
provide students with self-tests, helpful hints, and Exploration activities. Tests are scored instantly and contain a detailed explanation of all answers.

Probeware Lab Manual—provides detailed instructions for using probeware to perform selected labs. Blackline masters of labs are included.

Resource Pro® CD-ROM—electronic version of the Teaching Resources for all 15 books—ideal for creating integrated science lessons. Contains Planning Express software and Computer Test Bank. Organized by chapter to save you time.

Science Explorer Web Site—activities and teaching resources for every chapter at: www.phschool.com

Science Explorer Videotapes and Videodiscs —explore and visualize concepts through spectacular short documentaries containing computer animations. Videotapes also available in Spanish.

Lab Activity Videotapes—provide step-by-step instruction with students performing activities from every chapter. Promote and teach proper lab techniques, inquiry skills, and safety procedures.

iText—An interactive text version of the Student Edition at www.phschool.com containing animations, simulations, and videos to enhance student understanding and retention of concepts.

Interactive Physics—explore physics concepts with computer simulations that encourage what-if questions.

Computer Test Bank Book with CD-ROM— comprehensive collection of assessment resources containing Computer Test Bank Software with Dial-A-Test; provides you with unparalleled flexibility in creating tests.

ADDITIONAL RESOURCES

Materials Kits—Prentice Hall and Science Kit, Inc. have collaborated to develop a Consumable Kit and Nonconsumable Kit for each book. Ordering software makes it easy to customize!

Interdisciplinary Explorations—designed to help you connect science topics to social studies, math, language arts, and students' daily lives.

Options for Pacing *Chemical Interactions*

The Pacing Chart below suggests one way to schedule your instructional time. The **Science Explorer** program offers many other aids to help you plan your instructional time, whether regular class periods or **block scheduling.** Refer to the Chapter Planning Guide before each chapter to view all program resources with suggested times for Student Edition activities.

Pacing Chart

	Days	Blocks		Days	Blocks
Nature of Science: Saving the Ozone Layer	1	$\frac{1}{2}$	**1** Working With Solutions	5	$2\frac{1}{2}$
Chapter 1 Chemical Reactions			**2** Describing Acids and Bases	3	$1\frac{1}{2}$
Chapter 1 Project Keep a Chemical Change Log	Ongoing	Ongoing	**3** Acids and Bases in Solution	4	2
1 Matter and Changes in Matter	5	2–3	**4** Integrating Life Science: Digestion and pH	$1\frac{1}{2}$	$\frac{1}{2}$–1
2 Describing Chemical Reactions	4	2	Chapter 3 Review and Assessment	1	$\frac{1}{2}$
3 Controlling Chemical Reactions	4	2	**Chapter 4 Exploring Materials**		
4 Integrating Health: Fire and Fire Safety	$2\frac{1}{2}$	1–2	Chapter 4 Project Polymer Profiles	Ongoing	Ongoing
Chapter 1 Review and Assessment	1	$\frac{1}{2}$	**1** Polymers and Composites	$5\frac{1}{2}$	2–3
Chapter 2 Atoms and Bonding			**2** Integrating Technology: Metals and Alloys	$2\frac{1}{2}$	1–2
Chapter 2 Project Molecule Models	Ongoing	Ongoing	**3** Ceramics and Glass	$2\frac{1}{2}$	1–2
1 Inside an Atom	$2\frac{1}{2}$	1–2	**4** Radioactive Elements	4	2
2 Atoms in the Periodic Table	4	2	Chapter 4 Review and Assessment	1	$\frac{1}{2}$
3 Ionic Bonds	3	$1\frac{1}{2}$	Interdisciplinary Exploration: Bread on the Rise		
4 Covalent Bonds	$3\frac{1}{2}$	1–2			
5 Integrating Earth Science: Crystal Chemistry	$1\frac{1}{2}$	$\frac{1}{2}$–1			
Chapter 2 Review and Assessment	1	$\frac{1}{2}$			
Chapter 3 Acids, Bases, and Solutions					
Chapter 3 Project Make Your Own Indicator	Ongoing	Ongoing			

RESOURCE PRO®

The Resource Pro® CD-ROM is the ultimate scheduling and lesson planning tool. Resource Pro® allows you to preview all the resources in the *Science Explorer* program, organize your chosen materials, and print out any teaching resource. You can follow the suggested lessons or create your own, using resources from anywhere in the program.

Thematic Overview of *Chemical Interactions*

The chart below lists the major themes of *Chemical Interactions*. For each theme, the chart supplies a big idea, or concept statement, describing how a particular theme is taught in a chapter.

	Chapter 1	Chapter 2	Chapter 3	Chapter 4
Patterns of Change	A chemical reaction changes the original reactants into new substances with different properties.	Elements with similar properties are grouped together in the periodic table. Elements react in predictable ways, depending on the behavior of their electrons. Interactions of electrons between atoms lead to the formation of new substances.	Acids and bases cause predictable color changes when in contact with indicators. Acids and bases form salts when they react together. Food is broken down into smaller particles through mechanical and chemical digestion.	Ceramics, glass, and metal alloys may be made by heating their starting materials under controlled conditions. Radioactive elements decay into nonradioactive elements over time.
Scale and Structure	The types of atoms and how they are joined determine the properties of a substance. Elements combine to form compounds. Molecules are made of atoms bonded together.	Atoms are made of smaller particles—protons, neutrons and electrons. An element is made of atoms that all have the same number of protons, or atomic number.	When solutes dissolve in a solvent, the solute particles separate and become surrounded by solvent particles.	Polymers consist of long chains of monomers and differ based on the types of monomers from which they are made. The mixing of polymers to form composites yields products with the most desirable qualities of each material.
Unity and Diversity	Chemical reactions produce new substances. Different kinds of reactions may be classified by the types of changes substances undergo.	Chemical bonds form as a result of changes involving the electrons of atoms. The way in which these changes occur depends on the number of valence electrons and how they interact with other atoms.	Acids and bases produce ions in water solution. Acids produce hydrogen ions, and bases produce hydroxide ions.	Alloys have the properties of metals and always contain at least one metal. The properties of an alloy differ from the metals from which it is made and from other alloys.
Systems and Interactions	Increasing the temperature, concentration, or surface area of the reactants usually increases reaction rates. Catalysts can increase reaction rates.	Ionic bonding involves the transfer of electrons (one atom gains; the other loses) and the formation of ions. Covalent bonds involve the sharing of electrons and the formation of molecules.	The solubility of a solute varies with conditions, such as temperature and the nature of the solvent. Solutes affect the boiling points and freezing points of solvents. Acids and bases neutralize each other.	Polymer technologies and uses of radioactive materials may have undesirable side effects, such as waste disposal problems and health hazards.
Energy	Chemical reactions involve changes in energy that may be exothermic or endothermic. Activation energy is required to begin any reaction.		The solubility of most solid solutes may be changed by heating the solvent. Gases become less soluble when temperature is increased.	Nuclear decay releases radiation in the form of particles and high-energy waves.
Stability	Mass is always conserved in chemical reactions.	The reactivity of an element depends on the number of its valence electrons. Bonds between atoms form when the result is more stable structures.		Many polymers do not break down in the environment, so they last a long time unchanged. Unstable atomic nuclei undergo nuclear decay.
Modeling	Chemical equations use symbols and formulas to represent changes in substances during reactions.	Electron dot models can be used to compare atoms and ions of different elements, and to represent molecules.		

Inquiry Skills Chart

The Prentice Hall *Science Explorer* program provides comprehensive teaching, practice, and assessment of science skills, with an emphasis on the process skills necessary for inquiry. The chart lists the skills covered in the program and cites the page numbers where each skill is covered.

Basic Process SKILLS				
	Student Text: Projects and Labs	Student Text: Activities	Student Text: Caption and Review Questions	Teacher's Edition: Extensions
Observing	12–13, 22–23, 38–39, 70–71, 78–79, 102–103, 110–111	14, 24, 27, 32, 40, 55, 63, 65, 72, 80, 83, 90, 96, 98, 104, 112, 118, 123, 128, 131, 150	25, 73	16–18, 35, 51, 63, 68, 81, 84, 92, 114, 130
Inferring	12–13, 102–103	18, 32, 63, 65, 104, 112, 128, 150	24, 77, 135, 143	16, 20, 27, 33, 60, 68, 84, 86–87, 92, 100, 118, 124, 126, 130, 136
Predicting	22–23, 38–39, 58, 88–89, 102–103, 120–121, 140	36, 37, 50, 72, 87, 98, 133, 135, 150	47, 77, 87, 95, 101, 106, 109, 129–130	15, 26, 30, 36, 53, 81, 84–85, 99, 101
Classifying	12–13, 22–23, 110–111	56, 57, 83, 90, 118, 127, 151	21, 29, 31, 47, 60, 77, 81, 143	34, 82, 91, 124
Making Models	48–49, 58, 140	24, 27, 50, 59, 74, 133, 151	109	15, 28, 52, 54, 57, 61, 66, 98, 113, 117, 136
Communicating	12–13, 22–23, 38–39, 48–49, 78–79, 88–89, 110–111	34, 43, 44, 53, 68, 92, 115, 117, 122, 127, 131, 138, 151	46, 76, 142	14–15, 19, 25, 30, 34, 36, 40, 42, 50, 55, 61, 73, 80, 82, 84, 86, 90, 93, 99–100, 114, 128, 137
Measuring	38–39, 102–103	27, 36, 50, 128, 152–153		26, 36, 84, 99
Calculating	38–39, 58, 140	24, 28, 36, 50, 118, 128, 137, 153	57, 77, 108, 143	36, 136–137
Creating Data Tables	12–13, 22–23, 38–39, 58, 70–71, 88–89, 102–103, 110–111, 120–121, 140	83, 160	37	99, 137
Graphing	38–39, 58, 88–89, 140	85, 160–162		36, 118
Advanced Process SKILLS				
Posing Questions	12–13	55, 154	77	
Developing Hypotheses	38–39, 88–89, 120, 121	40, 123, 154	109	84, 114, 137
Designing Experiments	38–39, 70–71, 78–79, 88–89, 102–103, 110–111, 120–121	36, 67, 86, 155		35, 81, 84, 99, 114, 137

Advanced Process SKILLS (continued)

	Student Text: Projects and Labs	Student Text: Activities	Student Text: Caption and Review Questions	Teacher's Edition: Extensions
Controlling Variables	38–39, 70–71, 78–79, 88–89, 120–121	67, 86, 155		137
Forming Operational Definitions	12–13	96, 155		
Interpreting Data	22–23, 38–39, 58, 70–71, 78–79, 88–89, 102–103, 140	36, 55, 62, 85, 98, 155	47	85
Drawing Conclusions	38–39, 70–71, 88–89, 102–103, 120–121	83, 155	109, 119	53, 84, 99, 114

Critical Thinking SKILLS

	Student Text: Projects and Labs	Student Text: Activities	Student Text: Caption and Review Questions	Teacher's Edition: Extensions
Comparing and Contrasting	22–23, 48–49, 78–79, 102–103, 110–111, 120–121	32, 36, 44, 80, 83, 104, 122, 156	69, 74, 84, 95, 109, 114, 143	74, 81, 93, 114, 134
Applying Concepts	38–39, 58, 88–89, 102–103, 140	24, 80, 156	16, 30–31, 41, 47, 51, 54, 57, 77, 91, 109, 124, 127, 131–132, 143	20, 29, 51, 62, 64, 66, 83, 97, 100, 126
Interpreting Diagrams, Graphs Photographs, and Maps		55, 145, 147, 156	17, 28, 33, 40, 54, 66, 82, 99–100, 105, 109, 113, 136, 143	19, 57, 61, 85, 93–94, 125
Relating Cause and Effect	12–13, 38–39, 88–89	37, 123, 128, 146, 157	35, 37, 47, 85, 87	
Making Generalizations	12–13, 22–23, 58	157	63, 77, 97, 126, 132	26
Making Judgments	102–103, 120–121	44, 122, 157	42–43, 119, 139, 143	
Problem Solving	22–23, 70–71, 88–89, 102–103, 120–121	122, 157	27, 47, 64, 77, 127	30, 41, 118

Information Organizing SKILLS

	Student Text: Projects and Labs	Student Text: Activities	Student Text: Caption and Review Questions	Teacher's Edition: Extensions
Concept Maps		158	46, 108	72, 112, 128
Compare/ Contrast Tables		158	142	134
Venn Diagrams		159	76	128
Flowcharts		159		60, 104, 128
Cycle Diagrams		159		40, 128

The *Science Explorer* program provides additional teaching, reinforcement, and assessment of skills in the Inquiry Skills Activities Book and the Integrated Science Laboratory Manual.

Throughout the *Science Explorer* program, every effort has been made to keep the materials and equipment *affordable, reusable,* and *easily accessible.*

The *Science Explorer* program offers an abundance of activity options so you can pick and choose those activities that suit your needs. To help you order supplies at the beginning of the year, the Master Materials List cross-references the materials by activity. If you prefer to create your list electronically, you can use the Materials List CD-ROM.

There are two kits available for each book of the *Science Explorer* program: a Consumable Kit and a Nonconsumable Kit. These kits are produced by **Science Kit and Boreal Laboratories,** the leader in providing science kits to schools. Prentice Hall and Science Kit collaborated throughout the development of *Science Explorer* to ensure that the equipment and supplies in the kits precisely match the requirements of the program activities.

The kits provide an economical and convenient way to get all of the materials needed to teach each book. For each book, Science Kit also offers the opportunity to buy equipment and safety items individually. For additional information about ordering materials to accompany *Science Explorer,* please call:

1-800-848-9500

or access the *Science Explorer* Internet site at: **www.phschool.com**

Master Materials List

Consumable Materials

*	Description	Quantity per class	Textbook Section(s)	*	Description	Quantity per class	Textbook Section(s)
C	Aluminum Foil, Roll, 12" × 25'	1	1-1 (Lab)	C	Epsom Salt, 500 g	1	2-4 (Lab)
C	Ammonia Solution, 2 M, 500 mL	1	3-2 (DIS) 3-3 (DIS)	SS	Fabric	5	4-1 (Lab)
SS	Antacid, Liquid, 30 mL, Various Brands	5	3-3 (Lab)	C	Filter Paper, 11 cm Diam, Pkg/100	1	1-3 (Lab)
C	Bag, Plastic Zip Lip, 6" × 8" (1 qt)	5	4-2 (DIS)	SS	Fruit Juice	1	3-1 (TT)
C	Baking Soda, 454 g	1	1-1 (DIS) 1-4 (DIS) 2-4 (Lab) 3-1 (TT) 3-2 (DIS)	C	Gelatin, Box of 4 Packets	1	1-3 (SYS)
				SS	Glue, White, 4 oz	1	4-1 (DIS)
				SS	Graph Paper, Sheet	10	3-1 (SYS) 4-4 (Lab)
C	Battery, Carbon Zinc, AA, 1.5 V	10	4-3 (TT)	SS	Hand Cream	1	3-1 (TT)
C	Battery, Size D	10	2-4 (Lab)	C	Hydrochloric Acid, 1 L, 1.0 M	1	1-1 (Lab) 3-3 (Lab)
C	Borax, 4 oz	1	4-1 (DIS)	C	Hydrogen Peroxide, 3%, 230 mL	1	1-3 (Lab) 2-4 (Lab)
SS	Bread, Crusty	5	3-4 (DIS)				
C	Bubble Wrap, 6" × 12"	5	4-1 (Lab)	SS	Ice, Bucket	1	3-1 (Lab)
C	Bulb, Miniature, #14 (2.47 V)	5	2-4 (Lab)	C	Iodine (Starch Test) Reagent Solution, 100 mL	1	1-3 (DIS) 4-1 (Lab)
C	Candles, Birthday, Pkg/36	1	1-1 (Lab) 1-4 (DIS)	C	Lemon Juice, 15 oz	1	3-2 (DIS) 3-3 (DIS)
SS	Cardboard	5	4-1 (Lab)				
C	Chalk, White, Pkg/12	1	3-1 (TT)	C	Limewater Solution, 500 mL	1	1-1 (TT)
C	Clay, Modeling (Cream), lb (water-resistant)	1	1-1 (Lab) 1-4 (DIS)	C	Litmus Test Paper, Blue, Vial/100	1	3-2 (DIS)
				C	Litmus Test Paper, Red, Vial/100	1	3-2 (DIS)
C	Cup, Plastic, Clear, Cocktail, 9 oz	50	1-1 (DIS) 1-1 (TT) 1-1 (Lab) 1-3 (DIS) 2-3 (TT) 3-1 (DIS) 3-1 (TT) 3-3 (DIS) 3-3 (TT) 3-3 (Lab) 4-1 (DIS) 4-1 (Lab) 4-4 (Lab)	SS	Liver Preparation (Catalase)	1	1-3 (Lab)
				C	Matches, Wood Safety, Box/30	5	1-1 (Lab) 1-4 (DIS)
				C	Methyl Orange, 0.1% Indicator Solution, 100 mL	1	3-3 (Lab)
				SS	Milk, Powdered Skim	1	2-4 (Lab)
				C	Nail, Small, 2.5 cm	5	4-2 (DIS)
				C	Nails, 2.5 cm, Pkg/50	1	4-2 (DIS)
				C	Oil, Vegetable, 16 oz	1	2-4 (DIS) 2-4 (Lab)
				SS	Orange Juice	1	2-4 (Lab) 3-2 (DIS)
C	Cupric Sulfate, 500 g, Science Grade Powder	1	1-1 (Lab)				
C	Detergent, Household, 14.7 oz (dish detergent)	1	2-4 (DIS) 3-2 (DIS)	SS	Paper Towel Roll (120 sheets)	1	4-2 (DIS) 4-3 (DIS)
SS	Ecofoam	5	4-1 (Lab)	SS	Paper, Sheet	15	2-1 (DIS) 4-1 (Lab) 4-4 (DIS)
SS	Eggs, Hard-boiled (Optional)	5	4-1 (Lab)	C	Peanuts, Foam, Pkg/200	1	4-1 (Lab)

KEY: **DIS**: Discover; **SYS**: Sharpen Your Skills; **TT**: Try This; **Lab**: Lab
* Items designated **C** are in the Consumable Kit, **NC** are in the Nonconsumable Kit, and **SS** are School Supplied.

Quantities based on 5 lab groups per class.

Master Materials List

Consumable Materials (cont.)

*	Description	Quantity per class	Textbook Section(s)	*	Description	Quantity per class	Textbook Section(s)
C	Pepper, 2 oz	1	3-1 (DIS)	C	Soap, Ivory, Bar	1	3-1 (TT)
SS	Pencil	5	2-3 (TT)	C	Sodium Carbonate Anhydrous, 500 g, Science Grade Granular	1	1-1 (Lab)
SS	Pencils, Colored, Pkg/12	5	4-4 (Lab)				
C	pH Test Paper—Wide Range, 100/Vial, 1/4" × 2"	5	3-3 (TT)	C	Sugar, Granulated, 454 g	1	1-1 (Lab) 2-4 (Lab)
SS	Popcorn	1	4-1 (Lab)	SS	Tape, Masking, 3/4" × 60 yd	1	4-1 (Lab)
SS	Red Cabbage Juice	1	3-3 (DIS)	C	Thread, White, 200 yd Spool (polyester)	1	2-3 (TT)
C	Salt, Kosher, lb	1	3-1 (Lab)				
C	Salt, Non-Iodized, 737 g	2	2-3 (TT) 2-4 (Lab) 3-1 (DIS) 3-1 (Lab) 3-2 (DIS) 4-2 (DIS)	C	Tyvek	5	4-1 (Lab)
				C	SS	3	1-1 (DIS) 1-4 (DIS) 2-4 (Lab) 3-2 (DIS)
C	Salt, Rock, lb	1	2-3 (TT) 2-5 (DIS) 3-1 (Lab)	C	Vitamin C (l-Ascorbic Acid) 25 g, Science Grade Powder	1	1-3 (DIS)
				SS	Water, Carbonated, 5 mL	5	1-1 (TT)
C	Sawdust, lb Bag	1	4-1 (Lab)	SS	Wood Shavings	5	4-1 (Lab)

Nonconsumable Materials

*	Description	Quantity per class	Textbook Section(s)	*	Description	Quantity per class	Textbook Section(s)
NC	Battery Holder w/Fahnestock Clips, D-Cell	10	2-4 (Lab)	NC	Cylinder, PP Graduated, 100 mL	5	2-4 (Lab) 3-1 (Lab)
NC	Beaker, Pyrex Low Form, 100 mL	5	2-4 (Lab) 3-1 (Lab)	NC	Dropper, Plastic	15	3-2 (DIS) 3-3 (DIS) 3-3 (TT) 3-3 (Lab)
NC	Bolt, Short Round Head, 10–32, 2"	25	1-2 (TT) 4-2 (DIS)				
NC	Bowl, Opaque, 2 L, 6-1/4" Diam. × 4-1/4" High	5	1-1 (DIS) 1-3 (Lab) 4-3 (DIS) 4-4 (DIS)	NC	Dropping Bottle, Barnes, 30 mL	5	1-1 (Lab) 1-3 (DIS)
				NC	Fiber Optic Cable, 2 m Piece	2	4-3 (TT)
NC	Checkers, Pkg/24	5	2-3 (DIS)	NC	Flashlight, Penlight	5	4-3 (TT)
SS	Coins, Assorted	120	1-2 (DIS)	SS	Flower Pot, Clay, Unglazed	5	4-3 (DIS)
SS	Compass with Pencil	5	2-2 (Lab)	SS	Flower Pot, Clay, Glazed	5	4-3 (DIS)
NC	Cup, Polypropylene Measuring, 8 oz	5	1-4 (DIS)	NC	Forceps, Student, 115 mm, Straight	5	1-3 (Lab)
NC	Cylinder, PP Graduated, 10 × 0.2 mL	5	1-1 (TT) 1-1 (Lab) 3-1 (Lab)	SS	Glass	5	1-4 (DIS)
				SS	Household Materials for pH Testing	5	3-3 (TT)

KEY: **DIS**: Discover; **SYS**: Sharpen Your Skills; **TT**: Try This; **Lab**: Lab
* Items designated **C** are in the Consumable Kit, **NC** are in the Nonconsumable Kit, and **SS** are School Supplied.

Nonconsumable Materials (cont.)

*	Description	Quantity per class	Textbook Section(s)
NC	Jar, Plastic, 60 mL	5	2-4 (DIS)
NC	Knife, Plastic	5	1-3 (SYS)
NC	Lid, Metal, 53 mm, Screw Type	5	2-4 (DIS)
NC	Light Socket, Mini w/Fahn. Clips	5	2-4 (Lab)
NC	Magnifying Glass, 3x, 6x	5	2-5 (DIS) 4-1 (Lab)
NC	Nut, Hex, Zinc Plated, 3/16"	25	1-2 (TT)
SS	Pennies	500	4-4 (Lab)
SS	Ruler, Plastic, 12"/30 cm	5	2-1 (DIS) 4-4 (DIS)
SS	Scissors	5	4-1 (Lab) 4-4 (DIS)
NC	Spoon, Metal Tablespoon	5	1-4 (DIS) 2-5 (DIS) 4-1 (DIS)
NC	Spoons, Plastic, Pkg/24	1	1-1 (DIS) 1-1 (Lab) 1-3 (DIS) 2-3 (TT) 2-4 (Lab) 3-1 (DIS) 3-1 (TT) 3-1 (Lab) 3-3 (TT)
NC	Stirring Rod, Glass, 5 × 150 mm	5	3-1 (Lab)
NC	Stopper, Rubber, Size 2, 1-Hole, lb	1	1-3 (Lab)
NC	Stopper, Rubber, Size 2, Solid, lb	1	3-1 (Lab)
NC	Stopwatch, Electronic LED	5	1-3 (Lab) 3-1 (Lab) 4-1 (Lab)
NC	Test Tube Support, Wood, Holds 6-21 mm tubes, w/6 drying pins	5	3-1 (Lab)
NC	Test Tube, 18 × 150 mm, 27 mL	15	1-3 (Lab) 3-1 (Lab)
NC	Thermometer, Red Liquid, −20° to 110°C, Partial Immersion to 76 mm	5	1-3 (DIS) 3-1 (SYS) 3-1 (Lab) 4-1 (Lab)
NC	Tongs, Flask and Test Tube	5	1-1 (Lab)
SS	Weights (or Books)	30	4-1 (Lab)
NC	Wire, Insulated Copper, 22 Gauge, 25 m (4 oz. Spool)	1	2-4 (Lab)

Equipment

*	Description	Quantity per class	Textbook Section(s)
SS	Apron, Vinyl	30	1-1 (TT) 1-1 (Lab) 1-3 (DIS) 1-3 (Lab) 2-4 (Lab) 3-2 (DIS) 3-3 (DIS) 3-3 (TT) 3-3 (Lab) 4-1 (Lab)
SS	Balance, Triple Beam	5	1-2 (TT) 3-1 (SYS) 3-1 (Lab) 4-1 (Lab) 4-3 (DIS)
SS	Calculator	5	2-2 (Lab)
SS	Goggles, Chemical Splash - Class Set	1	1-1 (DIS) 1-1 (TT) 1-1 (Lab) 1-3 (DIS) 1-3 (Lab) 1-4 (DIS) 2-4 (Lab) 2-5 (DIS) 3-1 (TT) 3-1 (Lab) 3-2 (DIS) 3-3 (DIS) 3-3 (TT) 3-3 (Lab) 4-1 (DIS) 4-1 (Lab)
SS	Hot Plate	5	3-1 (SYS) 3-1 (Lab)

KEY: **DIS**: Discover; **SYS**: Sharpen Your Skills; **TT**: Try This; **Lab**: Lab
* Items designated **C** are in the Consumable Kit, **NC** are in the Nonconsumable Kit, and **SS** are School Supplied.

PRENTICE HALL SCIENCE EXPLORER

Chemical Interactions

Book-Specific Resources

Student Edition
Annotated Teacher's Edition
Teaching Resources with Color Transparencies
Consumable and Nonconsumable Materials Kits
Guided Reading Audio CDs
Guided Reading Audiotapes
Guided Reading and Study Workbook
Guided Reading and Study Workbook, Teacher's Edition
Lab Activity Videotapes
Science Explorer Videotapes
Science Explorer Web Site at **www.phschool.com**

Program-Wide Resources

Computer Test Bank Book with CD-ROM
How to Assess Student Work
How to Manage Instruction in the Block
Inquiry Skills Activity Book
Integrated Science Laboratory Manual
Integrated Science Laboratory Manual, Teacher's Edition
Interactive Student Tutorial CD-ROM
Prentice Hall Interdisciplinary Explorations
Probeware Lab Manual
Product Testing Activities by Consumer Reports™
Program Planning Guide
Reading in the Content Area with Literature Connections
Resource Pro® CD-ROM (Teaching Resources on CD-ROM)
Science Explorer Videodiscs
Standardized Test Preparation Book
Student-Centered Science Activity Books
Teacher's ELL Handbook: Strategies for English Language Learners

Spanish Resources

Spanish Student Edition
Spanish Guided Reading Audio CDs with Section Summaries
Spanish Guided Reading Audiotapes with Section Summaries
Spanish Science Explorer Videotapes

Science Explorer Student Editions

From Bacteria to Plants

Animals

Cells and Heredity

Human Biology and Health

Environmental Science

Inside Earth

Earth's Changing Surface

Earth's Waters

Weather and Climate

Astronomy

Chemical Building Blocks

Chemical Interactions

Motion, Forces, and Energy

Electricity and Magnetism

Sound and Light

Acknowledgments

Acknowledgment for pages 148–149: Excerpt from *Grandma Always Made the Bread* by Janet Knickerbocker. Copyright © 1995 by Countryside & Small Stock Journal.

ISBN 0-13-054094-3
2 3 4 5 6 7 8 9 10   05 04 03 02 01

Cover: The chemical reactions of fireworks fill a night sky with color and beauty.

Teacher's Edition ISBN 0-13-054095-1

Program Authors

Michael J. Padilla, Ph.D.
Professor
Department of Science Education
University of Georgia
Athens, Georgia

Michael Padilla is a leader in middle school science education. He has served as an editor and elected officer for the National Science Teachers Association. He has been principal investigator of several National Science Foundation and Eisenhower grants and served as a writer of the National Science Education Standards.

As lead author of *Science Explorer,* Mike has inspired the team in developing a program that meets the needs of middle grades students, promotes science inquiry, and is aligned with the National Science Education Standards.

Ioannis Miaoulis, Ph.D.
Dean of Engineering
College of Engineering
Tufts University
Medford, Massachusetts

Martha Cyr, Ph.D.
Director, Engineering
    Educational Outreach
College of Engineering
Tufts University
Medford, Massachusetts

Science Explorer was created in collaboration with the College of Engineering at Tufts University. Tufts has an extensive engineering outreach program that uses engineering design and construction to excite and motivate students and teachers in science and technology education.

Faculty from Tufts University participated in the development of *Science Explorer* chapter projects, reviewed the student books for content accuracy, and helped coordinate field testing.

CHAPTER PROJECT

Book Authors

David V. Frank, Ph. D.
Head, Department of Physical Sciences
Ferris State University
Big Rapids, Michigan

John G. Little
Science Teacher
St. Mary's High School
Stockton, California

Steve Miller
Science Writer
State College, Pennsylvania

Contributing Writers

Mary Sue Burns
Science Teacher
Pocahontas County
    High School
Dunmore,
    West Virginia

Peter Kahan
Former Science Teacher
Dwight-Englewood
    School
Englewood,
    New Jersey

Thomas L. Messer
Science Teacher
Cape Cod Academy
Osterville,
    Massachusetts

Linda Shoulberg
Science Teacher
Millbrook High School
Raleigh,
    North Carolina

Thomas R. Wellnitz
Science Teacher
The Paideia School
Atlanta, Georgia

Reading Consultant

Bonnie B. Armbruster, Ph.D.
Department of Curriculum
    and Instruction
University of Illinois
Champaign, Illinois

Interdisciplinary Consultant

Heidi Hayes Jacobs, Ed.D.
Teacher's College
Columbia University
New York, New York

Safety Consultants

W. H. Breazeale, Ph.D.
Department of Chemistry
College of Charleston
Charleston, South Carolina

Ruth Hathaway, Ph.D.
Hathaway Consulting
Cape Girardeau, Missouri

Tufts University Program Reviewers

Content Reviewers

Teacher Reviewers

Stephanie Anderson
Sierra Vista Junior
    High School
Canyon Country, California

John W. Anson
Mesa Intermediate School
Palmdale, California

Pamela Arline
Lake Taylor Middle School
Norfolk, Virginia

Lynn Beason
College Station Jr. High School
College Station, Texas

Richard Bothmer
Hollis School District
Hollis, New Hampshire

Jeffrey C. Callister
Newburgh Free Academy
Newburgh, New York

Judy D'Albert
Harvard Day School
Corona Del Mar, California

Betty Scott Dean
Guilford County Schools
McLeansville, North Carolina

Sarah C. Duff
Baltimore City Public Schools
Baltimore, Maryland

Melody Law Ewey
Holmes Junior High School
Davis, California

Sherry L. Fisher
Lake Zurich Middle
    School North
Lake Zurich, Illinois

Melissa Gibbons
Fort Worth ISD
Fort Worth, Texas

Debra J. Goodding
Kraemer Middle School
Placentia, California

Jack Grande
Weber Middle School
Port Washington, New York

Steve Hills
Riverside Middle School
Grand Rapids, Michigan

Carol Ann Lionello
Kraemer Middle School
Placentia, California

Jaime A. Morales
Henry T. Gage Middle School
Huntington Park, California

Patsy Partin
Cameron Middle School
Nashville, Tennessee

Deedra H. Robinson
Newport News Public Schools
Newport News, Virginia

Bonnie Scott
Clack Middle School
Abilene, Texas

Charles M. Sears
Belzer Middle School
Indianapolis, Indiana

Barbara M. Strange
Ferndale Middle School
High Point, North Carolina

Jackie Louise Ulfig
Ford Middle School
Allen, Texas

Kathy Usina
Belzer Middle School
Indianapolis, Indiana

Heidi M. von Oetinger
L'Anse Creuse Public School
Harrison Township, Michigan

Pam Watson
Hill Country Middle School
Austin, Texas

Activity Field Testers

Nicki Bibbo
Russell Street School
Littleton, Massachusetts

Connie Boone
Fletcher Middle School
Jacksonville Beach, Florida

Rose-Marie Botting
Broward County
    School District
Fort Lauderdale, Florida

Colleen Campos
Laredo Middle School
Aurora, Colorado

Elizabeth Chait
W. L. Chenery Middle School
Belmont, Massachusetts

Holly Estes
Hale Middle School
Stow, Massachusetts

Laura Hapgood
Plymouth Community
    Intermediate School
Plymouth, Massachusetts

Sandra M. Harris
Winman Junior High School
Warwick, Rhode Island

Jason Ho
Walter Reed Middle School
Los Angeles, California

Joanne Jackson
Winman Junior High School
Warwick, Rhode Island

Mary F. Lavin
Plymouth Community
    Intermediate School
Plymouth, Massachusetts

James MacNeil, Ph.D.
Concord Public Schools
Concord, Massachusetts

Lauren Magruder
St. Michael's Country
    Day School
Newport, Rhode Island

Jeanne Maurand
Glen Urquhart School
Beverly Farms, Massachusetts

Warren Phillips
Plymouth Community
    Intermediate School
Plymouth, Massachusetts

Carol Pirtle
Hale Middle School
Stow, Massachusetts

Kathleen M. Poe
Kirby-Smith Middle School
Jacksonville, Florida

Cynthia B. Pope
Ruffner Middle School
Norfolk, Virginia

Anne Scammell
Geneva Middle School
Geneva, New York

Karen Riley Sievers
Callanan Middle School
Des Moines, Iowa

David M. Smith
Howard A. Eyer Middle School
Macungie, Pennsylvania

Derek Strohschneider
Plymouth Community
    Intermediate School
Plymouth, Massachusetts

Sallie Teames
Rosemont Middle School
Fort Worth, Texas

Gene Vitale
Parkland Middle School
McHenry, Illinois

Zenovia Young
Meyer Levin Junior
    High School (IS 285)
Brooklyn, New York

Contents

Chemical Interactions

PRENTICE HALL SCIENCE EXPLORER

Prepare your students with rich, motivating content

Science Explorer is crafted for today's middle grades student, with accessible content and in-depth coverage. **Integrated Science Sections** support every chapter and the **Interdisciplinary Exploration** provides an engaging final unit.

Check your compass — regularly assess student progress.

Self-assessment tools are built right into the student text and **on-going assessment** is woven throughout the Teacher's Edition. You'll find a wealth of **assessment technology** in the Resource Pro®, Interactive Student Tutorial, and Assessment Resources CD-ROMs.

Activities

Guide your students to become science explorers.

A wide range of **student-tested** activities, **from guided to open-ended,** with options for **short-** and **long-term** inquiry.

Draw upon the world around you.

Interdisciplinary Activities connect to every discipline and give science a meaningful, real-world context.

Saving the Ozone Layer

Focus on Chemistry

This four-page feature introduces the process of scientific inquiry by involving students in a high-interest, magazine-like article about a working scientist, Mario Molina. Using Dr. Molina's investigation of the effect of pollution on the ozone layer, the article focuses on curiosity, persistence, reasoning, and relating cause and effect as key elements of scientific inquiry.

Chemical reactions are presented in Chapter 1, Sections 1-1, 1-2, and 1-3 of this book. However, students need not have any previous knowledge of that chapter's content to understand and appreciate this feature.

Scientific Inquiry

◆ Before students read the feature, let them read the title, examine the pictures, and read the captions on their own. Then ask: **What questions came into your mind as you looked at these pictures?** *(Students might suggest questions such as "What is the ozone layer? Why do we need to save the ozone layer? Do we know how to save it? How can a hole in the ozone over Antarctica affect people in the United States? Do we know how to make more ozone? What might happen to us if we did nothing to protect the ozone layer?")* Point out to students that just as they had questions about what they were seeing, scientists too have questions about what they observe.

SAVING THE OZONE LAYER

As a child growing up in Mexico, long before he won a Nobel Prize in chemistry, Mario Molina enjoyed playing with science. "I was always interested in chemistry sets or toy microscopes. With the microscope in front of me, I'd take a piece of lettuce, put it in water, and let it rot and really stink. To see the life teeming in a drop of water—that for me was fascinating. Even then I realized it would be great if I could become a research scientist."

What Mario wanted to do, he decided, was "actually use science for things that affect society." Mario Molina began by looking at the chemicals people put into the air.

Dr. Mario Molina Born in Mexico City, chemist Mario Molina is now a Professor of Earth, Atmospheric, and Planetary Sciences at the Massachusetts Institute of Technology in Cambridge, Massachusetts. In 1995, Professor Molina, Sherwood Rowland, and Paul Crutzen won the Nobel Prize in Chemistry for their work on CFCs and the ozone layer.

Background

Chemistry is the study of properties of materials, such as their structure and composition. Chemists also study how different materials interact and how adding or removing energy from materials changes them.

Photochemistry is one branch of chemistry. Scientists in this branch study how chemicals are affected by visible light and other forms of electromagnetic radiation (such as ultraviolet rays). Photochemists also study how radiation from the sun causes ozone to be formed. Other branches of chemistry include organic chemistry and analytical chemistry. Organic chemists study carbon-containing compounds. They may be concerned with such things as developing new medicines to researching new types of synthetic materials.

Cycle of Ozone Destruction

Chlorine **Ozone** → **Chlorine monoxide** + **Oxygen**

1 Chlorine from CFCs and ozone (O_3) combine to form chlorine monoxide and oxygen.

Chlorine monoxide + **Chlorine monoxide** → **Chlorine peroxide**

2 Two chlorine monoxide molecules combine to form chlorine peroxide.

Chlorine peroxide + **Sunlight** → **Chlorine** + **Oxygen**

3 Chlorine peroxide reacts with sunlight to form oxygen and chlorine. The chlorine atoms are then free to begin the cycle again.

Asking Simple Questions

In the early 1970s, one of Dr. Molina's co-workers, Sherwood Rowland, heard about a group of compounds called chlorofluorocarbons, or CFCs. CFCs were used in air conditioners, refrigerators, and aerosol spray cans, but leaked into the air. "It is something that is not natural, but is now in the atmosphere all over the planet." What happens to these compounds in the air, Rowland and Molina wondered, and what do they do to the air?

"We didn't know ahead of time if CFCs were doing damage or not," Dr. Molina explains. "So what we did was study what was going on. We learned that CFCs aren't changed much down near Earth. But we expected that if they got high enough in the atmosphere, solar radiation would destroy them."

Radiation is how energy from the sun reaches Earth. Ultraviolet (UV) rays, a form of radiation, break compounds apart and change them. "Above a certain altitude, everything falls apart. We had to learn how high CFCs went and how long it took them to get there. Then we asked: What does it mean that CFCs are up there?"

A Protective Shield in the Sky

In his laboratory, Dr. Molina studied how ultraviolet light changes CFCs. "It became clear that these molecules would be destroyed by UV rays in the stratosphere—the upper atmosphere, where the ozone layer is. At the time, I didn't even know what the ozone layer was."

But Mario Molina learned fast. The ozone layer is a thin layer of the atmosphere that contains ozone, a form of oxygen. The ozone blocks out UV rays from the sun. UV rays would be dangerous to living things if they reached Earth's surface.

In a 1987 international treaty, the United States and other industrial nations agreed to reduce the use of CFCs in spray cans and other products.

◆ Encourage students to tell about ways they have explored chemistry, for example, playing with chemistry sets, crystals, or studying items using a microscope or magnifying glass.

◆ Encourage students to tell what they already know about the ozone layer. Some students may know that ozone in the lower atmosphere is considered a pollutant. Another term concerning the environment that they may have heard is "greenhouse effect." Make it clear to students that the greenhouse effect and ozone depletion are two different phenomena. Refer interested students to the background information on page 10.

◆ Explain the ozone destruction cycle one stage at a time. Have student volunteers read the captions aloud. Point out that the source for chlorine in step 1 is the breakdown of CFCs by sunlight.

◆ Extend this exploration by using it to help students appreciate cause and effect. Lead students to recognize that use of aerosols in the United States can hurt the ozone over Antarctica, which in turn has the potential to cause catastrophic harm all over the globe. Ask students to think of other examples of local actions that could have global repercussions.

◆ Ask: **Why did people manufacture products that they knew leaked CFCs?** (Answers may vary. Sample: People did not imagine that CFCs could be harmful.) **Do you think people will continue to manufacture products that leak CFCs now that they know CFCs are harmful?** (Answers may vary. Samples: Some people may be skeptical that CFCs are the cause of the ozone holes. Some people may not want to spend the money to develop a product that does not leak CFCs.)

Background

Ozone (O_3) in the upper atmosphere is formed when sunlight acts on oxygen (O_2). As well as CFCs being able to destroy ozone, other chemicals, such as those found in fertilizers, may also be destructive.

As the ozone layer thins, scientists expect increases in skin cancer, cataracts, and damage to plankton. Since plankton are the basis for a huge food chain, even a small amount of plankton damage could have far-reaching effects.

During the winter of 1995–96, scientists observed that the ozone layer over one third of the northern hemisphere was depleted by 45 percent for several days. Scientists think the temporary depletion was due to a combination of chlorine compounds and clouds with unusually low temperatures.

- If students seem particularly interested in ozone or the greenhouse effect, share the information in the Backgrounds. Also suggest that they consult library books to learn more about global warming. (See Further Reading, page 11.)
- Ask: **What did Dr. Molina and his colleagues set out to study?** *(They wanted to study what happened to CFCs in the atmosphere.)* **What did the scientists find out?** *(In the process, CFCs are destroyed by solar radiation. Chlorine is released. The chlorine destroys ozone.)*
- Ask: **Why does Dr. Molina conclude that very small amounts of CFCs can have very big effects on ozone?** *Chlorine is not changed by the reaction with ozone, so it is free to break up more ozone molecules.*
- Challenge students to find out more about the different layers in the atmosphere. Ask students to find out what the stratosphere is and how it relates to the ozone layer.
- Ask: **Why do you think scientists would be skeptical that the ozone layer was being damaged?** *(It seems hard to believe that a small amount of CFCs could do so much damage.)* Point out that some people are still skeptical that there is a problem.

Changes in the ozone layer over Antarctica, 1979 to 1993

In 1979, thinning of the ozone layer was visible in satellite images.

In 1985, a hole in the ozone layer was clearly visible.

In 1989, the hole in the ozone layer was expanding.

In 1993, the damage to the ozone layer was even worse.

← Less ozone   More ozone →

These images of the South Pole, taken by satellite between 1979 and 1993, show a hole developing in the ozone layer of the atmosphere. The changing size and color of the image over the pole represent how quickly the hole increased.

Dr. Molina learned something very disturbing. When the sun's rays break CFCs apart, chlorine forms. A chain of chemical changes that destroys ozone then begins. "Very small amounts of CFCs can have very big effects on ozone."

A Scary Prediction Comes True

Mario Molina and his co-workers made a frightening prediction. If CFCs can reach the stratosphere, they will eventually damage the protective ozone layer. Other scientists thought Mario Molina was wrong or exaggerating. But more and more evidence came in. Researchers sent balloons up into the stratosphere with scientific instruments to measure chlorine formed by CFCs. They found that CFCs were in the stratosphere and that the sun's rays were breaking them down.

Was the ozone layer being hurt? Yes. Over Antarctica, there was an "ozone hole," an opening in the ozone layer. The hole lets in harmful radiation from the sun. "That was a surprise to us and to everybody. It was a very large effect that we hadn't predicted. Some scientists thought the ozone hole was natural, but we thought it was caused by CFCs. We checked it out by doing experiments from Antarctica. In a couple of years it became very clear that this hole was a result of the CFCs."

Scientist and Speaker

Dr. Molina now had to convince people to stop making and using CFCs. "We were lucky that the effect

Shown here is the ER-2 aircraft, which was used to measure gases in the ozone hole over Antarctica. ▶

Background

The ozone layer is not very dense. If all the ozone molecules that make up the ozone layer were compressed at Earth's surface, they would form a layer about as thick as a pie crust!

In 1987, 24 countries signed an agreement called the Montreal Protocol that calls for gradually phasing out and eventually ending the production of many CFCs. Now, over 150 countries have agreed to these goals.

"Greenhouse effect" is a term that describes how the atmosphere keeps Earth warm. Greenhouse gases include carbon dioxide, methane, and water vapor. Greenhouse gases are being studied for their effect on Earth's climate. In 1997, 160 nations agreed to the Kyoto Protocol. This agreement would commit industrialized countries to reduce emissions of six greenhouse gases to below 1990 levels by 2012.

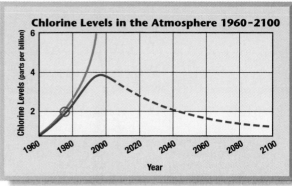

Chlorine Levels in the Atmosphere 1960–2100

The graph shows that the level of chlorine in the atmosphere would have increased rapidly if controls on CFCs had not been passed. With controls in place, the amount of chlorine in the atmosphere should gradually decrease to levels in the light blue region of the graph. The ozone hole should then close.

— Predicted levels without controls
— Actual levels with controls
○ Antarctica ozone hole found
- - Predicted levels with controls

over Antarctica was so large. That made it easy to measure and test. But similar effects exist everywhere. As scientists we had to inform the public and the government. If you're convinced that you're right and that something dangerous is going to happen, you need to risk speaking out."

Mario Molina went to the U.S. Senate and to other governments. He was able to show how UV radiation was causing damage. "There was damage to some crops, damage to growing fish, damage that we can already see and measure today."

Finally, the world listened. Through the United Nations, an agreement was signed by most industrial nations to stop using CFCs by the year 2000.

Work Still to Do

"Everybody has to work together," chemist Molina says. He has done more than his share. He gave $200,000 of his Nobel Prize money to help train scientists from Latin America and other developing countries. "There is a need to understand our planet, and we need very good minds to work on these problems. There are big challenges out there," he says with a confident smile, "but fortunately science is fascinating."

In Your Journal

Mario Molina particularly wants to know how chemicals made by people get into the atmosphere and change it. Take a walk in your neighborhood. Make a list of ways you can observe—or think of—that people put chemicals into the air. Remember that smoke is a mixture of chemicals.

L ◆ 11

- ◆ **Ask: What would a scientist risk by speaking out on a controversial subject?** *(Answers may vary. Sample: A scientist's professional reputation could be hurt if people did not take the scientist seriously.)*
- ◆ Draw students' attention to the graph. Point out that from 1978 to 1998, the level of chlorine in the atmosphere rose each year but did not rise as much as it would have had there been no controls in place. Encourage students to study the satellite images of the ozone hole and make predictions about how quickly the entire ozone layer could have been destroyed had scientists not persuaded politicians to enact legislation.
- ◆ Point out that it may take over 100 years for the chlorine levels in the atmosphere to drop back to where they were in 1960.
- ◆ Challenge interested students to find out how scientists believe the ozone layer will close. Students may also want to research whether scientists are exploring ways of removing the excess chlorine from the atmosphere.

In Your Journal Students can combine their lists to make a classroom display. If students need help thinking of chemicals emitted, point out that anything that has an odor (such as perfume or pine cleaner) is likely to be releasing chemicals of some sort. After students make their lists, ask: **What questions occurred to you as you wrote down ideas?** *(Sample: Chemicals may be harmless individually, but is it possible that they combine in the atmosphere to make something harmful?)*

Introducing Chemical Interactions

Have students look through the table of contents and the book to find the parts that relate most closely to this article. *(Chapter 1, Chemical Reactions, particularly section 1-2, Describing Chemical Reactions, and section 1-3, Controlling Chemical Reactions.)* Ask: **Besides chemical reactions, what else is this book about?** *(atoms, chemical bonds, acids, bases, solutions, chemistry applications)* **What kinds of things do you think you will be learning about?** *(Accept all responses without comment.)*

READING STRATEGIES

Further Reading
- ◆ Benedick, Richard Elliot. *Ozone Diplomacy: New Directions in Safeguarding the Planet.* Harvard University Press, 1997.
- ◆ Pringle, Laurence. *Vanishing Ozone: Protecting Earth from Ultraviolet Radiation,* Vol. 1. William Morrow & Company, 1995.
- ◆ Philander, S. George. *Is the Temperature Rising?: The Uncertain Science of Global Warming.* Princeton University Press, 1998.
- ◆ Gelbspan, Ross. *The Heat Is on: The High Stakes Battle over Earth's Threatened Climate.* Addison Wesley Longman, 1997.

Sections	Time	Student Edition Activities	Other Activities	
CHAPTER PROJECT 1 **Keep a Chemical Change Log** p. L13	Ongoing (2 weeks)	Check Your Progress, pp. L21, L31 Project Wrap Up, p. L47	TE	Chapter 1 Project Notes, pp. L12–13
1 Matter and Changes in Matter pp. L14–23 ◆ 1.1.1 Define and compare elements, compounds, mixtures, atoms, and molecules. ◆ 1.1.2 Compare chemical changes to physical changes. ◆ 1.1.3 Explain how chemical bonds are changed during chemical reactions. ◆ 1.1.4 Identify evidence of chemical reactions.	5 periods/ 2–3 blocks	**Discover** What Happens When Chemicals React?, p. L14 **Try This** Mostly Cloudy, p. L18 **Skills Lab: Making Observations** Where's the Evidence?, pp. L22–23	TE TE TE TE TE ISLM	Building Inquiry Skills: Predicting, p. L15 Math Toolbox, p. L16 Demonstration, p. L16 Demonstration, p. L17 Addressing Naive Conceptions, p. L18 L-1, "The Law of Definite Proportions"
2 Describing Chemical Reactions pp. L24–31 ◆ 1.2.1 Describe the information conveyed in a chemical equation. ◆ 1.2.2 Apply the principle of conservation of mass to chemical reactions. ◆ 1.2.3 Identify and describe the three categories of chemical reactions.	4 periods/ 2 blocks	**Discover** Do You Lose Anything?, p. L24 **Try This** Still There, p. L27 **Sharpen Your Skills** Calculating, p. L28	TE TE TE	Inquiry Challenge, p. L26 Including All Students, p. L28 Demonstration, p. L30
3 Controlling Chemical Reactions pp. L32–39 ◆ 1.3.1 Explain that every chemical reaction requires activation energy to get started. ◆ 1.3.2 List factors that control the rate of chemical reactions.	4 periods/ 2 blocks	**Discover** Can You Speed Up or Slow Down a Reaction?, p. L32 **Sharpen Your Skills** Interpreting Data, p. L36 **Science at Home** p. L37 **Real-World Lab: How It Works** Peroxide, Catalase, & You!, pp. L38–39	TE TE TE	Demonstration, p. L35 Inquiry Challenge, p. L35 Inquiry Challenge, p. L36
4 🔵 **INTEGRATING HEALTH** **Fire and Fire Safety** pp. L40–44 ◆ 1.4.1 Identify the three conditions necessary to maintain a fire. ◆ 1.4.2 Explain how water inhibits combustion. ◆ 1.4.3 List fire-safety measures for the home.	$2\frac{1}{2}$ periods/ 1-2 blocks	**Discover** How Does Baking Soda Affect a Fire?, p. L40 **Science at Home** p. L43	TE	Demonstration, p. L41
Study Guide/Assessment pp. L45–47	1 period/ $\frac{1}{2}$ block		ISAB	Provides teaching and review of all inquiry skills

 For Standard or Block Schedule The Resource Pro® CD-ROM gives you maximum flexibility for planning your instruction for any type of schedule. Resource Pro® contains Planning Express®, an advanced scheduling program, as well as the entire contents of the Teaching Resources and the Computer Test Bank.

Key: **SE** Student Edition
PLM Probeware Lab Manual
ISAB Inquiry Skills Activity Book

CHAPTER PLANNING GUIDE

Program Resources	Assessment Strategies	Media and Technology
TR Chapter 1 Project Teacher Notes, pp. L6–7 **TR** Chapter 1 Project Overview and Worksheets, pp. L8–11	**TE** Check Your Progress, pp. L21, L31 **TE** Performance Assessment: Chapter 1 Project Wrap Up, p. L47 **TR** Chapter 1 Project Scoring Rubric, p. L12	🌐 Science Explorer Internet Site 🎧 Audio CDs and Audiotapes, English-Spanish Section Summaries
TR 1-1 Lesson Plan, p. L13 **TR** 1-1 Section Summary, p. L14 **TR** 1-1 Review and Reinforce, p. L15 **TR** 1-1 Enrich, p. L16 **TR** Skills Lab blackline masters, pp. L29–31	**SE** Section 1 Review, p. L21 **SE** Analyze and Conclude, p. L23 **TE** Ongoing Assessment, pp. L15, L17, L19 **TE** Performance Assessment, p. L21	💿 Exploring Physical Science Videodisc, Unit 2 Side 2, "Designing Fireworks" 📼 Lab Activity Videotape, *Chemical Interactions*, 1
TR 1-2 Lesson Plan, p. L17 **TR** 1-2 Section Summary, p. L18 **TR** 1-2 Review and Reinforce, p. L19 **TR** 1-2 Enrich, p. L20 **SES** Book E, *Environmental Science*, Chapter 5	**SE** Section 2 Review, p. L31 **TE** Ongoing Assessment, pp. L25, L27, L29 **TE** Performance Assessment, p. L31	📽 Transparency 1, "Balancing an Equation"
TR 1-3 Lesson Plan, p. L21 **TR** 1-3 Section Summary, p. L22 **TR** 1-3 Review and Reinforce, p. L23 **TR** 1-3 Enrich, p. L24 **TR** Real-World Lab blackline masters, pp. L32–33 **SES** Book C, *Cells and Heredity*, Chapter 2	**SE** Section 3 Review, p. L37 **SE** Analyze and Conclude, p. L39 **TE** Ongoing Assessment, pp. L33, L35 **TE** Performance Assessment, p. L37	💿 Exploring Physical Science Videodisc, Unit 2 Side 2, "Fast Reactions?"; Unit 2 Side 2, "Endothermic and Exothermic Reactions" 📼 Lab Activity Videotape, *Chemical Interactions*, 2 📽 Transparencies 2, "Energy in Chemical Reactions"; 3, "Activation Energy"; 4, "How an Enzyme Works"
TR 1-4 Lesson Plan, p. L25 **TR** 1-4 Section Summary, p. L26 **TR** 1-4 Review and Reinforce, p. L27 **TR** 1-4 Enrich, p. L28	**SE** Section 4 Review, p. L43 **TE** Ongoing Assessment, p. L41 **TE** Performance Assessment, p. L43	📽 Transparencies 5, "Fire Safety Tips"; 6, "Fire-Safe House"
GSW Provides worksheets to promote student comprehension of content **RCA** Provides strategies to improve science reading skills **ELL** Provides multiple strategies for English language learners	**SE** Study Guide/Assessment, pp. L45–47 **TR** Performance Assessment, pp. L134–136 **TR** Chapter 1 Test, pp. L137–140 **CTB** *Chemical Interactions*, Chapter 1 Test **STP** Provides standardized test practice	💿 Computer Test Bank, *Chemical Interactions*, Chapter 1 Test 💿 Interactive Student Tutorial CD-ROM, L-1

TE Teacher's Edition **TR** Teaching Resources **CTB** Computer Test Bank
RCA Reading in the Content Area **ISLM** Integrated Science Laboratory Manual **STP** Standardized Test Preparation Book
GSW Guided Study Workbook **ELL** Teacher's ELL Handbook **SES** Science Explorer Series Text

Meeting the National Science Education Standards and AAAS Benchmarks

National Science Education Standards	Benchmarks for Science Literacy	Unifying Themes
Science as Inquiry (Content Standard A) ◆ **Communicate scientific procedures and explanations** Students report on how successfully they were able to observe chemical reactions in the world around them. *(Skills Lab)* **Physical Science** (Content Standard B) ◆ **Properties and changes of properties in matter** A chemical reaction changes the original reactants into new substances with different properties. *(Sections 1–2)* ◆ **Transfer of energy** Chemical reactions always involve transfer of energy between reactants and changes in the energy level of products. *(Sections 1, 3)* **Science and Technology** (Content Standard E) ◆ **Abilities of technological design** Technology is available to control fires and reduce fire danger. *(Section 4)* **Science in Personal and Social Perspectives** (Content Standard F) ◆ **Science and technology in society** Technology is available to control fires and reduce fire danger. *(Section 4)*	**1A The Scientific World View** Chemistry and chemical processes are all around us and are essential for understanding the world. *(Chapter Project)* **3A Technology and Science** Technology is available to control fires and reduce fire danger. *(Section 4)* **4D The Structure of Matter** Matter is composed of a few simple building blocks called elements. Elements can form compounds with properties different from the elements. *(Sections 1, 2)* **4E Energy Transformations** Chemical reactions always involve energy changes. *(Sections 1, 3; Real-World Lab)* **11C Constancy and Change** Mass is always conserved in chemical reactions. *(Section 2)*	◆ **Energy** The energy of the reactants changes during a chemical reaction. A chemical reaction can give off energy or absorb energy. The reactants must be given enough energy to overcome the activation energy before the reaction will occur. *(Sections 1, 3; Real-World Lab)* ◆ **Patterns of Change** A chemical reaction changes the original reactants into new substances with different properties. *(Sections 1, 2)* ◆ **Scale and Structure** The types of atoms and how they are joined determine the properties of a substance. Elements combine to form compounds. Molecules are made of atoms bonded together. *(Sections 1, 2)* ◆ **Unity and Diversity** All chemical reactions share certain characteristics. Different kinds of chemical reactions can be classified. *(Sections 1–4; Skills Lab; Real-World Lab)* ◆ **Systems and Interactions** Increasing the temperature, concentration, or surface area of the reactants usually increases reaction rates. Catalysts can increase reaction rates. *(Section 3; Real-World Lab)* ◆ **Stability** Mass is always conserved in chemical reactions. *(Section 2)*

Take It to the Net

 Interactive text at www.phschool.com

Science Explorer comes alive with iText.

- **Complete student text** is accessible from any computer with Internet service or a CD-ROM drive.

- **Animations, simulations, and videos** enhance student understanding and retention of concepts.

- **Self-tests and online study tools** assess student understanding.

- **Teacher management tools** help you make the most of this valuable resource.

STAY CURRENT with **SCIENCE NEWS**®

Find out the latest research and information about chemical interactions at: **www.phschool.com**

Go to **www.phschool.com** and click on the Science icon. Then click on <u>Science Explorer</u> under PH@school.

ACTIVITY	Time (minutes)	Materials *Quantities for one work group*	Skills
Section 1			
Discover, p. 14	10	**Consumable** baking soda, white vinegar, clear plastic cups **Nonconsumable** large bowls	**Observing**
Try This, p. 18	10	**Consumable** carbonated water, limewater, tap water, plastic cups **Nonconsumable** graduated cylinder	**Inferring**
Skills Lab, pp. 22–23	40	**Consumable** 4 small plastic cups; 2 plastic spoons; matches; sodium carbonate (powder); aluminum foil, about 10-cm square; dilute hydrochloric acid in a dropper bottle; copper sulfate solution; sodium carbonate solution; sugar **Nonconsumable** tongs; graduated cylinder, 10 mL; birthday candles; clay	**Observing**
Section 2			
Discover, p. 24	10	**Nonconsumable** about 24 coins of various denominations	**Making Models**
Try This, p. 27	15	**Nonconsumable** hex nuts and short bolts, balance	**Making Models**
Sharpen Your Skills, p. 28	10	No special materials are required.	**Calculating**
Section 3			
Discover, p. 32	10	**Consumable** clear plastic cups, solutions of vitamin C tablets and water at three different temperatures, tincture of iodine **Nonconsumable** 3 500-mL heat-resistant beakers, spoon	**Inferring**
Sharpen Your Skills, p. 36	15	**Consumable** gelatin cubes, plastic knife **Nonconsumable** ruler	**Interpreting Data**
Science at Home, p. 37	home	**Consumable** nail, fine-grade steel wool, 2 plastic cups, water	**Predicting**
Real-World Lab, pp. 38–39	50	**Consumable** 0.1% hydrogen peroxide solution, filter paper disks soaked in liver preparation (catalase enzyme) and kept at four different temperatures (room temperature, 0–4°C, 37°C, and 100°C) **Nonconsumable** test tube with a one-hole stopper, forceps, container to hold water (beaker or bowl), stopwatch	**Measuring, Controlling Variables, Drawing Conclusions**
Section 4			
Discover, p. 40	15	**Consumable** matches, water, vinegar, baking soda **Nonconsumable** aluminum pie pan, small candles, clay or candle holder, beaker or glass	**Developing Hypotheses**
Science at Home, p. 43	home	No special materials are required.	**Communicating**

A list of all materials required for the Student Edition activities can be found beginning on page T15. You can obtain information about ordering materials by calling 1-800-848-9500 or by accessing the Science Explorer Internet site at: **www.phschool.com**

Keep a Chemical Change Log

Many students think of "chemistry" as something that happens only in the school lab. They may think that chemistry has nothing to do with them. As students learn about the concepts of chemical reactions, they will discover the large number of chemical changes that occur around them and how these reactions are an important part of their daily lives.

Purpose In this project, students will keep a log of chemical changes that they observe in their daily lives. They will use the signs of chemical change mentioned in Section 1 to distinguish between physical and chemical changes and will further classify these changes. They will also design their own record-keeping format for recording their observations.

Skills Focus Students will be able to
◆ form operational definitions about physical and chemical changes;
◆ pose questions and make inferences based on observations of chemical reactions;
◆ create tables to record observations;
◆ classify chemical reactions as synthesis, decomposition, or replacement reactions.

Project Time Line The project requires almost two weeks. On the first day, have students survey the chapter to learn what is meant by a chemical change. Use the Chapter 1 Project Worksheet 1 to help students start thinking about differences between physical and chemical changes. On the second or third day, have students list the signs of a chemical reaction and discuss their lists in pairs. On the next day, students should prepare data tables. Students should then spend a week making their observations and completing the tables.

Before beginning the project, see Chapter 1 Project Teacher Notes on pages 6–7 in Teaching Resources for more details on carrying out the project. Also distribute the Students' Chapter 1 Project Overview and Worksheets and Scoring Rubric on pages 8–12 in Teaching Resources.

CHAPTER

1 Chemical Reactions

WEB ACTIVITY www.phschool.com

SECTION **1** Matter and Changes in Matter
Discover **What Happens When Chemicals React?**
Try This **Mostly Cloudy**
Skills Lab **Where's the Evidence?**

SECTION **2** Describing Chemical Reactions
Discover **Do You Lose Anything?**
Try This **Still There**
Sharpen Your Skills **Calculating**

SECTION **3** Controlling Chemical Reactions
Discover **Can You Speed Up or Slow Down a Reaction?**
Sharpen Your Skills **Interpreting Data**
Real-World Lab **Peroxide, Catalase, and You!**

12 ◆ L

Suggested Shortcuts To save time, students can observe and record the chemical reactions they observe during a 24-hour period.

Possible Materials Students need only paper and pencil to record data for the project. Students should design their own record-keeping sheets, using Chapter 1 Project Worksheet 2 as an example.

Keep a Chemical Change Log

Look around. All sorts of changes are taking place. Some changes involve growth. For example, you and your classmates are growing. Other changes produce something that wasn't there before. A factory turns raw materials into desirable products, for instance. Rust coats the surface of a once-silvery fence. Even the green color of the Statue of Liberty comes from a change to the statue's copper metal covering. All of these changes are the result of chemical reactions, or changes in which substances react to form new substances.

In this chapter, you will learn more about the changes in matter that result from chemical reactions. Your project involves keeping a log of chemical changes occurring around you.

Your Goal To identify and observe chemical changes in your daily life and to record evidence for those changes.

To complete the project you must
◆ determine what evidence indicates that a chemical change has taken place
◆ record observations of the different chemical changes you notice in your life during one week
◆ classify the types of chemical changes you observe
◆ follow the safety guidelines in Appendix A

Get Started Begin by previewing the chapter to learn what a chemical change is. With a group, discuss some changes you observe regularly. Try to decide if each change is a chemical change.

Check Your Progress You'll be working on this project as you study this chapter. To keep your project on track, look for Check Your Progress boxes at the following points.

Section Review 1, page 21: List evidence of chemical changes.
Section Review 2, page 31: Construct a table for observations.

Wrap Up At the end of the chapter (page 47), you will compare your table of chemical changes with those of your classmates and classify the changes.

SECTION
4
Integrating Health
Fire and Fire Safety

Discover **How Does Baking Soda Affect a Fire?**

The copper-covered Statue of Liberty has stood in Upper New York Bay for more than 100 years.

L ◆ 13

Program Resources

◆ **Teaching Resources** Chapter 1 Project Teacher's Notes, pp. 6–7; Chapter 1 Project Overview and Worksheet, pp. 8–11; Chapter 1 Project Scoring Rubric, p. 12

Media and Technology

 Audio CDs and **Audiotapes** English-Spanish Section Summaries

WEB ACTIVITY
www.phschool.com

You will find an Internet activity, chapter self-tests for students, and links to other chapter topics at this site.

Launching the Project To illustrate physical change, cut a piece of paper into smaller parts and point out that the small pieces are still paper. Then burn a piece of paper and show students the ash. Explain that this is a chemical change. Point out that the key difference between chemical and physical changes is that a chemical change produces substances that were not there before the reaction. Explain that sometimes it is difficult to tell if a new substance is produced. Hold up a battery. Tell students that a chemical change occurs inside the battery, but it is not visible or obvious.

Distribute copies of the Chapter 1 Project Worksheet 1 on page 10 in Teaching Resources and have small groups of students discuss the project. To ensure that every student participates in discussions, limit group size to 3 students.

Allow time for students to read the description of the project in their text and the Chapter Project Overview on pages 8–9 in Teaching Resources.

Performance Assessment

The Chapter 1 Project Scoring Rubric on page 12 of Teaching Resources will help you evaluate how well students complete the Chapter 1 Project. You may wish to share the scoring rubric with your students so they are clear about what will be expected of them. Students will be assessed on
◆ their understanding of and ability to identify chemical change;
◆ the number of different observations dealing with chemical change that they are able to accumulate during one week;
◆ the accuracy of their classifications of the types of chemical changes observed;
◆ their participation in classroom discussions.

Objectives

After completing the lesson, students will be able to

◆ define and compare elements, compounds, mixtures, atoms, and molecules;

◆ compare chemical changes to physical changes;

◆ explain how chemical bonds are changed during chemical reactions;

◆ identify evidence of chemical reactions.

Key Terms chemistry, element, compound, mixture, solution, physical change, chemical change, chemical reaction, precipitate, atom, molecule, chemical bond

1 Engage/Explore

Activating Prior Knowledge

Invite volunteers to name some changes in matter they are familiar with. Prompt students by suggesting rusting bicycle chains, growing plants, burning candles, melting ice, and so on. Record students' responses on the board and refer to them as they work through the section.

DISCOVER

Skills Focus observing **ACTIVITY**
Materials *safety goggles, baking soda, white vinegar, clear plastic cups, large bowl or sink*
Time 10 minutes
Tips Demonstrate the wafting technique (see Appendix A, Science Safety Rules). Remind students not to taste the mixture.
Expected Outcome The mixture will fizz, the contents of the cup will become cooler, and the vinegar smell will disappear.
Think It Over Students may say they could hear the products fizzing, feel the cup become cool, and smell that the mixture no longer smelled like vinegar.

SECTION 1 Matter and Changes in Matter

DISCOVER **ACTIVITY**

What Happens When Chemicals React?

1. Put on your safety goggles.

2. Put 2 teaspoons of baking soda into a clear plastic cup.

3. Holding the cup over a large bowl or sink, add about 125 mL of vinegar. Swirl the cup gently.

4. Observe any changes to the material in the cup. Feel the outside of the cup. What do you notice about the temperature?

5. Carefully fan some air over the liquid toward you. What does the mixture smell like?

Think It Over

Observing Looking at an experiment is not the only way to get information. Your other senses can be equally useful in making observations. What changes did you detect using your senses of smell and touch?

GUIDE FOR READING

◆ What simple substances make up matter?

◆ How can you tell a chemical reaction has occurred?

◆ What happens to chemical bonds in chemical reactions?

Reading Tip As you read, use the headings of the section to make an outline describing matter and its changes.

A jet sits on the runway, waiting to fly across the ocean. On a signal from the control tower, the pilot eases the plane forward. Suddenly there is a rumbling sound. The plane starts to shake and picks up speed. Passengers looking out the window watch the runway zip by as the jet moves faster and faster. Suddenly the jet is off the ground. As the thrust of the engines shoots the plane into the air, the passengers feel as though they are being pushed back into their seats.

The jet's giant engines move matter from one city to another. **Matter** is anything that has mass and takes up space. The jet, and the people and the baggage on it, are forms of matter. In fact, everything you can see, taste, touch, or smell is matter.

Inside the jet's powerful engines, the energy needed for the flight comes from changes in the matter that makes up the fuel supply. When the fuel reacts with oxygen from the air, new materials are made and tremendous amounts of energy are released. The release of this energy moves the huge jet fast enough to keep it in the air and speeding on its way.

Chemistry is the study of the properties of matter and how matter changes. Some changes are spectacular, like those in the engines that power a jet. Others are as quiet as a cake baking in an oven. But however dramatic or calm a change is, it always involves matter.

◀ The engines of this jet get their energy from chemical changes.

READING STRATEGIES

Reading Tip As students create their outlines, remind them to write each main topic next to a Roman numeral, using the section headings as main topics. As a class, outline the first main topic, Building Blocks of Matter. Write the subtopics Elements, Compounds, and Mixtures under the main topic. Then have volunteers suggest details that support each subtopic.

Study and Comprehension After students read the section, have them use the outlines they created to generate questions about matter and its changes. Have partners quiz each other using the questions based on the outlines. Suggest that students save their questions to use as study guides for the section.

Figure 1 A geodesic dome, a bridge, and a skyscraper are all made from steel, but their appearances and uses are very different.

Building Blocks of Matter

Take an imaginary walk through your city or town and notice all the buildings. Their shapes, sizes, and uses are very different. You would never confuse a doghouse with an airport terminal or a gas station with a 50-story office tower. But they are all constructed of a few kinds of materials. Bricks, wood, glass, stone, concrete, and steel are some of the most common building materials. Using these materials, people have built many different structures. No two are exactly alike.

Elements Just as many different buildings are made from just a few kinds of materials, all the different kinds of matter in the universe are made from about 100 different substances, called elements. An **element** is a substance that cannot be broken down into any other substances by chemical or physical means.

You have seen some elements in their pure form in the world around you. Examples include aluminum in foil, carbon in the form of graphite pencil lead, copper that coats pennies, and tungsten that composes the wire that glows in a light bulb. **All the matter around you is composed of one element or a combination of two or more elements.**

Program Resources

◆ **Teaching Resources** 1–1 Lesson Plan, p. 13; 1–1 Section Summary, p. 14
◆ **Guided Reading and Study Workbook** Section 1-1

2 *Facilitate*

Building Blocks of Matter

Building Inquiry Skills: Predicting

Materials *1/4-20 hex nuts, 1/4-20 square nuts, 1/4-20 × 1/2" bolts, 1/4-20 × 1" bolts*
Time 10 minutes

ACTIVITY

Have students work in small groups to assemble as many "elements" and "compounds" as they can from these four different kinds of "atoms." You may have to show students how to assemble a "molecule" with two bolts and one nut by screwing both bolts part way into the same nut. Students should be able to assemble at least 12–15 different "compounds." Ask students if it is possible to make a compound that contains only bolts or only nuts. *(No)* Then ask students to predict how many different substances they could assemble if they had 100 different kinds of "atoms." *(Sample: millions)* The nut and bolt analogy is useful, but it can be carried only so far. Since it will be used in other activities in this chapter, don't overwork it at this time. **learning modality: kinesthetic**

Using the Visuals: Figure 1

Have students examine the figure. Ask them what properties of steel make it valuable as a building material. *(It has a high strength compared to its weight. It is strong in both compression and tension, and can be made very stiff. It can be formed into many different shapes. It can be easily worked with machine tools.)*
learning modality: visual

Ongoing Assessment

Writing Ask students to explain how the elements relate to the study of chemistry. *(Chemistry is the study of the properties of matter and how matter changes, and all matter is made of elements.)*

Building Blocks of Matter, continued

Math TOOLBOX

Encourage students to use ratios to compare items in the classroom. Ask them to find the ratio of boys to girls, brown eyes to blue eyes, and so on. Point out that in each case they may write the ratio, 1 to 4, or use symbols, 1 : 4. Have students use the information they gather to compose sentences. For example, "In this class, the ratio of boys to girls is 12 to 13." **learning modality: logical/mathematical**

Demonstration

Materials *iron filings, sulfur powder, clear plastic cup, magnet, crucible with cover, crucible tongs, high output burner, glass stirring rod*
Time 15 minutes

 Place a magnet near the sulfur, then near the iron filings and have students observe what happens. *(It attracts the iron filings but not the sulfur.)* Next, mix some iron filings and sulfur in a plastic cup. Ask: **What is in the cup?** *(A mixture of iron and sulfur)* **How could you separate the different parts of this mixture?** *(Use the magnet to attract the iron filings.)* Wrap clear plastic around the magnet and demonstrate how to separate the filings.

Now combine iron and sulfur to form the compound iron sulfide. CAUTION: *Complete the remainder of this activity under a fume hood or in a well ventilated area.* Thoroughly mix 2.0 g of iron filings with 1.0 g of sulfur in the crucible. Cover the crucible and use the burner to heat it strongly for at least 10 minutes. When the reaction is complete, allow the crucible to cool, dump out the reacted mass, and crumble it up with a stirring rod. Ask: **What happens when I bring the magnet close to the substance?** *(It is not attracted.)* Ask: **What can you infer about elements in a compound?** *(Elements can lose their original properties.)* **learning modality: visual**

Math TOOLBOX

Ratios

A ratio compares two numbers. It tells you how much you have of one item in comparison to how much you have of another. For example, a recipe for cookies calls for 2 cups of flour for every 1 cup of sugar. You can write the ratio of flour to sugar as:

2 to 1 or 2 : 1

The elements in a compound are present in a specific ratio. If two compounds contain the same elements in different ratios, they are different compounds.

Figure 2 Some items in this picture are made of compounds, while others are mixtures. *Applying Concepts What do the compositions of all these items have in common?*

16 ◆ L

Compounds Most elements are not found in their pure form in nature. They are more likely found as parts of compounds. A **compound** is a substance made of two or more elements chemically combined in a specific ratio, or proportion. For example, the carbon dioxide gas (CO_2) you breathe out of your lungs is made of carbon atoms and oxygen atoms in a 1 to 2 ratio (one part carbon to two parts oxygen).

You use many compounds every day. The sugar that makes juice taste sweet, the water you drink when you're thirsty, and the cavity-fighting ingredient in your toothpaste are all compounds made from different combinations of elements.

Sugar, for example, is made of the elements carbon, hydrogen, and oxygen. Think about the white crystals in a sugar bowl. Do they seem much like the black powdery carbon of pencil lead, and colorless hydrogen and oxygen gases? When elements combine to make a compound, the resulting compound has properties that are different from the elements.

Mixtures Most matter you find in your environment occurs as parts of mixtures. A **mixture** consists of two or more pure substances—elements, compounds, or both—that are in the same place but are not chemically combined. Unlike in a compound, the parts of a mixture may be present in varying ratios. Soil, for example, can be any combination of sand, clay, water, and other materials. Yet it is still soil. Also, the different parts of a mixture keep their individual properties. You can easily distinguish the many parts of a handful of soil just by looking closely at it.

In some mixtures the individual substances are not easily seen. A **solution** is a well-mixed mixture. If you have ever tasted sea water, you know the salt is present even though you can't see it in the water. But if you let a glass of salt water sit on a sunny windowsill for a few days, the water evaporates and only the salt remains. When the salt and water mix, they are still salt and water. No new materials form.

☑ *Checkpoint* Why can you call elements the building blocks of matter?

Changes in Matter

Chemistry is not just the study of kinds of matter but also of the changes in matter. Clouds, a plant seed, gasoline in a lawn mower engine, a book of matches—all of these are examples of matter. All of them are useful. They are useful as a result of the changes they undergo.

Physical Change Not all changes produce different material. A change that alters the form or appearance of a material but does not convert the material into new substances is called a **physical change.**

When you think about water in its different forms, you are thinking about physical changes. When it is cooled in a freezer or at the cold regions of Earth, liquid water becomes solid ice. You can change ice to liquid water by leaving an ice cube on your kitchen counter. If it is heated on your stove or by the energy of the sun, liquid water becomes an invisible gas called water vapor. When water vapor becomes liquid again, it returns to the ground as rain. These are all physical changes. Water is still the same substance in all three forms. It is still made of two parts hydrogen and one part oxygen (H_2O).

Chemical Change A change in matter that forms one or more new substances is called a **chemical change.** The new substances are made of the same elements as the original substance, but are now in different combinations. Elements and compounds rearrange to make new materials. Elements may combine to make compounds, compounds may be broken down into elements, or compounds may change into other compounds.

Think about elements and compounds as if they were letters and words. Every word is made of specific letters in a certain combination. Likewise, every compound is made of specific elements in a certain combination. A physical change is like printing the same word in a different style of type:

$$\text{stampedes} \;\rightarrow\; \mathit{stampedes}$$

A chemical change, or **chemical reaction,** is like scrambling the letters of a word to make new words:

$$\text{stampedes} \;\rightarrow\; \text{made} + \text{steps}$$

Figure 3 Matter commonly exists in three different forms, or states. *Interpreting Photographs Name two states of water shown in this photograph. Which state of water is invisible?*

Using the Visuals: Figure 3

As students identify the states of water in the figure, ask: **What might cause water to change to ice or to a vapor?** (*A change in temperature*) Ask: **Is this a physical change or a chemical change?** (*Physical*) **Why?** (*Because the form or appearance of the water is changed, but it is not made into something different.*) **learning modality: logical/mathematical**

Demonstration

Materials *2 small pieces of dark fabric, hydrogen peroxide, water, plastic dropper* **Time** 10 minutes plus 30 minutes waiting time

Students may have difficulty understanding that combining the same elements in different proportions produces different compounds. Explain that both water and hydrogen peroxide are made of oxygen and hydrogen, but the elements are combined in different ratios. Show students the two pieces of fabric. On one, place a few drops of water. On the other, place a few drops of hydrogen peroxide. After 30 minutes, ask students to observe each piece of fabric. Ask: **What evidence is there that hydrogen peroxide and water are different compounds?** (*They have different properties—hydrogen peroxide bleaches fabric, water does not.*) **learning modality: visual**

Program Resources

◆ **Integrated Science Laboratory Manual** L-1, "The Law of Definite Proportions"

Media and Technology

 Exploring Physical Science Videodisc Unit 2, Side 2, "Designing Fireworks"

Chapter 3

Answers to Self-Assessment

Caption Questions

Figure 2 They are all forms of matter. The building blocks of compounds and mixtures are elements.

Figure 3 Solid (ice) and liquid (flowing water); gases (water vapor and air) are invisible.

☑ *Checkpoint*

Because all matter is made from elements.

Ongoing Assessment

Oral Presentation Ask students to explain how compounds differ from mixtures or how chemical changes differ from physical changes.

L ◆ 17

Addressing Naive Conceptions

Materials *polished silver or silver-plated spoon, hard-boiled egg*
Time 10 minutes

Some students may think that all chemicals are dangerous substances. To challenge this, point out that chemicals are everywhere, and chemical changes occur in everyday objects. Display the spoon. Place the yolk of the egg on the spoon. At the end of the period, show the spoon again. Ask students to describe what happened. Tell them that they have observed a chemical change; the sulfur in the egg yolk reacts with silver to form a black film called silver sulfide. **learning modality: visual**

Observing Chemical Reactions

Skills Focus inferring
Materials *carbonated* *water, limewater, tap water, plastic cups, graduated cylinder, safety goggles, lab apron*
Time 10 minutes
Tips To make limewater, dissolve solid lime (calcium hydroxide, available at garden centers) in water until no more solid will dissolve. CAUTION: *Wear safety goggles.* Filter the solution.
Expected Outcome The reaction in the limewater cup will produce a white precipitate (calcium carbonate). As it settles, it will form a layer on the bottom of the cup. There will be no reaction in the plain water cup.
Inferring There was a chemical reaction in the limewater cup. The evidence for this is the white precipitate.
Extend Ask students: **How can you be sure there was no chemical reaction in the other cup?** *(Sample: None of the indicators of a chemical reaction were observed.)*

Figure 4 Over time, the surface of a polished bronze statue darkens as it reacts with oxygen in air.

Mostly Cloudy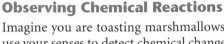

How can you tell if a chemical reaction is taking place?

1. Put on your safety goggles and apron.
2. Pour about 5 mL of limewater into a plastic cup.
3. Pour an equal amount of plain water into another plastic cup.
4. Add about 5 mL of carbonated water to each of the cups.

Inferring In which cup do you think a chemical reaction occurred? What evidence supports your inference?

Examples of chemical reactions are commonplace in your life. Rusting turns the strong iron metal of a car body into iron oxide, a compound you can easily knock a hole through. When wood burns, the compounds that make up the wood combine with oxygen in the air to make carbon dioxide and water.

☑ *Checkpoint* How is a physical change different from a chemical change?

Observing Chemical Reactions

Imagine you are toasting marshmallows over a campfire. You use your senses to detect chemical changes. You see the burning logs change from a hard solid to a pile of soft ash. You hear popping and hissing sounds as gases produced by the reaction cause the wood to expand. You smell the smoke. You feel the heat. You even taste the results of one chemical change. The brown surface and gooey interior of the toasted marshmallow is a big change from the soft, white marshmallow just out of its bag.

You can detect many chemical reactions by observing changes in the properties of the materials, or matter, involved. Such changes result when new substances form. But how can you tell when a new substance is present? Sometimes a gas is produced, which you might see as bubbles in a liquid. Other times, a solid may appear when two solutions are mixed. A solid that forms from solution during a chemical reaction is called a **precipitate** (pree SIP uh tayt). Still other times, a color change or a change in other properties may tell you that a new substance has formed.

All of these kinds of evidence are good indicators of a chemical reaction. But they do not necessarily mean that a chemical reaction has taken place. Sometimes physical changes give similar results. Take, for example, the changes to water described earlier. When water boils, gas bubbles form. When water freezes, solid ice crystals appear. The properties of solid, liquid, and gaseous water differ also. Ice is a hard, sometimes milky white, brittle solid. Liquid water is clear and colorless. Some of the properties differ, but water vapor, ice, and liquid water all are made of hydrogen and oxygen in a 2 to 1 ratio. **The key characteristic of a chemical reaction is the production of new materials that are chemically different from the starting materials.**

Background

Facts and Figures One very obvious chemical reaction is the oxidation that occurs when photochromatic eyeglasses get dark when exposed to sunlight, and lighten when the light is reduced.

Some photochromatic lenses contain tiny crystals of silver chloride (AgCl) and copper chloride (CuCl) which are added during manufacture. The crystals become uniformly embedded in the glass.

When light hits the silver chloride, the chloride ions lose an electron to become chlorine atoms. The silver ions grab the free electrons and become ordinary silver. The presence of silver in the glass makes it darker. Normally, the chlorine gas would escape and the lenses would be permanently darkened, but the copper ions convert the chlorine back to chloride ions.

EXPLORING Evidence for Chemical Reactions

Chemical reactions produce new substances. The signs of a reaction vary, but many reactions include one or more of the following types of evidence.

Color Change A color change often is a sign that a chemical reaction has occurred. The brilliant colors of fall foliage result when green chlorophyll in leaves breaks down. Then colors of other substances in the leaves become visible.

Precipitation Two clear solutions react when mixed, forming a red precipitate. The presence of the precipitate tells you a new substance has formed. So you know a chemical change has taken place.

Gas Production Oxygen bubbles formed during photosynthesis collect on the leaves of this underwater plant. Oxygen is a product of the reaction between carbon dioxide and water inside the cells of the plant.

Changes in Temperature The burning of natural gas (a chemical reaction) supplies heat to boil water (a physical change). An increase or decrease in temperature can result from the changes in energy during a chemical reaction.

Changes in Properties Baking turns flour, water, and other ingredients into light, flaky bread. The loaf of bread with its crunchy crust has very different properties from the soft dough that went into the oven.

Draw students' attention to the photograph showing a precipitate forming in solution. Ask: **Why is the formation of a precipitate in solution evidence of a chemical change?** (*The precipitate is a new material formed by a chemical reaction of the original materials.*) Have students explain how they know a chemical reaction is represented in each photo. Make sure students understand that the water is undergoing a physical change as it boils, but the natural gas is producing heat as a result of a chemical reaction. The color changes in autumn leaves are due, in part, to the *cessation* of a chemical reaction. The plants stop making chlorophyll while existing chlorophyll is broken down. **learning modality: verbal**

Extend Have students work in pairs to prepare a storyboard or poster about a chemical-reaction detective. The poster should illustrate, with examples other than those shown in the text, five clues the detective can use to tell if a chemical reaction has taken place.

Answers to Self-Assessment

☑ Checkpoint

In a physical change, the properties of the substances remain the same. In a chemical change, a new substance is formed with different chemical properties.

Ongoing Assessment

Skills Check Ask students to state several kinds of evidence for a chemical reaction. Have them identify what kind of evidence is most reliable.

Chemical Reactions on a Small Scale

Using the Visuals: Figure 6

Use Figure 6 to help students visualize molecular models. Draw students' attention to the art representing the oxygen molecule. Ask: **How many oxygen atoms combine to form a single molecule of oxygen?** *(two)* **How many oxygen atoms are in one molecule of water?** *(one)* Ask students to infer what happens to the oxygen molecules when oxygen reacts with hydrogen to form water. *(The oxygen molecule is broken apart into individual atoms.)* **learning modality: visual**

Building Inquiry Skills: Applying Concepts

Inform students that the human body contains only about 35 elements, and that the most common elements in the body (by weight) are oxygen, carbon, hydrogen, nitrogen, calcium, and phosphorus. Have students use the letters in the names of the six listed elements to make new words. Then ask: **Were there some combinations of letters that did not form words?** *(Yes)* Point out that the rules of English determine what combinations of letters form words. Encourage students to speculate about whether there are also principles governing how the atoms of elements combine to form molecules. *(Students may speculate that there are principles that determine which chemical bonds can occur between elements to form compounds.)* **learning modality: verbal**

If you walk along a beach, you leave footprints in the sand. Over time, the incoming tide erases them. A beach is constantly changing, as each wave carries new sand in from the ocean and takes some of the shore sand back with it. Sometimes a violent storm can change the outline of a shore in just a few hours, but mostly the beach is changed by wind and water moving sand a little at a time.

Chemical reactions also occur one small step at a time. When you observe evidence of a chemical change, you are detecting the combined effect of countless small, invisible changes. These changes involve tiny particles of matter.

Atoms and Molecules The matter you see is made of particles you can't see. The smallest particle of an element is an **atom.** All the atoms of an element have the same chemical properties, and these are different from the properties of atoms of other elements. Atoms are unbelievably small. One grain of sand on a beach contains more atoms than there are sand grains on the entire beach!

A **molecule** is a particle made of two or more atoms bonded together. Some molecules are made of atoms that are all alike, as in the oxygen gas (O_2) that you breathe. Most molecules, though, are made of more than one type of atom. Water molecules have 2 hydrogen atoms combined with 1 oxygen atom (H_2O).

Figure 5 The sandy cliffs protecting this lighthouse from the ocean have been worn away as wind and water shifted sand one tiny grain at a time. Moving one piece of sand on a large beach doesn't make a change you can see, but moving billions of pieces changes the shoreline forever.

EROSION CONTROL AREA CLOSED

Background

History of Science While the concept of atoms was first developed by Democritus and other ancient Greeks, the Greek atomic theory has no modern scientific value, based as it was on philosophical considerations about the soul and the illusion of change. While the notion of atoms, once discovered, was never completely lost, the only part of Democritus' theory that has been retained in modern times is the word *atom*, which comes from the ancient Greek word *atomos*, meaning indivisible.

The concept of atoms as the basic particle of matter reappeared again in the latter half of the nineteenth century. Even without direct observation to support the idea, it prevailed because it was so useful in explaining the behavior of matter.

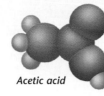

Oxygen   **Water**   **Acetic acid**

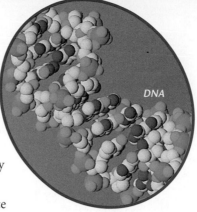

DNA

Acetic acid, the compound that gives vinegar its sharp odor and sour taste, has 2 carbon atoms, 4 hydrogen atoms, and 2 oxygen atoms ($C_2H_4O_2$). Some of the molecules in your body are made of millions of atoms.

Chemical Bonds and Chemical Reactions   The force that holds atoms together is called a **chemical bond.** You can think of chemical bonds as the "glue" that makes atoms "stick" to each other. The types of atoms and how they are joined by chemical bonds determine the properties of a substance. **Chemical reactions occur when chemical bonds break or when new bonds form.** When bonds are broken and new ones are formed, atoms are shuffled, making new substances with different properties.

Some chemical bonds are strong and hard to change. Others break apart easily. Glass is unreactive because the chemical bonds that hold it together are strong. Windows in buildings hundreds of years old show no damage from weather, while wood frames around the glass have rotted away. The wood is made of compounds that react easily with other substances in the environment. It can be softened by water and rotted by fungi. Or it can burn in a fire.

Figure 6 Molecules may be as simple as oxygen. Or, they may be as complex as the DNA in living cells. However, all molecules are made of atoms. (The computer image of DNA was made using a color code for atoms different from the code used in this book.) *Classifying Which one of these is a molecule of an element? How do you know?*

Section 1 Review

1. Tell how an element, a compound, and a mixture differ.
2. What forms of evidence show that a chemical reaction has taken place?
3. What is the difference between an atom and a molecule?
4. What happens to the chemical bonds in a molecule during a chemical reaction?
5. **Thinking Critically Classifying** Classify each of the following as a chemical or a physical change: ice cream melting; sugar dissolving in water; a candle burning; a bathroom mirror fogging as someone showers; milk turning sour.

Check Your Progress   CHAPTER PROJECT 1

Use the information from the section to make a list of signs or evidence that a chemical reaction is taking place. Discuss your list with another classmate. (*Hint:* Look outside your home, think about reactions inside your body, and look for reactions that may occur either very slowly or very quickly.)

Program Resources

◆ **Teaching Resources** 1-1 Review and Reinforce, p. 15; 1-1 Enrich, p. 16

Answers to Self-Assessment

Caption Question

Figure 6 Oxygen, because it is the only molecule made from one kind of atom.

3 Assess

Section 1 Review Answers

1. An element is the simplest kind of substance and cannot be broken down into other substances. A compound is a substance made up of two or more elements combined in a specific ratio. A mixture is made from two or more substances that are not chemically combined as a new substance.
2. The formation of one or more new substances; evidence may be a color change, precipitation, gas production, changes in temperature, changes in properties.
3. An atom is the smallest particle of an element; a molecule is a combination of two or more atoms.
4. Bonds are broken, then new bonds may form.
5. ice cream melting: physical; sugar dissolving: physical; a candle burning: chemical; mirror fogging: physical; milk souring: chemical

Check Your Progress   CHAPTER PROJECT 1

Have students work together to make their lists and check each others' work. Students should develop rules for classifying situations in which evidence of a chemical change may actually signal a physical change. If students have difficulty thinking of places to look for chemical changes, suggest they list rooms in their homes, places they visit during a day, and products they use.

Performance Assessment

Oral Presentation Suggest students prepare three-minute consumer news bulletins to break the news that all matter is composed of elements. They should include information about elements and describe physical and chemical changes in terms of atomic properties.

 Students can save their news bulletins in their portfolios.

L ◆ 21

Where's the Evidence?

Preparing for Inquiry

Key Concept There is often visible evidence that a chemical change is taking place or has taken place. Production of gas bubbles, color change, or production of a precipitate are all indications of chemical reactions.

Skills Objectives Students will be able to
◆ make predictions of results of reactions;
◆ observe evidence of chemical reactions;
◆ infer that a chemical reaction has occurred.

Time 40 minutes

Advance Planning Prepare copper   sulfate solution by dissolving 25 g of $CuSO_4 \cdot 5H_2O$, in 1 liter of water. Prepare sodium carbonate solution by dissolving 13 g of $Na_2CO_3 \cdot H_2O$, in 1 liter of water. Prepare 1.0 M HCl solution by carefully adding 83 mL of concentrated HCl into enough water to make 1,000 mL of solution. CAUTION: *Always add acid to water, never the other way around.* Pour the dilute HCl into individual dropper bottles for student use.

Guiding Inquiry

Invitation

Review the difference between a physical change and a chemical change. Ask students to describe the difference between making careful observations and reaching a conclusion by inference. *(Observations describe only what is taking place. Reaching a conclusion by inference means interpreting the meaning of those observations.)*

Introducing the Procedure

Have students read through the procedure and predict some of the observations they will make during each reaction.

Troubleshooting the Experiment

◆ Part 1: Students will probably call the bubbles air bubbles. Remind them that not all gases are air and they should not jump to conclusions without further evidence.

Skills Lab

Where's the Evidence?

Chemical reactions occur all around you. In this lab you will observe different types of evidence of chemical reactions.

Problem

What are some signs that a chemical reaction has taken place?

Materials

4 small plastic cups	birthday candles
2 plastic spoons	sugar
tongs	clay
matches	
sodium carbonate (powder)	
graduated cylinder, 10 mL	
aluminum foil, about 10-cm square	
dilute hydrochloric acid in a dropper bottle	
copper sulfate solution	
sodium carbonate solution	

Procedure

Preview the steps for each reaction and copy the data table into your notebook.

Part 1

1. Put a pea-sized pile of sodium carbonate into a clean plastic cup. Record the appearance of the sodium carbonate in the data table.
2. Observe a dropper containing hydrochloric acid. Record the appearance of the acid. **CAUTION:** *Hydrochloric acid can burn you or anything else it touches. Wash spills with water.*
3. Make a prediction about how you think the acid and the sodium carbonate will react when mixed. Record your prediction.
4. Add about 10 drops of hydrochloric acid to the sodium carbonate. Swirl to mix the contents of the cup. Record your observations.

Part 2

5. Fold up the sides of the aluminum foil square to make a small tray.
6. Use a plastic spoon to place a pea-sized pile of sugar into the tray.
7. Carefully describe the appearance of the sugar in your data table.

DATA TABLE				
Reaction	Observations Before Reaction	Predictions	Observations During Reaction	Observations After Reaction
1. Sodium carbonate (powder) + hydrochloric acid				
2. Sugar + heat				
3. Copper sulfate + sodium carbonate solutions				

Program Resources

◆ **Teaching Resources** Skills Lab blackline masters, pp. 29–31

Media and Technology

 Lab Activity Videotape *Chemical Interactions*, 1

Safety

Caution students not to mix or burn any materials except as directed in the procedure. Fire safety should be reviewed before students perform Part 2. Instruct students how to safely light the candle. Review the safety guidelines in Appendix A.

8. Secure a small candle on your desktop in a lump of clay. Carefully light the candle with a match only after being instructed to do so by your teacher. **CAUTION:** *Tie back long hair and loose clothing.*

9. Predict what you think will happen if you heat the sugar. Record your prediction.

10. Use tongs to hold the aluminum tray. Heat the sugar slowly by moving the tray gently back and forth over the flame. Make observations while the sugar is heating.

11. When you think there is no longer a chemical reaction occurring, blow out the candle.

12. Allow the tray to cool for a few seconds and set it down on your desk. Record your observations of the material left in the tray.

Part 3

13. Put about 2 mL of copper sulfate solution in one cup. **CAUTION:** *Copper sulfate is poisonous and can stain your skin and clothes. Do not touch it or get it in your mouth.* Put an equal amount of sodium carbonate solution in another cup. Record the appearance of both liquids.

14. Predict what you think will happen when the two solutions are mixed. Record your prediction.

15. Combine the two solutions and record your observations. **CAUTION:** *Dispose of the solutions as directed by your teacher.*

16. Wash your hands when you have finished working.

Analyze and Conclude

1. How do the results of each reaction compare with your predictions for that reaction?

2. How did you know when Reaction 1 was over?

3. Was the product of the reaction in Part 1 a solid, a liquid, or a gas? How do you know?

4. How are the properties of the material remaining after the reaction in Part 2 different from those of the sugar?

5. Was the product of the reaction in Part 3 a solid, a liquid, or a gas? How do you know?

6. How do you know if new substances were formed in each reaction?

7. **Think About It** What senses did you use to make observations during this lab? How might you use scientific instruments to extend your senses in order to make more observations?

More to Explore

Use your observation skills to find evidence of chemical reactions involving foods in your kitchen. Look for production of gases, color changes, and formation of precipitates. Share your findings with your classmates.

- **Part 2:** Students must pay attention so they don't miss the melting of the sugar before the chemical reaction begins. They will probably say that "smoke" is produced. It is actually water vapor produced by the decomposition of the sugar. The solid product is pure carbon.
- **Part 3:** The green color of the copper carbonate precipitate may be difficult to see in the blue copper sulfate solution.

Expected Outcome

- **Part 1:** Sodium carbonate and hydrochloric acid react to produce carbon dioxide gas as one of the products.
- **Part 2:** Sugar melts and then decomposes into pure carbon and water vapor. Students will see vapor and a black crusty product. They will smell a cotton candy smell.
- **Part 3:** The solutions of copper sulfate and sodium carbonate react to produce copper carbonate (a green precipitate) as well as sodium sulfate solution in a double replacement reaction.

Analyze and Conclude

1. Accept all well-explained, logical answers relating predictions to observations.

2. Students may suggest that there was no more bubbling or vapor.

3. The product is a gas. It made gas bubbles in the liquid.

4. The product is black and crusty.

5. Solid. A precipitate was produced.

6. The properties (color, physical state, solubility) changed for the substances in the reactions. This is evidence that there are new substances present.

7. Answers may include sight, sound, smell, or touch. Thermometers could be used to measure changes in temperature. Balances could be used to measure the masses of reactants and products. Microscopes could be used to observe the formation of the precipitate.

Extending the Inquiry

More to Explore Possible answers include: an egg white changing color and texture as an egg is fried; meat changing color when it is cooked; the rising of a cake as a gas (CO_2) is released inside the cake.

Sample Data Table

Reaction	Observations Before Reaction	Predictions	Observations During Reaction	Observations After Reaction
1. Sodium carbonate (powder) + hydrochloric acid	white powder and colorless liquid	accept all answers	bubbles and foaming	colorless liquid, maybe some white solid
2. Sugar + heat	white, granular crystals	accept all answers	bubbles, smoke, turning black	black solid
3. Copper sulfate + sodium carbonate solutions	blue liquid and colorless liquid	accept all answers	reaction too fast	green precipitate

SECTION 2 Describing Chemical Reactions

Objectives

After completing the lesson, students will be able to

◆ describe the information conveyed in a chemical equation;

◆ apply the principle of conservation of mass to chemical reactions;

◆ identify and describe the three categories of chemical reactions.

Key Terms chemical equation, symbol, chemical formula, subscript, reactant, product, conservation of mass, coefficient, synthesis, decomposition, replacement reaction

1 Engage/Explore

Activating Prior Knowledge

As a class, brainstorm a list of symbols that the students are familiar with. Ask: **What symbols did you observe on your way to school today?** *(Samples: bus stop sign, stop sign, crosswalk)* Ask students to use examples to illustrate how symbols are helpful.

········· **DISCOVER** ·········

Skills Focus making models

Materials *about 24 coins of various denominations*

Time 10 minutes

Tips Suggest that students use data tables to record their counts for each trial.

Think It Over The total value and types of coins did not change. Rearranging the coins did not change any individual coins. Students should infer that, like the total value and kinds of coins in the activity, the total number of atoms and the kinds of atoms do not change during chemical reactions.

DISCOVER ···ACTIVITY····

Do You Lose Anything?

1. Place about two dozen coins on a table. Sort them into stacks of pennies, nickels, dimes, and quarters.

2. Count and record the number of coins in each stack. Calculate and record the value of each stack and the total value of all stacks combined.

3. Mix all the coins together and then divide them randomly into four unsorted stacks.

4. Again calculate the value of each stack and the total amount of money. Count the total number of each type of coin.

5. Repeat Steps 3 and 4.

Think It Over
Making Models What happened to the total value and types of coins in this activity? Did rearranging the coins change any individual coin? If you think of the coins as representing different types of atoms, what does this model tell you about chemical reactions?

GUIDE FOR READING

◆ What does a chemical equation tell you?

◆ How does mass change during a chemical reaction?

◆ What are three categories of chemical reactions?

Reading Tip As you read, describe how each boldfaced word relates to a chemical reaction.

Suppose you were to take a walk in a foreign country where the language is unfamiliar to you. Think of the signs you might see—two doors with drawings of a man and a woman, the receiver of a telephone, a drawing of a bicycle, and a picture of a trash can with something dropping into it. You would have no trouble figuring out what these signs mean.

Symbols express a concept in a shorter form. "Hydrogen molecules react with oxygen molecules to form water molecules" is a sentence that describes the reaction between hydrogen and oxygen. But writing it is slow and awkward. A **chemical equation** is a shorter, easier way to show chemical reactions, using symbols instead of words.

Figure 7 Symbols are used as short and easy-to-recognize ways of saying something. *Inferring What information does each of these symbols tell you?*

24 ◆ L

READING STRATEGIES

Reading Tip Before students begin reading, have them preview the chapter to look for boldfaced words. Direct students to write these words on a sheet of notebook paper, leaving at least two lines of space between each term. As students read each section, have them write descriptions of how the key terms relate to chemical reactions.

Study and Comprehension After students finish reading, have them review each section and jot down the main points and important details. Then have students use these notes to write summaries of the information in the section. Students may also want to use the descriptions they wrote for the Reading Tip to summarize the section. Remind students that in a summary, they should briefly state the main points and key details in their own words.

Symbols of Common Elements			
Element	**Symbol**	**Element**	**Symbol**
Oxygen	O	Gold	Au
Hydrogen	H	Silver	Ag
Carbon	C	Sulfur	S
Helium	He	Calcium	Ca
Nitrogen	N	Neon	Ne
Chlorine	Cl	Phosphorus	P
Aluminum	Al	Potassium	K
Iron	Fe	Iodine	I
Sodium	Na	Silicon	Si

Figure 8 The symbols for most elements are the first one or two letters of their names. Some elements have symbols that come from their Latin, Greek, or Arabic names.

Writing Chemical Equations

To write a chemical equation, you have to know what chemicals you are starting with and what new chemicals you get during the reaction. Then you can use symbols to stand for the elements and compounds involved. A **symbol** in chemistry is a one-letter or two-letter set of characters used to identify an element.

Chemical Formulas Most elements are represented by a one- or two-letter symbol. So, how do you represent a compound? If you've looked at Figure 9, you may already know the answer: with a formula. A **chemical formula** is a combination of symbols that represent the elements in a compound. For example, NaCl is the formula for table salt. If you think of symbols of the elements as being like letters of the alphabet, a formula is like a "word" that represents a compound.

Look at the formula for propane in Figure 9. The formula tells you that the compound propane is made of the elements carbon and hydrogen. But a formula does more than just identify the elements in a compound. Notice that there are numbers in the formula that are written smaller and lower than the letter symbols. These numbers are subscripts. **Subscripts** show the number of atoms of an element in a molecule or the ratio of elements in a compound. The formula for propane shows that it has three atoms of carbon and eight atoms of hydrogen.

If a letter symbol in a chemical formula doesn't have a subscript, the number 1 is understood to be there. Carbon dioxide (CO_2), for example, has one carbon atom and two oxygen atoms. Its ratio of carbon atoms to oxygen atoms is 1 to 2. How many atoms in total does a water molecule (H_2O) have? Since the absence of a subscript means that there is one oxygen atom, there are three atoms altogether in a water molecule.

Figure 9 Formulas for compounds tell you what elements as well as how many atoms of each element are present. ***Observing*** *How many oxygen atoms are present in water, carbon dioxide, and sugar?*

Formulas of Familiar Compounds	
Compound	**Formula**
Water	H_2O
Carbon dioxide	CO_2
Carbon monoxide	CO
Methane	CH_4
Propane	C_3H_8
Sugar (sucrose)	$C_{12}H_{22}O_{11}$
Rubbing alcohol	C_3H_8O
Ammonia	NH_3
Sodium chloride	NaCl
Washing soda	Na_2CO_3
Baking soda	$NaHCO_3$

2 Facilitate

Writing Chemical Equations

Language Arts Connection

Students may not understand why not all symbols for elements are made up of the first one or two letters of their names. Inform them that the elements with symbols coming from Latin, Greek, or Arabic are the elements that were discovered earliest. Interested students can research the history of the symbols for gold and silver. **limited English proficiency**

Using the Visuals: Figure 9

Make sure students understand that ionic compounds do not occur as individual molecules (except in the gaseous state). The subscripts in ionic compound formulas represent ratios of atoms in the compound, not atoms in a molecule. After students study the table of formulas in Figure 9, ask: **How many elements make up rubbing alcohol?** *(three)* **How many atoms are in each sugar molecule?** *(12 + 22 + 11 = 45)* Invite students to work in small groups to develop a three-question quiz based on data found in the table. Prompt students' creativity by asking: **Which molecule has 2 elements and 11 atoms?** *(propane)* **Which compounds have the same number of sodium (Na) atoms in their formulas?** *(sodium chloride, baking soda)* Allow groups to exchange and answer their quizzes. **cooperative learning**

Program Resources

- **Teaching Resources** 1-2 Lesson Plan, p. 17; 1-2 Section Summary, p. 18
- **Guided Reading and Study Workbook** Section 1-2

Answers to Self-Assessment

Caption Questions

Figure 7 Bicycle path; rest rooms; traffic signal; waste basket; telephone; No U-turn
Figure 9 1 oxygen atom in water, 2 oxygen atoms in carbon dioxide, 11 oxygen atoms in sugar

Ongoing Assessment

Skills Check Have each student choose three compounds from Figure 9 other than water, carbon dioxide, or sugar, then list the elements that are present in the compounds and how many atoms of each element are in the formulas.

Writing Chemical Equations, continued

Building Inquiry Skills: Making Generalizations

Ask students to compare the general chemical equation and the two equations for specific reactions shown on this page. Ask: **Are there any elements on the left side of the equations that are not also on the right side?** *(No)* Have students rewrite each equation as a sentence. *(Hydrogen combines with oxygen to form hydrogen peroxide; iron plus sulfur yields iron sulfide.)* **learning modality: logical/mathematical**

Conservation of Mass

Inquiry Challenge: Making Measurements

Materials *self-seal plastic bag, baking soda, 10 mL vinegar, small spoon, plastic cup, balance, safety goggles*

ACTIVITY

Time 20 minutes

Tips CAUTION: *Vinegar is a mild acid. Wash spills with water. Make sure students wear goggles.* To begin the activity, have students put a small spoonful of baking soda in the corner of a dry plastic bag and use the balance to find the mass of the baking soda and the bag. Then have students find the mass of an empty plastic cup, add about 10 mL of vinegar, and find the combined mass. Then subtract to find the mass of the vinegar. Ask: **What will the mass of the product and the plastic bag be after the baking soda and vinegar react?** *(It will be equal to the mass of the baking soda, vinegar, and bag before the reaction.)* Then instruct students to carefully pour the vinegar into the bag containing the baking soda and quickly zip the bag closed. After the contents of the bag mix, students can find the total mass and compare it to their predictions. **learning modality: kinesthetic**

Structure of an Equation A chemical equation summarizes a reaction. It tells you the substances you start with and the substances you get at the end. The materials you have at the beginning are called the **reactants.** When the reaction is complete, you have different materials, called the **products** of the reaction. **A chemical equation uses symbols and formulas to show the reactants and the products of a chemical reaction.**

Chemical equations have a definite structure. The formulas for all the reactants are written on the left side of the equation, followed by an arrow. You read the arrow as "yields." The formulas for all the products are on the right:

$$\text{Reactant} + \text{Reactant} \rightarrow \text{Product} + \text{Product}$$

The number of reactants and products can vary. Some reactions have only one reactant or product. Other reactions have two, three, or more reactants or products. Look at the equation for a reaction that forms hydrogen peroxide and count the number of reactants:

$$\underset{\text{Reactant}}{H_2} \quad + \quad \underset{\text{Reactant}}{O_2} \quad \rightarrow \quad \underset{\text{Product}}{H_2O_2}$$

Conservation of Mass

No matter how many reactants and products are involved, all the atoms present at the start of a reaction are present at the end. Think about what happens when classes change at your school. A class is made up of a group of students and a teacher together in one room. When the bell rings, people from each class move from room to room, ending up in different classes. The number of students and teachers in the school has not changed. But their arrangement is different and the new groups interact differently.

Figure 10 When iron filings and sulfur are mixed and heated, the product is the compound iron sulfide. *Interpreting Diagrams How do you know that mass has been conserved in the reaction?*

$$\underset{\text{Iron}}{Fe} \quad + \quad \underset{\text{Sulfur}}{S} \quad \rightarrow \quad \underset{\text{Iron sulfide}}{FeS}$$

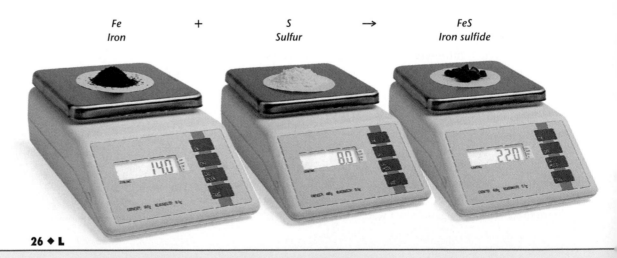

Background

History of Science The principle of conservation of mass was first expressed by Antoine Lavoisier (1743–1794). Lavoisier is often called "The Father of Modern Chemistry." He was a meticulous experimenter and was one of the first to apply quantitative analysis to chemical experiments. He experimented with burning sulfur and phosphorus, carefully measuring the mass of the reactants and the products.

He also duplicated Joseph Priestly's investigations into the combustion of mercury oxide. In these investigations, Lavoisier precisely measured the reactants and products. He concluded that the mass of the reactants in a chemical equation was the same as the mass of the products of that same reaction—nothing is created or destroyed. Lavoisier published his findings in 1789.

Figure 11 Burnt wood and gray ash are all that remain from a roaring fire.
Problem Solving When wood burns, it reacts with oxygen in the air. What masses would you need to measure before and after the fire to show conservation of mass?

Now imagine that all the students and teachers are atoms, and each class is a molecule. At the end of a reaction (similar to a class change), the same atoms are present, but they are grouped together in different molecules. **The amount of matter in a chemical reaction does not change. Therefore, the total mass of the reactants must equal the total mass of the products.** This principle, called the **conservation of mass,** means that during a chemical reaction, matter is not created or destroyed.

At first glance, some reactions seem to violate the principle of conservation of mass. If you measured the cooled ash left from a wood fire, for example, it wouldn't have the same mass as the wood that had been burned. What happened to the missing mass? Much of it escaped into the air as carbon dioxide gas and water vapor. If you could trap and measure these gases, you'd be able to prove that the mass didn't change.

☑ *Checkpoint* *How do the numbers and masses of the atoms in the reactants of a chemical reaction compare with the atoms in the products?*

Balancing Chemical Equations

What does the principle of conservation of mass mean for a chemical equation? Matter is not created or destroyed in a reaction. This means that the same number of atoms exists in the products as in the reactants. To accurately describe a reaction, a chemical equation must show the same number of each type of atom on both sides of the equation. When it does, chemists say the equation is balanced. To balance an equation, first look at the formulas.

$$H_2 \quad + \quad O_2 \quad \rightarrow \quad H_2O$$

How many atoms does an oxygen molecule have? How about hydrogen? How many of each kind of atom are present in one water molecule?

Still There

ACTIVITY

Use nuts and bolts to model the principle of conservation of mass.

1. Measure the mass of a collection of bolts, each with a nut attached to it.
2. Remove all the nuts from the bolts. Measure the total mass of the nuts. Then do the same with the bolts. Add these values.
3. Rearrange your collection, putting two or three nuts on one bolt, one nut on another bolt, and so on. You can even leave a few pieces unattached.
4. Measure the total mass again. Compare this figure with the totals from Steps 1 and 2.

Making Models How are the nuts and bolts similar to atoms and molecules in a chemical reaction? How do your observations model conservation of mass?

Skills Focus making models
Materials *hex nuts and short bolts (from the activity on p. 15), balance*
Time 15 minutes
Tips Encourage students to think of the bolts and nuts as reactants and the combined nuts and bolts as products.
Expected Outcome The total mass of the nuts and bolts will be the same.
Making Models The nuts and bolts are similar to the atoms and molecules in a chemical reaction because even though they are rearranged during the activity, no nuts or bolts are created or destroyed.
Extend Have students use the nuts and bolts to model a reaction. Let the bolts represent iron atoms and the hex nuts represent sulfur atoms. Then model the reaction: $Fe + S \rightarrow FeS$. **learning modality: logical/mathematical**

Balancing Chemical Equations

Building Inquiry Skills: Inferring

On the board, write "Carbon reacts with oxygen to form carbon dioxide." Ask a volunteer to write the appropriate chemical equation below this statement. Ask: **How can we tell this is a balanced equation?** *(It has the same number of carbon and oxygen atoms in the product as in the reactants.)* Explain that when carbon burns in a limited supply of oxygen, carbon monoxide (CO) is formed instead of carbon dioxide. Ask: **How would the balanced equation for this new reaction be different from the one we just completed?** *($2C + O_2 \rightarrow 2CO$)* **learning modality: logical/mathematical**

Answers to Self-Assessment
Caption Questions
Figure 10 The mass of the reactants (14 grams + 8 grams) equals the mass of the product (22 grams).
Figure 11 Measure the masses of the oxygen and wood before the fire, and the ashes and escaped gases afterward.

☑ *Checkpoint*
The numbers of atoms remain equal and their total mass is unchanged.

Ongoing Assessment

Writing Have students explain conservation of mass in chemical reactions in terms of atoms.

Balancing Chemical Equations, continued

Including All Students

Materials *two colors of modeling clay, 2 paper plates, marker*
Time 20 minutes

Some students may need extra help to understand how to balance chemical equations. Write these statements on the board:

◆ One molecule of oxygen has two oxygen atoms.
◆ One molecule of hydrogen has two hydrogen atoms.
◆ One molecule of water has two hydrogen atoms and one oxygen atom.

Direct students to use the clay to model an oxygen molecule, a hydrogen molecule, and a water molecule. Have students label one paper plate "Reactants" and the other "Products," then place their model molecules on the appropriate plates. Ask: **What do you need to do to make the product balance the reactants?** *(Add one hydrogen molecule to the reactants and one water molecule to the product.)* Allow students who are still mastering English to demonstrate their answers with their models. **limited English proficiency**

Sharpen your *Skills*

Calculating

Time 10 minutes
Tips Have volunteers show their calculations on the board. Students should multiply the subscript by the coefficient to find the number of atoms of a substance. If there is no coefficient, the subscript is the number of atoms.

Expected Outcome 3 H_2O: 6 H atoms, 3 O atoms; 2 H_2SO_4: 4 H atoms, 2 S atoms, 8 O atoms; 4 Fe_2O_3: 8 Fe atoms, 12 O atoms; 6 NaCl: 6 Na atoms, 6 Cl atoms; NO_2: 1 N atom, 2 O atoms

Extend Have students compute the number of atoms of each element in some other chemical compounds.
learning modality: logical/ mathematical

Calculating ACTIVITY
Each chemical formula below is written just as it might be in a balanced chemical equation. For each formula, calculate the number of each kind of atom.

3 H_2O
2 H_2SO_4
4 Fe_2O_3
6 NaCl
NO_2

When a coefficient is in front of a formula, how do you find the total number of atoms of one kind? What do you do if there is no coefficient?

Look at the chemical equation and models for the reaction:

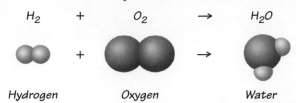

$$H_2 \quad + \quad O_2 \quad \rightarrow \quad H_2O$$

Hydrogen   Oxygen   Water

Count the number of atoms of each element on each side of the equation. You find 2 atoms of oxygen in the reactants but only 1 atom of oxygen in the products.

How can you get the number of oxygen molecules on both sides to be the same? You might be tempted to balance the oxygen by changing the formula for water to H_2O_2. Don't even think about it! Remember that H_2O_2 is the formula for hydrogen per-oxide, a completely different compound.

To balance the equation, use a coefficient. A **coefficient** (koh uh FISH unt) is a number placed *in front of* a chemical formula in the equation. It tells you how many atoms or molecules of each reactant and product take part in the reaction. If the coefficient is 1, you don't need to write it. Balance the number of oxygen atoms by writing the coefficient 2 for water. It's like saying "2 × H_2O." Now there are 2 oxygen atoms in the product.

$$H_2 \quad + \quad O_2 \quad \rightarrow \quad 2\ H_2O$$

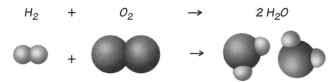

Okay, you've balanced the oxygen atoms. But now there are 2 hydrogen atoms in the reactants and 4 in the product. How can you balance the hydrogen? Try doubling the number of hydrogen atoms on the left side of the equation by changing the coefficient for hydrogen to 2. You've got it! Here is the balanced equation:

$$2\ H_2 \quad + \quad O_2 \quad \rightarrow \quad 2\ H_2O$$

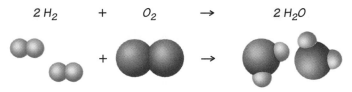

Now there are 4 hydrogen atoms and 2 oxygen atoms on each side. The equation is balanced. It tells you that 2 molecules of hydrogen react with 1 molecule of oxygen to yield 2 molecules of water. Count the atoms in the last diagram. Prove to yourself that the balanced equation is correct.

Background

Integrating Science Students may suggest that photosynthesis and cell respiration are, respectively, examples of synthesis and decomposition reactions. From a chemist's perspective, however, these reactions do not fit the strict definitions of the terms. A decomposition yields two or more simple products from one complex reactant. A synthesis does just the opposite, forming one product from two or more simpler reactants.

Photosynthesis yields two products (sugar and oxygen), while cell respiration, an oxidation reaction, uses two reactants (glucose and oxygen).

The classification of chemical reactions is useful for understanding basic mechanisms, but only to a point. Many reactions involve more than one kind of change and/or several steps, and cannot be cleanly categorized.

Sample Problem

When magnesium metal, Mg, reacts with oxygen, O_2, the product of the reaction is magnesium oxide, MgO. Write a balanced equation for this reaction.

Write the word equation.	Magnesium + Oxygen $\rightarrow$ Magnesium oxide
Write the chemical equation.	$Mg + O_2 \rightarrow MgO$
Count the number of atoms of each element on each side of the equation.	Mg O Mg O one two one one
Choose coefficients to balance the equation.	$2\,Mg + O_2 \rightarrow 2\,MgO$
Think about it.	The answer shows 2 magnesium atoms and 2 oxygen atoms on each side, so the equation is balanced.

Practice Problems

1. Balance the equation: $C + Cl_2 \rightarrow CCl_4$

2. Balance the equation: $Al_2O_3 \rightarrow Al + O_2$

Classifying Chemical Reactions

Chemical reactions can be classified by what happens to the reactants and products. Substances may add together to make a more complex substance. They may break apart to make simpler substances. Or substances may even exchange parts. In each case, new materials form. **Many chemical reactions can be classified in one of three categories: synthesis, decomposition, or replacement.** As you read about each of these kinds of reactions, look at the examples. Compare the reactants and the products to see how they change.

Synthesis Have you ever listened to music from a synthesizer? You can hear many different notes and types of musical sounds. The synthesizer combines these sounds to make a complicated piece of music. When two or more substances (elements or compounds) combine to make a more complex substance, the process is called **synthesis** (SIN thuh sis). To synthesize is to put things together. Look back at the reaction of hydrogen and oxygen to make water. You should see now that this is a synthesis reaction—two elements come together, making a compound.

 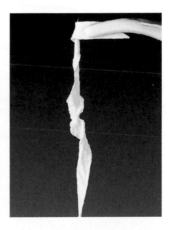

Figure 12 When a ribbon of magnesium metal burns in air (left), it combines with oxygen to form magnesium oxide (right). The shiny metal and colorless gas become a white powdery solid. *Classifying Why is this a synthesis reaction?*

Sample Problem

Have a volunteer demonstrate how to count the number of atoms of each element on each side of the equation. Invite a second volunteer to explain how to choose coefficients that will balance the equation.

Practice Problems
1. $C + 2\,Cl_2 \rightarrow CCl_4$
2. $2\,Al_2O_3 \rightarrow 4\,Al + 3\,O_2$

Classifying Chemical Reactions

Building Inquiry Skills: Applying Concepts

To help students understand the classifications for chemical reactions, write these statements on the board:
◆ hand + kerchief $\rightarrow$ handkerchief
◆ schoolbook $\rightarrow$ school + book
◆ television screen + door knob $\rightarrow$ television knob + screen door
Tell students the letters in the statement represent atoms and the words represent molecules. Inform them that the first statement represents *synthesis* (letters in words combine to make a more complex word), the second statement represents *decomposition* (a word broken apart to make simpler words), and the third represents *replacement* (words combine to form new words) Challenge students to come up with new statements for each type of reaction. **learning modality: verbal**

Answers to Self-Assessment

Caption Question

Figure 12 Two elements, magnesium and oxygen, combine to form a compound.

Ongoing Assessment

Writing Have students prepare step-by-step directions explaining how to write a balanced equation for tarnished silver. The reactants are silver (Ag) and hydrogen sulfide (H_2S). The products are Ag_2S and H_2. ($2\,Ag + H_2S \rightarrow Ag_2S + H_2$)

Classifying Chemical Reactions, continued

Integrating Environmental Science

Open the discussion by asking what students know about acid rain. Then have them visit the Environmental Protection Agency's Web site at **www.epa.gov** to find information on acid rain. Or you may have students do research in the library. When they have finished, students can prepare reports about the problem and suggest ways the amount of acid rain might be reduced.
learning modality: verbal

Demonstration

Materials *safety goggles, lab aprons, granulated sugar, concentrated sulfuric acid, 50-mL heat-resistant beaker, 100-mL graduated cylinder*

ACTIVITY

Time 15 minutes

Tips CAUTION: *Sulfuric acid will burn skin and clothing. Avoid direct contact. You and your students should wear safety goggles and lab aprons, and you should wear protective gloves. Wash spills and splashes with plenty of water. Remind students that the* formula for sugar is $C_{12}H_{22}O_{11}$. Ask them to predict what will happen when sulfuric acid is added to sugar. Then pour in ordinary table sugar to the 20-mL mark on the beaker. CAUTION: *You may wish to use a slightly larger beaker because the volume of the product will be significantly greater than the volume of the sugar, and it will overflow if the beaker is too small.* Next, slowly add 7–10 mL of the acid to the sugar. The reaction takes 60–90 seconds to finish, and the beaker will be VERY hot. Explain that the black column formed is primarily carbon. Students may notice the water vapor that is given off. Ask: **Is this reaction synthesis, decomposition, or replacement? Why?** *(Decomposition, because the sugar was broken down into the simpler products.)* The simplest way of explaining this reaction is to tell students that sulfuric acid attracts water so strongly that it will pull hydrogen and oxygen right out of the sugar, forming water and leaving the carbon behind.
learning modality: visual

 INTEGRATING ENVIRONMENTAL SCIENCE Acid rain is a product of synthesis reactions. In one case, sulfur dioxide, oxygen, and water combine to make sulfuric acid. Look at the equation for the reaction. Can you find the 8 oxygen atoms on each side of the equation?

$$2\,SO_2 \quad + \quad O_2 \quad + \quad 2\,H_2O \quad \rightarrow \quad 2\,H_2SO_4$$

Sulfur dioxide   Oxygen   Water   Sulfuric acid

Sulfur dioxide comes from car engines or from power plants that burn coal. Oxygen and water vapor are in the air. Together they produce sulfuric acid, which causes rainwater to become corrosive. This acid water then eats away at stone and metal, and can damage living organisms.

Decomposition While a synthesis reaction builds compounds from simpler reactants, a process called **decomposition** breaks down compounds into simpler products. Remember the bottle of hydrogen peroxide used to clean cuts? If you keep such a bottle for a very long time, you'll have water instead. The hydrogen peroxide decomposes into water and oxygen gas.

$$2\,H_2O_2 \rightarrow 2\,H_2O + O_2$$

The oxygen that is produced escapes into the air.

✓ *Checkpoint* *How do synthesis and decomposition differ?*

Figure 13 Safety airbags in cars inflate as a result of a decomposition reaction. On impact, a detonator cap inside the air bag explodes. The explosion causes a compound made of sodium and nitrogen to decompose. One product is a large quantity of nitrogen gas.
Applying Concepts Why would quick inflation of airbags be important?

Background

Facts and Figures Sulfuric acid, also called oil of vitriol, or hydrogen sulfate, is a dense, colorless, oily, corrosive liquid. The acid, sometimes referred to as the "king of chemicals" is produced worldwide in enormous quantities. Annual production in the United States, the world's leading producer, is well over 39 billion kilograms. Nearly half the manufactured acid is used to produce phosphates and other fertilizers. Other uses for sulfuric acid include the manufacture of high-octane gasoline, explosives, rayon, the processing of uranium, and the pickling of steel. The acid also is used in the manufacture of pigments, dyes, drugs, and detergents. In its most familiar application, sulfuric acid is the electrolyte in lead-acid storage batteries.

Replacement When one element replaces another in a compound, or when two elements in different compounds trade places, the process is called **replacement**. Copper metal, for example, can be obtained by heating rock containing copper oxide in the presence of charcoal. The carbon of the charcoal takes the place of copper in the copper oxide. You can write the reaction as:

$$2\,CuO + C \rightarrow 2\,Cu + CO_2$$

Obtaining copper metal from rock is a simple replacement reaction. However, not all chemical reactions can be classified clearly as synthesis, decomposition, or replacement. Look carefully at the formulas of the reactants and products for clues to what type of reaction the equation shows.

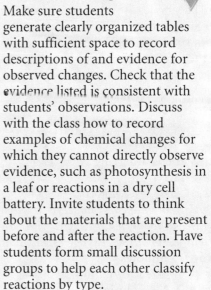

Figure 14 Copper metal can be chemically obtained from copper ore. Copper oxide (in the ore) reacts with carbon in a replacement reaction.

Section 2 Review

1. What information do you need in order to write a chemical equation?
2. What is the principle of conservation of mass?
3. List and define three categories of chemical reactions.
4. **Thinking Critically Applying Concepts**
   Balance the following chemical equations by adding coefficients:
   a. $HCl + NaOH \rightarrow H_2O + NaCl$
   b. $Fe_2O_3 + C \rightarrow Fe + CO_2$
   c. $SO_2 + O_2 \rightarrow SO_3$
5. **Thinking Critically Classifying** Classify each of the following reactions as synthesis, decomposition, or replacement:
   a. $2\,NH_4NO_3 \rightarrow 2\,N_2 + O_2 + 4\,H_2O$
   b. $2\,Al + Fe_2O_3 \rightarrow Al_2O_3 + 2\,Fe$
   c. $MgCl_2 + K_2S \rightarrow MgS + 2\,KCl$
   d. $P_4O_{10} + 6\,H_2O \rightarrow 4\,H_3PO_4$

Check Your Progress CHAPTER PROJECT 1

Prepare a table to keep track of the chemical changes you observe. Have your teacher check your table to be sure it contains the proper headings. Record the different chemical changes you observe for a week. Make sure you can describe the evidence for each chemical change. If possible, classify each reaction as a synthesis, decomposition, or replacement reaction. Also classify it as occurring in a living or nonliving setting.

Section 2 Review Answers

1. The reactants, the products, and their chemical formulas
2. In a chemical reaction, the total mass of the reactants is equal to the total mass of the products.
3. In a synthesis reaction, substances combine to form a new substance. In a decomposition reaction, compounds break apart into simpler substances. In a replacement reaction, one element replaces another in a compound.
4. **a.** already balanced;
   b. $2\,Fe_2O_3 + 3\,C \rightarrow 4\,Fe + 3\,CO_2$;
   c. $2\,SO_2 + O_2 \rightarrow 2\,SO_3$
5. **a.** decomposition; **b.** replacement;
   c. replacement; **d.** synthesis

Check Your Progress CHAPTER PROJECT 1

Make sure students generate clearly organized tables with sufficient space to record descriptions of and evidence for observed changes. Check that the evidence listed is consistent with students' observations. Discuss with the class how to record examples of chemical changes for which they cannot directly observe evidence, such as photosynthesis in a leaf or reactions in a dry cell battery. Invite students to think about the materials that are present before and after the reaction. Have students form small discussion groups to help each other classify reactions by type.

Program Resources

Science Explorer Series
Environmental Science, Chapter 5
◆ **Teaching Resources** 1-2 Review and Reinforce, p. 19; 1-2 Enrich, p. 20

Answers to Self-Assessment

Caption Question
Figure 13 In a car crash, the airbags must inflate in time to stop the passengers from hitting the dashboard or windshield.

☑ *Checkpoint*
Synthesis reactions build compounds from simpler reactants; decomposition reactions break down compounds into simpler substances.

Performance Assessment

Drawing Direct students to compose posters explaining how to classify a chemical reaction. Posters should describe the differences and similarities between the types of reactions.

 Students can save their posters in their portfolios.

L ◆ 31

SECTION
3 Controlling
Chemical
Reactions

Objectives

After completing the lesson, students will be able to

◆ explain that every chemical reaction requires activation energy to get started;
◆ list factors that control the rate of chemical reactions.

Key Terms exothermic reaction, endothermic reaction, activation energy, concentration, catalyst, enzyme, inhibitor

1 Engage/Explore

Activating Prior Knowledge

Ask students to explain why milk, meat, and vegetables are kept cool. Most students will say that this keeps them from spoiling. Ask: **Does food ever spoil in the refrigerator?** *(Yes)* Elicit the idea that the reactions that spoil food slow down at lower temperatures.

•••••••••• **DISCOVER** ••••••••

Skills Focus inferring
Materials *clear plastic cups, 3 heat-resistant beakers(500-mL), solutions of vitamin C tablets and water at three different temperatures, tincture of iodine, spoon, safety goggles, lab apron*
Time 10 minutes
Tips Prepare the vitamin C 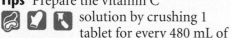 solution by crushing 1 tablet for every 480 mL of water. Each group will need 120 mL of the solution at each temperature. Pour one-third of the prepared solution into each beaker. Leave one at room temperature, chill one in an ice water bath, and heat the third in the beaker to about 75°C on a hot plate. Do not boil. Caution students to avoid spills and splashes—iodine can stain skin and clothing.
Expected Outcome Vitamin C reacts with iodine and turns it colorless.
Think It Over At higher temperatures, the vitamin C and iodine react faster.

DISCOVER •••••••••••••••••••••••• ACTIVITY•••

Can You Speed Up or Slow Down a Reaction?

1. Put on your safety goggles and lab apron.

2. Obtain about 125 mL each of three solutions of vitamin C and water—one at room temperature, one at about 75°C, and one chilled to between 5° and 10°C.

3. Add three drops of iodine solution to each container and stir each with a clean spoon. Compare changes you observe in the solutions.

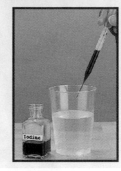

4. Clean up your work area and wash your hands.

Think It Over
Inferring What conclusion can you make about the effect of temperature on the reaction of iodine and vitamin C?

GUIDE FOR READING

◆ How is energy related to chemical reactions?
◆ How can you control the rate of a chemical reaction?

Reading Tip As you read, make a list of factors affecting reaction rate.

You are working on an engineering team that tears down buildings. "3, 2, 1 . . . Let it go!" You push a button and suddenly a loud rumbling sound starts. The ground shakes, and clouds of dust pour into the street. In 15 seconds, a tall building is reduced to a pile of rubble. Careful control of energy in the explosion is critical to collapse the building without even breaking a window next door. If the demolition expert on your team doesn't understand the chemical reactions used, people could be injured or property damaged.

Although you may never demolish a building, you do use energy from controlled chemical reactions every day. Every time your body converts your lunch into the energy to play sports or you go for a ride in a car, you are using controlled reactions.

Figure 15 Building demolition requires a good understanding of chemical reactions.

READING STRATEGIES

Reading Tip Have students write "What Can Affect Reaction Rate?" on a sheet of paper. Then, as students read the section, instruct them to list and briefly describe the factors that affect reaction rate.

Study and Comprehension Have students preview the section by reading the headings, subheadings, and captions and looking at the pictures.

Program Resources

◆ **Teaching Resources** 1-3 Lesson Plan, p. 21; 1-3 Section Summary, p. 22
◆ **Guided Reading and Study Workbook** Section 1-3

Energy in Chemical Reactions

Light is a type of energy. Other forms of energy include electricity and the energy of a moving object. **Every chemical reaction involves a change of energy. Some reactions release energy and others absorb energy.**

The reaction between gasoline and oxygen in a car engine yields carbon dioxide, water, and other products. It also releases a lot of energy. You can detect one form of this energy as heat. The engine of a car gets hot enough to burn you if you touch it. A reaction that releases energy in the form of heat is called an **exothermic reaction** (ek soh THUR mik).

If you did the Discover activity in Section 1, you observed that the mixture became colder. When baking soda (sodium bicarbonate) reacts with vinegar, the reaction takes heat from the solution, making it feel cooler. This kind of reaction, which absorbs energy, is called an **endothermic reaction** (en doh THUR mik).

Figure 17 compares the changes in energy of exothermic and endothermic reactions. Notice that the energy of the products in an exothermic reaction is lower than the energy of the reactants. In an exothermic reaction, energy is released. This is the case when gasoline burns. Now see how an endothermic reaction is different. In an endothermic reaction, the energy of the products is greater than the energy of the reactants. This means energy is absorbed. That's what happened with the baking soda and vinegar.

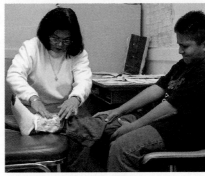

Figure 16 The endothermic reaction inside a cold pack helps cool this boy's injured ankle. Such rapid treatment after an injury reduces pain and speeds up healing.

Getting Reactions Started

Trace each diagram in Figure 17 from left to right with your finger. As your finger moves, do you notice how the curve goes up and over a rise? Then your finger moves down toward the products. All chemical reactions need energy to get started. The **activation energy** is the minimum amount of energy needed to start a chemical reaction.

Figure 17 Every chemical reaction needs a certain amount of energy to get started. *Interpreting Diagrams Where are increases and decreases in energy shown in each diagram?*

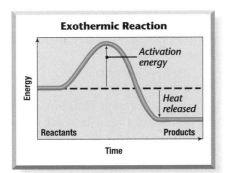

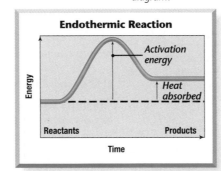

Chapter 1 **L ◆ 33**

Media and Technology

Transparencies "Energy in Chemical Reactions," Transparency 2

Exploring Physical Science Videodisc
Unit 2, Side 2, "Fast Reactions?"

Chapter 5

Answers to Self-Assessment

Caption Question

Figure 17 In both diagrams, energy increases until the energy level is high enough for the reaction to start, then energy decreases. In an exothermic reaction, the energy level decreases as the products form. In an endothermic reaction, the energy level increases as the products form.

---

2 Facilitate

Energy in Chemical Reactions

Including All Students

Some students may need extra help to remember the difference between the terms "exothermic" and "endothermic." Suggest students say to themselves "Exo—go out; endo—go in" to help them remember that during an exothermic reaction, energy moves outward, and during an endothermic reaction, energy is absorbed. **limited English proficiency**

Getting Reactions Started

Using the Visuals: Figure 17

Have students describe the general shape of each graph in the figure. Ask: **What does the "hump" in each graph represent?** *(The energy needed to start a reaction)* Challenge students to infer what happens before a reaction starts. Ask: **If energy is added to a mixture or substance and there is no reaction, does that mean the elements cannot react with each other?** *(No. It may mean there is not enough energy to start the reaction.)* **learning modality: logical/ mathematical**

Ongoing Assessment

Skills Check Call on students to tell you what kind of reaction it is when the products feel hot and when they feel cold.

L ◆ 33

Social Studies CONNECTION

Inform students that the *Hindenburg* carried twenty tons of water ballast that could be dropped in order to make an emergency ascent. Ask: **Why do you think this water did not stop the fire?** *(Because the fire may have started in an area of the ship away from the water. It may have grown too large and too rapidly for the water to have an effect.)* Encourage students to infer what kind of reaction occurred during the disaster. *(exothermic)* Ask: **What evidence do you have?** *(Flames indicate that energy was released)*

In Your Journal Remind students that a good newspaper article includes the *who, what, when, where,* and *how* of a story. In this report, students should fully explain the *how* of the *Hindenburg* disaster. **learning modality: verbal**

Using the Visuals: Figure 18

Draw students' attention to the cartoon. Ask them to describe what is happening in their own words. They should compare the amount of energy given to the rock as it is lifted over the small hump to the amount of energy released as it falls. Then have students compare Figure 18 to Figure 17 and ask them to classify the "reaction" in Figure 18 as "exothermic" or "endothermic." *(Notice that the profile of the "mountain" resembles the exothermic reaction in Figure 17. However, don't push this analogy too far.)*

Figure 18 The rock at the top of this hill cannot roll down the hill until a small push gets it going.

Social Studies CONNECTION

In the early part of the 1900s, people sometimes traveled in airships called dirigibles. Unlike modern airships, which are filled with unreactive helium, some dirigibles contained flammable hydrogen. On May 6, 1937, the airship *Hindenburg* came in for a landing over Lakehurst, New Jersey. Somehow the ship caught fire. Seconds later, its 200,000 cubic meters of hydrogen gas burst into flame, killing 36 people. The *Hindenburg* was a tragic example of how much energy can be released during a chemical reaction.

In Your Journal

Pretend you are a reporter covering the *Hindenberg* disaster. Write a brief news article explaining how the reaction between hydrogen and oxygen affected the disaster.

The reaction that makes water from hydrogen and oxygen is very exothermic. It gives off tremendous amounts of energy. But if you make a mixture of hydrogen and oxygen, it could remain unchanged for years. For the reaction to start, a tiny amount of activation energy—just a spark—is needed. Once a few molecules of hydrogen and oxygen react, the rest will follow, because the large amount of energy released provides the activation energy for more molecules to react.

Think of a chemical reaction as being like a rock resting behind a ridge at the top of a hill. The rock stays put until someone or something adds energy by giving it a push. With enough energy, the rock can move over the hump and roll down the hill. The same idea applies to a chemical reaction. With enough energy, reactants can get "over the hump" and form products.

It's not always clear where the energy to start a reaction comes from. In the case of vinegar and baking soda, heat already in the solution provides the energy to get the reaction started. This reaction is endothermic. To keep it going, more energy is continually drawn from the solution. As a result, the mixture gets cooler.

☑ *Checkpoint* **What is the difference between an endothermic reaction and an exothermic reaction?**

Rates of Chemical Reactions

Chemical reactions don't all occur at the same rate. Some, like explosions, are very fast. Others, like the rusting of metal, are much slower. Also, a particular reaction can occur at different rates in different conditions. How fast a reaction happens depends on how easily the particles of the reactants can get together.

Background

Facts and Figures Before widespread use of the airplane, dirigibles (also called airships or zeppelins), such as the *Hindenburg,* made passenger flights across the Atlantic to Brazil and the United States. In 1936, the *Hindenburg* carried over 1,000 passengers on ten round trips between Germany and the United States. It could travel at a maximum speed of 135 km/h, and its typical cruising speed was 126 km/h.

The most visible of today's airships are the helium-filled blimps that are frequently seen at major sporting events and fairs. The largest of the Goodyear airships, the GZ-22, is about one-fourth the size of the gigantic *Hindenburg.*

If you want to make a reaction happen faster, you need to get more particles of the reactants together more often. To slow down a reaction, you need to do the opposite—get fewer particles together less often. Chemists do this by controlling the conditions of a reaction. **The rate of a chemical reaction is affected by such factors as concentration, surface area, and temperature, and by using substances called catalysts and inhibitors.**

Concentration One way to increase the rate of a reaction is to increase the concentration of the reactants. **Concentration** is the amount of one material in a given volume of another material. For example, adding a small spoonful of sugar to a glass of lemonade will make it sweet. But adding a large spoonful of sugar makes the lemonade a lot sweeter! The glass with more sugar has a greater concentration of sugar molecules.

Increasing the concentrations of the reactants makes more particles available to react. Compare the test tubes in Figure 19. In the test tube on the right, the greater concentration of acid means more acid particles are present to react with the magnesium metal. You can see evidence for the increased rate of reaction in the greater number of bubbles that are produced.

Surface Area When a chunk of solid material reacts with a liquid or a gas, only the particles on the surface of the solid come in contact with the other reactant. Now suppose you break the solid into smaller pieces. What happens? You've increased the

Figure 19 Bubbles of hydrogen form when magnesium reacts with an acid. The test tube on the left has a lower concentration of acid than the test tube on the right. *Relating Cause and Effect How does the concentration of acid affect the rate of the reaction?*

Figure 20 The concrete walls of this grain elevator in Kansas were blown apart by an explosion when grain particles and oxygen above the stored wheat exploded. Grain dust has a much greater surface area exposed to air than the top surface of a pile of grain does.

Chapter 1 **L ◆ 35**

Answers to Self-Assessment

Caption Question

Figure 19 The higher the concentration of the acid, the faster the reaction proceeds.

☑ *Checkpoint*

An endothermic reaction absorbs energy; an exothermic reaction releases energy.

Rates of Chemical Reactions, continued

Inquiry Challenge

Materials *fizzing antacid tablets, two cups, hot and cold tap water*

Time 15 minutes

Tips Divide the class into small groups. Give each group two antacid tablets and two plastic cups. For best results, use fresh antacid tablets. Have groups fill the cups with hot and cold tap water. Ask: **Do you think the antacid will react faster in the hot water or in the cold water?** Then have students drop the tablets into the water and observe what happens. Ask: **Why did this happen?** *(The energy from the faster moving particles in the warm water helped the antacid get over the energy hump.)*
learning modality: kinesthetic

Sharpen your Skills

Interpreting Data

Materials *gelatin cubes, plastic knife, ruler*

Time 15 minutes

Tips To prepare the gelatin, double the amount of gelatin called for. Use a hot knife to cut the solid gelatin into 5-cm squares. Make sure students understand they should compare the total surface area of the single whole cube with that of the two smaller half cubes.

Expected Outcome The total surface area increases when the cube is cut in half. Students should predict that cutting it in half again will increase the total surface area.

Extend Students can graph changes in surface area vs. the number of times the gelatin cube is cut in half. Have them use their graphs to predict the surface area if the original cube had been cut into sixteen equal-sized pieces.

Sharpen your Skills

Interpreting Data

1. Measure the length and width of a face of a gelatin cube.
2. Calculate the area of that face of the cube.
   Area = length × width
   Repeat for each of the other five faces. Then add the six values together to get the total surface area.
3. Using a plastic knife, cut the cube in half and repeat Steps 1 and 2 for each piece of gelatin. Add the surface areas of the two pieces to get the new total surface area.

4. How did the total surface area of the cube before it was cut compare with the total surface area after it was cut?
5. Predict what would happen to the total surface area if you cut each cube in two again. If you have time, test your prediction.

surface area of the solid. More particles of the material are exposed, so the reaction happens faster. That's also what happens when you chew your food. Chewing breaks the food into smaller pieces. Your digestive juices can then work more quickly to change the food into nutrients your body can use.

Temperature A third way to increase the rate of a reaction is to increase its temperature. When you heat a substance, its particles move faster. Faster-moving particles increase the reaction rate in two ways. First, they come in contact more often, which means there are more chances for a reaction to happen. Second, faster-moving particles have more energy. This energy helps the reactants get over the activation energy "hump."

Did you ever leave a glass of milk out on the kitchen counter when you left for school? When you picked it up again later, the milk may have had a sour smell. When foods are left unrefrigerated, bacteria in them reproduce quickly. As they live and reproduce, the bacteria carry out thousands of chemical reactions. Some reactions can cause food to spoil. Keeping foods cold slows these reactions and the growth of the organisms that cause them. Your food stays fresh longer.

Catalysts Another way to control the rate of a reaction is to change the activation energy. If you decrease the activation energy, the reaction happens faster. A **catalyst** (KAT uh list) is a material that increases the rate of a reaction by lowering the activation energy. Catalysts help with the reaction, but they are not permanently changed in the reaction. Therefore, they are not considered reactants.

Figure 21 Unrefrigerated foods quickly spoil from the chemical reactions carried out by microorganisms. Keeping foods cold slows these changes.

Many chemical reactions happen at temperatures that would be deadly to living things. Yet, some of these reactions are necessary for life. The cells in your body (as in all living things) contain biological catalysts called **enzymes** (EN zymz). Enzymes provide a surface on which reactions take place. This helps reactions happen at lower temperatures because it lowers activation energy. In this way, enzymes safely increase the reaction rates of chemical reactions necessary for life. An enzyme breaks away unchanged at the end of a reaction.

Inhibitors Sometimes a reaction is more useful when it can be slowed down rather than speeded up. A material used to decrease the rate of a reaction is called an **inhibitor.**

The discovery of one inhibitor had an important effect on the construction industry. Nitroglycerin is a powerful liquid explosive that decomposes quickly, releasing tremendous energy. An explosion can be caused just by shaking the bottle! In the 1860s, Alfred Nobel tried adding certain solid materials, such as wood pulp, to the nitroglycerin. The solids absorbed the liquid and kept it from reacting until it was detonated. This mixture could be handled more safely and still be used for blasting. Nobel's discovery is the more easily controlled material known as dynamite.

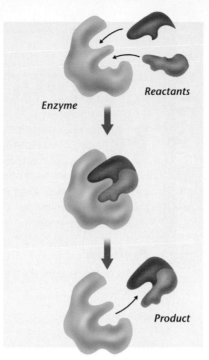
Reactants
Enzyme
Product

Figure 22 Enzyme molecules are shaped in ways that help reactant molecules come together.

Section 3 Review

1. Compare the change of energy in an exothermic reaction to that in an endothermic reaction.
2. Which has greater surface area: a sugar cube or an equal mass of sugar crystals? Explain.
3. Compare and contrast catalysts and inhibitors.
4. **Thinking Critically Relating Cause and Effect** Copy and complete the table below to show how some factors increase, decrease, or have no effect on rate of a reaction.

Changes	Effect on Reaction Rate
Decreased concentration	
Increased surface area	
Heat added	
Catalyst	

Science at Home

Place an iron nail in a plastic cup. Add enough water to almost cover the nail. Place a small piece of fine steel wool in another cup and add the same amount of water. Ask family members to predict what will happen overnight. The next day, examine the nail and steel wool. Compare the amount of rust on each. Were your family's predictions correct? Explain how reaction rates are affected by surface areas.

Chapter 1   **L ◆ 37**

Program Resources

◆ **Teaching Resources** 1-3 Review and Reinforce, p. 23; Enrich, p. 24

Media and Technology

Transparencies "How an Enzyme Works," Transparency 4

Exploring Physical Science Videodisc Unit 2, Side 2, "Endothermic and Exothermic Reactions"   Chapter 4

Explain to students that human body temperature is normally around 37°C. Ask: **Can the reactions necessary to support life occur at this temperature without enzymes?** (*No. These reactions would proceed too slowly.*) **learning modality: logical/mathematical**

3 Assess

Section 3 Review Answers

1. Exothermic reaction—energy of products is lower than energy of reactants; endothermic reaction—energy of products is higher than energy of reactants
2. The sugar crystals
3. A catalyst lowers the level of activation energy needed to start a reaction, so the reaction happens faster. An inhibitor causes a reaction to happen slower.
4. Decreased concentration—RR decreases; increased surface area—RR increases; heat added—RR increases; catalyst—RR increases

Science at Home

Materials *nail, fine-grade steel wool, 2 plastic cups, water*
Tips Students should use a nongalvanized nail. Point out that steel wool is made of iron mixed with carbon. Students should predict that much more rust will be visible on the steel wool because it has a greater surface area than the nail.

Performance Assessment

Oral Presentation Have students plan presentations that explain how to control chemical reactions. Presentations should discuss the factors affecting reaction rates and the role of catalysts and inhibitors and should use specific examples. Students can use drawings or demonstrations to illustrate their explanations.

L ◆ 37

Peroxide, Catalase, and You

Preparing for Inquiry

Key Concept Students will study the effect of temperature on catalyzed reactions.

Skills Objectives Students will be able to

◆ measure the time it takes for a reaction to occur;

◆ graph their data;

◆ draw conclusions about the effect of temperature on reaction rate.

Time 50 minutes

Advance Planning Prepare the catalase solution by placing fresh liver in a blender or food processor. Blend until it is soupy, add twice the volume of distilled water, and swirl to mix. Make about a dozen disks for each group by using a one-hole punch to punch disks out of filter paper. Place disks in the solution and stir gently. Divide the disks and solution into fourths and place in beakers. Keep one beaker at room temperature. Place one beaker in an ice water bath, one in a bath of 37°C water, and one in a boiling water bath. Monitor the temperatures of the baths. Dilute 3% hydrogen peroxide solution to 0.1% by adding 20 volumes of distilled water. (Add 500 mL of distilled water to 25 mL of 3% hydrogen peroxide.)

Suggested Shortcuts Have students work with partners. To reduce the time even more, the class can be divided into two groups. Have half of the class do two of the temperatures and the other half do the other two temperatures.

Guiding Inquiry

Invitation

Ask students who have used hydrogen peroxide to clean a wound to describe what happened. *(It foamed and bubbled. See the photo on p. 39.)* Explain that this is caused by a reaction between hydrogen peroxide and catalase, an enzyme found in organisms from potatoes to cattle. Humans have catalase in their blood, which explains why hydrogen peroxide bubbles when it contacts blood.

Peroxide, Catalase, & You!

Hydrogen peroxide is a poisonous waste product of reactions in living cells. An enzyme called catalase, found in the blood, speeds up the breakdown of hydrogen peroxide into harmless water and oxygen gas. In this lab, you will explore the action of catalase under changing conditions.

Problem

How does temperature affect the action of an enzyme?

Skills Focus

measuring, controlling variables, drawing conclusions

Materials

forceps
stopwatch
test tube with a one-hole stopper
0.1% hydrogen peroxide solution
filter paper disks soaked in liver preparation (catalase enzyme) and kept at four different temperatures (room temperature, 0–4°C, 37°C, and 100°C)
container to hold water (beaker or bowl)

Procedure

1. Form a hypothesis that predicts how the action of the catalase enzyme will differ at the different temperatures to be tested.

2. Fill a container with water. Then fill a test tube with 0.1% hydrogen peroxide solution until the test tube is overflowing. Do this over a sink or the container of water.

3. Make a data table similar to the one shown.

DATA TABLE		
Temperature (°C)	Time (sec)	Average Time for Class (sec)

Introducing the Procedure

Students should work in pairs. Tell students that they will measure the rate at which small paper disks that have been soaked in enzyme float to the top of an inverted test tube of hydrogen peroxide. They will do this with disks that have been in an ice water bath, at room temperature, at body temperature (37°C), and at 100°C.

Troubleshooting the Experiment

◆ Remind students that they must invert the test tube quickly and begin timing the rise of the disk at that point.

◆ It is important to keep the disks in the warm water close to 37°C to duplicate body temperature.

◆ You may wish to distribute the disks from the boiling water so students don't handle hot equipment.

4. Moisten the small end of a one-hole stopper with water.

5. Using forceps, remove a filter paper disk soaked in liver preparation (catalase enzyme) that has been kept at room temperature. Stick it to the moistened end of the one-hole stopper.

6. Your partner should be ready with the stopwatch for the next step.

7. Place the stopper firmly into the test tube, hold your thumb over the hole, and quickly invert the test tube. Start the stopwatch. Put the inverted end of the test tube into the container of water, as shown in the photograph, and remove your thumb.

8. Observe what happens to the filter paper inside the test tube. Record the time it takes for the disk to rise to the top. If the disk does not rise within 2 minutes, record "no reaction" and go on to Step 9.

9. Rinse the test tube and repeat the procedure with catalase enzyme disks kept at 0°C, 37°C, and 100°C. **CAUTION:** *When you remove the disk kept in the hot water bath, do not use your bare hands. Avoid spilling the hot water.*

Analyze and Conclude

1. What makes the disk float to the top of the test tube?

2. Calculate the average time for each temperature based on the results of the entire class. Enter the results in your data table.

3. Make a line graph of the data you collected. Label the horizontal axis (*x*-axis) "Temperature" with a scale from 0°C to 100°C. Label the vertical axis (*y*-axis) "Time" with a scale from 0 to 30 seconds. Plot the class average time for each temperature.

4. What evidence do you have that your hypothesis from Step 1 is either supported or not supported?

5. How is the time it takes the disk to rise to the top of the tube related to the rate of reaction?

6. What can you conclude about the activity of the enzyme at the various temperatures you tested? (*Hint:* Enzyme activity is greater when the rate of reaction is faster.)

7. Make a prediction about how active the enzyme would be at 10°C, 60°C, and 75°C. Give reasons to support your prediction.

8. **Apply** Oxygen kills many kinds of bacteria that can cause infection. Explain why hydrogen peroxide is often used as a treatment on cuts and scrapes.

Design an Experiment

The activity of an enzyme also depends upon the concentration of the enzyme. Design an experiment that explores the relationship between enzyme activity and enzyme concentration. (Your teacher can give you disks soaked with different enzyme concentrations.)

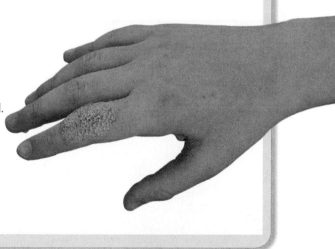

Sample Data Table

Temperature	Time (sec)	Average Time (sec)
0°C	5.1	
21°C	3.2	
37°C	1.0	
100°C	no reaction	

Program Resources

◆ **Teaching Resources** Real-World Lab blackline masters, pp. 32–33

Media and Technology

 Lab Activity Videotape
Chemical Interactions, 2

Expected Outcome

The 37°C trial will be the fastest, followed by the room temperature and 0°C. The 100°C trial will show no reaction.

Analyze and Conclude

1. Oxygen gas clings to the disk and causes it to float.

2. Answers should show time decreasing as temperature approaches 37°C, with no reaction at 100°C.

3. Students should graph results from Step 2.

4. If students hypothesized that the enzyme works better closer to body temperature, they should give evidence.

5. A slower reaction rate will result in a longer time for the disk to rise.

6. Activity appears to increase with temperature, but does not occur at 100°C.

7. Answers will vary depending on students' graphs. The activity of the enzyme at 10°C would be greater than at 0°C but less than at 37°C. Accept all answers for 60°C and 75°C.

8. Hydrogen peroxide reacts when it contacts the catalase in blood and produces oxygen.

Extending the Inquiry

Design an Experiment Students should design a procedure, similar to the one in this lab, to test disks treated with varying concentrations of enzyme. The expected outcome is that the activity will be higher for the higher enzyme concentration.

Safety

Students should wash their hands after performing the experiment.

SECTION 4 Fire and Fire Safety

Objectives

After completing the lesson, students will be able to
◆ identify the three conditions necessary to maintain a fire;
◆ explain how water inhibits combustion;
◆ list fire-safety measures for the home.

Key Terms combustion, fuel

1 Engage/Explore

Activating Prior Knowledge

Encourage students to share experiences they may have had involving fire. Ask them to describe the properties of things that burn and things that do not. Call on volunteers to explain how to control or put out different kinds of fires.

•••••• DISCOVER ••••••

Skills Focus developing hypotheses

Materials *aluminum pie pan, small candles, clay or candle holder, matches, beaker or glass, water, vinegar, baking soda, safety goggles*

Time 15 minutes

Tips Before lighting the candle, have students place the candle in the pie pan (to catch any spills). Demonstrate the safe way to light a candle with matches: close the matchbook or box, and strike the match away from your body. Show students how to hold the beaker to "pour out" the gas above the liquid without pouring out any liquid.

Expected Outcome The carbon dioxide gas produced by the reaction will extinguish the candle flame.

Think It Over Students may say that the carbon dioxide gas produced by the chemical reaction smothered the candle flame.

SECTION 4 Fire and Fire Safety

DISCOVER •••••••••••••••••••••• ACTIVITY

How Does Baking Soda Affect a Fire?

1. Put on your safety goggles.
2. Secure a small candle in a holder or some clay. After instructions from your teacher, use a match to light the candle.
3. Place a beaker next to the candle. Measure 1 large spoonful of baking soda into the beaker. Add about 112 mL of water and stir. Add about 112 mL of vinegar.
4. As soon as the mixture stops foaming, tip the beaker as if you are pouring something out of it onto the flame. **CAUTION:** *Do not pour any liquid on the candle.*
5. Observe what happens to the flame.

Think It Over
Developing Hypotheses The gas produced in the beaker was carbon dioxide. Based on the results of this experiment, develop a hypothesis to explain what you observed in Step 5.

GUIDE FOR READING

◆ What are the three things necessary to maintain a fire?
◆ How does water stop combustion?

Reading Tip Before you read, predict what conditions contribute to the start of a fire. Revise your predictions as you read.

What picture comes to mind when you hear the word *fire?* Do you think of a warm campfire on a cold night or a house reduced to a pile of ashes? All fires are chemically similar, but a fire can be useful or disastrous depending on whether or not it is controlled. You can keep fires under control, but only if you understand fire as a chemical reaction.

Understanding Fire

Fire is the result of **combustion,** a rapid reaction between oxygen and a substance called a fuel. A **fuel** is a material that releases energy when it burns. Some fuels you probably know about are oil, coal, wood, gasoline, and paper. Combustion of these types of fuel always produces carbon dioxide and water. Sometimes products such as smoke and poisonous gases may form from incomplete combustion or the presence of other materials.

READING STRATEGIES

Reading Tip After students complete their predictions, have small groups discuss their ideas. Alternatively, lead a class discussion of conditions that can contribute to the start of a fire. List these on the board. After students read the section, invite volunteers to add to the list.

Study and Comprehension After students read the section, have partners prepare a diagram of the fire triangle. Then add one corresponding method of controlling a fire to each corner of the fire triangle.

The Fire Triangle Although a combustion reaction is very exothermic and fast, a fire cannot start unless conditions are right. **Three things are necessary to start and maintain a fire—fuel, oxygen, and heat.**

You just read about some different fuels. The second part of the fire triangle is oxygen. Where does oxygen come from? About 20 percent of the air around you is composed of oxygen gas. If air can reach the fuel, so can oxygen. A large fire can actually draw oxygen toward it. As other gases in the air around the flame are heated, they move rapidly away from the fire. Cooler air flows toward the fire, bringing a fresh supply of oxygen. If you stand in front of a fire in a fireplace, you can often feel the flow of air to the fire.

The third part of the fire triangle is heat. Fuel and oxygen can be together, but they won't react until something provides enough activation energy to start the combustion reaction. This energy can come from a lighted match, an electric spark, lightning, or the heat from a stove. Once the reaction starts, the heat released by the combustion can keep the reaction going.

Once a fire has started, it can continue as long as all three components of the fire triangle are available. Coal in abandoned mines underneath the town of Centralia, Pennsylvania, started burning in 1962 and still burns. Many old ventilation shafts lead into the tunnels, but they have never been mapped. Since not all the shafts can be located and sealed, air (containing oxygen) continues to flow into the mines, supporting the fire. Heat and poisonous gases coming up from the fire through cracks in the ground made living in Centralia difficult. Everyone eventually moved away. No one knows how long this fire will burn.

☑ Checkpoint What is necesssary to start a fire?

Controlling Fire Use your knowledge of chemical reactions to think of ways to control a fire. What if you removed one part of the fire triangle? For example, you could get the fuel away from the flames. You could keep oxygen from getting to the fuel, or cool the combustion reaction below its activation energy. Any of these actions may help bring a fire under control.

Think about how firefighters put out a fire in a building. They use large hoses to spray huge amounts of water on the flaming part of the building.

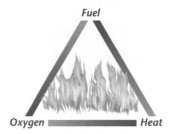

Fuel

Oxygen — *Heat*

Figure 23 If any point of the fire triangle is missing, a fire will not continue. *Applying Concepts How does putting a lid over a burning pot of food affect the fire triangle?*

Figure 24 Firefighters use water to cool a fire and prevent oxygen from reaching the fuel.

L ◆ 41

Program Resources

◆ **Teaching Resources** 1-4 Lesson Plan, p. 25; 1-4 Section Summary, p. 26
◆ **Guided Reading and Study Workbook** Section 1-4

Answers to Self-Assessment

Caption Question

Figure 23 It stops the flow of air containing oxygen from reaching the fire.

☑ Checkpoint

Fuel, oxygen, and heat are necessary to start and maintain a fire.

2 Facilitate

Understanding Fire

Demonstration

Materials *candle, match, heat-resistant beaker, tongs, water*

Time 15 minutes

 This demonstration illustrates the three parts of the fire triangle. Choose a beaker that is tall enough to completely cover the candle. Show students the candle and match, and ask them to identify which is the fuel *(wax)* and which is the source of activation energy *(match)*. Then light the candle. Ask: **How could you put out the flame using just the beaker?** *(Put the beaker over the candle.)* Ask: **When you do this, which part of the fire triangle are you taking away?** *(oxygen)* Then relight the candle, and ask students to name other ways they could put out the candle. Students should identify the part of the fire triangle their methods affect. *(Samples: Pinch the flame with tongs, which shuts off the flow of fuel; blow on the flame or douse it with water, which keeps the fuel from contacting oxygen and removes heat from the candle wick.)*
learning modality: visual

Ongoing Assessment

Skills Check Inform students that fire-safety experts suggest that a person "drop and roll" if their clothes are on fire. Invite a volunteer to demonstrate the drop and roll. Ask students to use the fire triangle to explain why this is sound advice.

Home Fire Safety

Addressing Naive Conceptions

Students may believe that water is effective at putting out all kinds of fires. Inform students that fires are grouped into four classes, according to the type of fuel. Class A fires—involving wood, paper, or similar dry fuels—are the most common fires and the only type of fire that should be put out with water. The other classes involve liquids such as cooking fat or paint thinner (Class B), electrical equipment (Class C), and highly reactive metals (Class D). Fighting these fires with water can be dangerous, but most of them can be put out with carbon dioxide. Class D fires are normally fought with dry chemicals.
learning modality: verbal

Real-Life Learning

Contact your local fire department to find out what educational opportunities are available. Students may be able to visit the fire station and have firefighters demonstrate the hoses and other equipment they use to fight fires, or a firefighter may be able to visit your class to demonstrate the proper use of fire extinguishers. Encourage students to prepare a list of questions before the visit. After the visit, groups of students can use their questions to develop presentations on what they learned. Have students select an audience and prepare a poster or an oral presentation about fire safety. **learning modality: verbal**

42 ◆ L

Water removes two parts of the fire triangle. First, water covers the fuel, which keeps it from coming into contact with oxygen. Second, evaporation of the water uses a large amount of heat, causing the fire to cool. Without heat, there isn't enough energy to reach the activation energy of combustion, so the reaction stops.

Home Fire Safety

Every year, fire claims thousands of lives in the United States. If you know how to prevent fires in your home and what to do if a fire starts, you are better prepared to take action. You may save your home or even your life!

Common Sources of Fires The two most common sources of home fires are small heaters and fires that start in the kitchen during cooking. Another common cause is faulty electrical wiring. The fires that cause the most deaths start from carelessness with cigarettes.

Fighting Fires You can fight a small fire by using what you know about the fire triangle. For example, carbon dioxide gas can be used to smother a fire by preventing contact between the fuel and oxygen in the air. If a small fire should start on the stove,

Figure 25 Families can take several steps to prevent fire and to be ready for action if one should start. *Making Judgments Which of these fire safety aids do you think a home should have?*

Fire Safety Tips

◆ Keep matches and other sources of flames away from young children.
◆ Replace frayed or broken electric cords, and repair appliances that aren't working right.
◆ Keep flammable things, like potholders, towels, and curtains, away from stove burners.
◆ Store gasoline outside the home and only in a safety can.
◆ Never use a gas or charcoal grill inside the home.
◆ Keep a box of baking soda in the kitchen to fight grease fires.
◆ Have at least one fire extinguisher in good working order and within easy reach in your home.
◆ Most importantly, make sure there is a working smoke detector on every level of your home. Check it regularly.

42 ◆ L

Background

Facts and Figures The National Fire Protection Association reports that 13 out of every 14 homes in the United States have at least one smoke detector. The agency estimates that having a working smoke detector in your home can cut your chances of dying in a fire nearly in half.

Photoelectric detectors use material that is sensitive to light to detect the presence of smoke. Photoelectric detectors detect smoke when the smoke particles interrupt or scatter a beam of light inside the detector, causing the alarm to sound.

The second type of smoke detector contains very small amounts of radioactive material that ionizes the air between a pair of electrodes inside the detector. This causes the air to carry a small current. Smoke particles attach to the ions in the air, and the current decreases, setting off the alarm.

42 ◆ L

covering it with baking soda may put the fire out. Liquids in food will react with baking soda to produce carbon dioxide. The baking soda itself will help smother the fire, too.

The smaller a fire is, the easier it is to control. You can cool a match enough to stop combustion just by blowing on it. A small fire in a trash can may be doused with a pan of water. If the fire spreads to the curtains, however, even a garden hose might not deliver enough water to put it out.

One of the most effective ways to fight a small fire is with a fire extinguisher. Extinguishers designed for home use are effective when used properly. But a fire that is growing as you fight it is out of control. If this happens, there is only one safe thing to do—get away from the fire and let the fire department handle it.

Preventing Trouble The best form of fire safety is fire prevention. With your family, check your home for fire hazards and fire-fighting aids. Look at the list on the opposite page for some things you and your family can do.

Fires can be dangerous and deadly, but many fires can be prevented if you are careful. Understanding the chemistry of fire gives you a way to reduce risk and increase your family's safety.

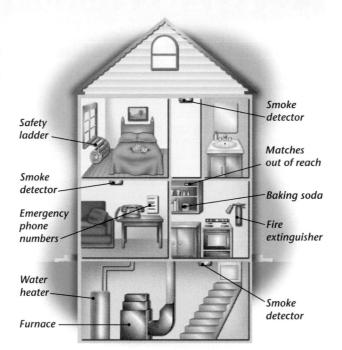

Labels: *Safety ladder*, *Smoke detector*, *Emergency phone numbers*, *Water heater*, *Furnace*, *Smoke detector*, *Matches out of reach*, *Baking soda*, *Fire extinguisher*, *Smoke detector*

Figure 26 This fire-safe house has many of the fire-prevention features listed in Figure 25. *Interpreting Illustrations* Which of those safety features can you find in the picture?

Section 4 Review

1. What are the three points of the fire triangle?
2. Why is water a good tool for fighting most fires?
3. List some of the products of combustion.
4. How does adding carbon dioxide gas to cover a fire control or stop it? Use the fire triangle in your answer.
5. **Thinking Critically Making Judgments** Why is fire prevention one of the best ways to fight fires?

Science at Home

Work with your family to formulate a fire safety plan. How can fires be prevented in your home? How can fires be put out if they occur? Is there a functioning smoke detector on each floor of the home, especially near the bedrooms? How can the fire department be contacted in an emergency? Design a fire escape route. Make sure all family members know the route as well as a meeting place outside.

Section 4 Review Answers

1. Fuel, oxygen, and heat
2. Water covers the fuel and keeps it from coming into contact with oxygen. Water also evaporates, absorbing a large amount of thermal energy from the fire.
3. Carbon dioxide, water, smoke, and poisonous gases
4. Carbon dioxide prevents contact between the fuel and oxygen in the air.
5. If you take steps ahead of time to prevent fires, they may never start at all. If a fire does start, you will be prepared to put it out quickly or get to safety.

Science at Home

Encourage students to assume responsibility for checking the batteries in smoke detectors and posting the phone number of the fire department near the telephone. A fire-safety plan should include the preventative measures mentioned in Figure 25, as well as: making sure electrical outlets are not overloaded, inspecting electrical cords for signs of wear, planning and rehearsing an escape route, and keeping the escape route free from obstacles.

Media and Technology

Transparencies "Fire Safety Tips," Transparency 5; "Fire-Safe House," Transparency 6

Answers to Self-Assessment

Caption Questions

Figure 25 Many students will select smoke detectors or fire extinguishers. Students should be able to support their choice.

Figure 26 The matches are out of reach of children; there is a fire extinguisher; baking soda is in the kitchen; there is a smoke detector on every floor of the house.

Performance Assessment

Oral Presentation Direct students to prepare and deliver 30-second public service announcements on home fire safety. Announcements should describe ways to prevent fires and ways to fight fires effectively and safely, as well as explaining when to get away from a fire and let the fire department handle it.

SCIENCE AND SOCIETY

Transporting Hazardous Chemicals Safely

Purpose

To encourage students to discuss some of the issues concerning the transport of hazardous chemicals.

Role-Play

Time a day to prepare; 45 minutes for the role-play

First have the class discuss the widespread use of hazardous chemicals in their community. These chemicals include gasoline, paints, paint strippers, solvents, pesticides, and so on. Have students discuss how these chemicals are transported into and out of their community.

Have groups of students role-play a city council meeting to discuss ways of reducing the risk of transporting hazardous chemicals. Some students should represent the views of industry, while others should represent consumer groups, emergency response teams, and chemists and other experts. Contact the appropriate local authority to obtain information about hazardous materials routes through your community. (Look in the government pages in the phone book for transportation departments or environmental services.) Provide students with a map of the area and help them identify the Hazardous Materials routes.

Extend Have students check to find out whether their city has a hazardous chemical response plan.

You Decide

Have students complete the first two steps as they read the feature. Students should note any questions they have and use them to prepare for the role-play activity. Have students complete the last step after the role-play, so they can use what they learned to help develop a list of regulations.

Transporting Hazardous Chemicals

Each year, millions of tons of hazardous substances criss-cross the country by truck and rail. These substances can be poisonous, flammable, and even explosive. But chemical reactions using these materials are also necessary to make the products that people use every day. They even make the trucks themselves run.

The chemical industry says that the transport of hazardous substances is safe and that problems are rare. But public health officials are worried. When accidents do happen, these compounds can damage the environment and threaten human lives. How can hazardous substances be transported safely?

The Issues

Why Do People Transport Hazardous Substances? Transporting hazardous substances can be dangerous. Useful products are made, however, from the hazardous materials that trucks and trains carry. Would people give up cars, computers, and CDs?

For example, CDs are made from plastics. To produce these plastics, manufacturers use compounds such as benzene and styrene. Benzene fumes are poisonous and flammable. Styrene can explode when exposed to air. Public health experts say it is important to find safe substitutes for dangerous substances. But finding alternatives will be difficult and expensive.

What Are the Risks? Serious accidents are rare. But in the United States in a recent year, there were over 300 accidents involving hazardous chemical releases. Public health experts say that some substances are too hazardous to transport on roads and railroads. An accidental release of these substances near a city could harm many people.

Some people say that vehicles carrying chemically reactive or hazardous substances should be restricted to isolated roads. However, many factories that use the chemical compounds are located in cities. Chemicals often must be transported from where they are made to where they are used. In the case of gasoline, cars are everywhere. Trucks and trains must transport the fuel to every neighborhood and region of the country.

How Should Transportation Be Regulated? Manufacturers that use hazardous chemicals say that there already are adequate laws. The Hazardous Materials Transportation Act (1975, revised 1994) requires carriers of hazardous substances to follow strict labeling and packaging rules. They must keep records of what they carry and where they travel. Local emergency officials in communities near transportation routes must also be trained to handle accidents involving these substances.

On the other hand, public health experts say there are not enough inspectors to check all trucks and trains and make sure rules are followed. But hiring more inspectors would cost additional tax money.

You Decide

1. Identify the Problem
In your own words, explain the problem of safely transporting hazardous substances.

2. Analyze the Options
Examine the pros and cons of greater regulation of the transport of hazardous substances. In each position, consider the effects on chemical industries and on the general public.

3. Find a Solution
Suppose there is a chemical factory in your city. You are the emergency planning director. Create regulations for transporting hazardous substances through your community.

Background

The Hazardous Materials Transportation Act (HMTA) is the primary statute affecting transportation of hazardous cargoes. The purpose of the HMTA, according to the policy stated by Congress, is ". . . to improve the regulatory and enforcement authority of the Secretary of Transportation to protect the Nation adequately against risks to life and property which are inherent in the transportation of hazardous materials in commerce." Regulations apply to ". . . any person who transports, or causes to be transported or shipped, a hazardous material; or who manufactures, fabricates, marks, maintains, reconditions, repairs, or tests a package or container which is represented, marked, certified, or sold by such person for use in the transportation in commerce of certain hazardous materials."

Concept Map Sample title: Characteristics of Chemical Reactions
a. New substances **b.** Coefficients
c. Elements **d.** Formulas

 SECTION 1

Matter and Changes in Matter

Key Ideas

◆ Matter may be in the form of elements, compounds, or mixtures.
◆ Chemical changes result in the formation of new substances. Physical changes do not.
◆ Chemical reactions occur when chemical bonds are formed or broken.

Key Terms

chemistry
element
compound
mixture
solution
physical change

chemical change
chemical reaction
precipitate
atom
molecule
chemical bond

 SECTION 2

Describing Chemical Reactions

Key Ideas

◆ A chemical equation uses symbols for the reactants and products of a chemical reaction.
◆ Chemical reactions may be classified by the types of changes in reactants and products.

Key Terms

chemical equation
symbol
chemical formula
subscript
reactants
products

conservation of mass
coefficient
synthesis
decomposition
replacement

SECTION 3

Controlling Chemical Reactions

Key Ideas

◆ A chemical reaction involves a change in energy.
◆ The rate of a chemical reaction can be controlled by such factors as concentration, surface area, temperature, and use of a catalyst or inhibitor.

Key Terms

exothermic reaction
endothermic reaction
activation energy
concentration

catalyst
enzyme
inhibitor

 SECTION 4

Fire and Fire Safety

INTEGRATING HEALTH

Key Ideas

◆ The fire triangle shows the three things necessary to start a fire and keep it burning: fuel, oxygen, and heat.
◆ Water stops combustion by keeping the fuel from coming in contact with oxygen. Also, evaporation of water uses a great deal of heat and cools the fire.

Key Terms

combustion   fuel

Concept Map Copy the concept map, then complete it and add a title.

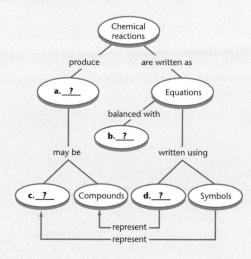

Chemical reactions

produce → **a.** ?
are written as → Equations

balanced with → **b.** ?

may be → **c.** ? / Compounds
written using → **d.** ? / Symbols

represent
represent

Reviewing Content
Multiple Choice
1. c 2. a 3. b 4. c 5. b

True or False
6. mixtures 7. true 8. true
9. endothermic 10. oxygen

Checking Concepts
11. Elements can combine in different ratios and in different combinations to make different compounds.
12. Changing the subscripts in a compound's formula changes it to the formula for a different compound.
13. No. The extra mass in rust (iron oxide) is from oxygen, which was not accounted for in the original measurement because it was in the air.
14. Carbon dioxide gas bubbles are produced by the reaction of the baking soda with the food.
15. Answers should include information that describes liquid water and water vapor as the same compound in different physical states. Although one is a gas and one is a liquid, both have the chemical formula H_2O. It is easy to change from one to the other by heating or cooling, which are both physical processes.

Thinking Critically
16. a. $Fe + 2 HCl \rightarrow FeCl_2 + H_2$; replacement **b.** $2 N_2 + 5 O_2 \rightarrow 2 N_2O_5$; synthesis **c.** balanced; decomposition **d.** balanced; replacement
17. Sample: Paint the metal on the ship so that the salt water is prevented from coming into contact with the metal.
18. The rooms in a burning building contain heat and additional fuel. When a door is opened, oxygen enters, and the fuel may burst into flame.

Reviewing Content

 For more review of key concepts, see the Interactive Student Tutorial CD-ROM.

Multiple Choice
Choose the letter of the best answer.

1. A chemical equation shows
   a. elements and mixtures.
   b. hydrogen and oxygen.
   c. reactants and products.
   d. chemical bonds.
2. You can balance a chemical equation by changing the
   a. coefficients.   b. products.
   c. reactants.   d. formulas.
3. The reaction between sulfur trioxide and water ($SO_3 + H_2O \rightarrow H_2SO_4$) is a
   a. replacement reaction.
   b. synthesis reaction.
   c. decomposition reaction.
   d. physical change.
4. The rate of a chemical reaction can be increased by all the following, except:
   a. increasing temperature.
   b. increasing concentration.
   c. decreasing concentration.
   d. increasing surface area.
5. To extinguish a fire, do *not*
   a. remove fuel.
   b. add oxygen.
   c. reduce heat.
   d. add baking soda.

True or False
If the statement is true, write true. If it is false, change the underlined word or words to make the statement true.

6. Air, soil, and sea water are all examples of <u>elements</u>.
7. A solid that falls out of solution during a chemical reaction is called a <u>precipitate</u>.
8. A <u>chemical</u> change occurs when new substances are formed.
9. An <u>exothermic</u> reaction is a chemical reaction that absorbs heat.
10. The three parts of the fire triangle are fuel, <u>carbon dioxide</u>, and heat.

Checking Concepts
11. How can millions of compounds exist if there are only about 100 elements?
12. Why can't you balance a chemical equation by changing the subscripts?
13. You find the mass of a piece of iron metal, let it rust, and measure the mass again. The mass has increased. Does this violate the law of conservation of mass? Explain.
14. A fire starts in a frying pan in your kitchen. You grab a box of baking soda and throw its contents into the pan. Bubbling and foaming occur, and the fire goes out. What is the evidence that a chemical reaction has occurred?
15. **Writing to Learn** Imagine you are teaching a group of younger students about the difference between chemical and physical changes. One of the students claims the change from liquid water to water vapor is chemical. Write a brief paragraph of what you would say to convince the student otherwise.

Thinking Critically
16. Applying Concepts Balance the following equations and tell whether they are synthesis, decomposition, or replacement reactions.
   a. $Fe + HCl \rightarrow FeCl_2 + H_2$
   b. $N_2 + O_2 \rightarrow N_2O_5$
   c. $H_2CO_3 \rightarrow H_2O + CO_2$
   d. $CuO + H_2SO_4 \rightarrow CuSO_4 + H_2O$
17. Problem Solving Steel that is exposed to water and salt rusts quickly. If you were a shipbuilder, how would you protect a new ship? Explain why your solution works.
18. Relating Cause and Effect Firefighters open doors very carefully, because sometimes a room will explode into flames when the door is opened. Based on your knowledge of reaction rates and the fire triangle, why does this happen?

Applying Skills
19. It is lower.
20. exothermic
21. The height of the curve would be lower because a catalyst would speed up the reaction by lowering activation energy. No. Adding heat does not affect the activation energy. It may only speed up the rate of the reaction.

Applying Skills

Use the energy diagram to answer Questions 19–21.

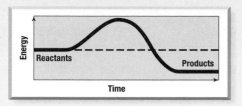

19. **Interpreting Data** How does the energy of the products compare with the energy of the reactants?
20. **Classifying** Tell whether this reaction is exothermic or endothermic.
21. **Predicting** What would happen to the graph if a catalyst were added to the reaction? Would adding heat to the reaction change the height of the curve? Explain.

Project Wrap Up Compare the reactions in your chemical change log with those of your classmates. How many of the same processes did you observe? Defend your opinions as to whether or not your observations were chemical changes. Together make a list of the types of evidence you observed, and classify the reactions as endothermic or exothermic.

Reflect and Record In your journal, answer these questions. What evidence of chemical change is easiest to detect? What types of chemical reactions did you observe most frequently? Give an example of a chemical reaction you suspect was taking place, but for which you could not find direct evidence.

Project Wrap Up As students compare their observations and compile a list, have them identify common observations and make sure they classified them the same way. It may help to have volunteers make a poster or a large data table on the board for students to fill in. Have students work together to classify the reactions as endothermic or exothermic.

Reflect and Record Students should identify changes that were easy to observe and classify, as well as those that were difficult. Students should give an example of a reaction they had trouble analyzing.

Test Preparation

22. a 23. b 24. c 25. c 26. d

Test Preparation *Use these questions to prepare for standardized tests.*

Read the information below. Then answer Questions 22–26.

A laboratory assistant was experimenting with chemical reactions when she combined a small amount of zinc (Zn) with hydrochloric acid (HCl). She discovered that zinc chloride ($ZnCl_2$) and hydrogen (H_2) were produced.

22. Which of the following substances are the reactants?
    a. $Zn + HCl$
    b. $ZnCl_2 + H_2$
    c. $Zn + H_2$
    d. $ZnCl_2 + HCl$

23. Which of the following substances are the products?
    a. $Zn + HCl$
    b. $ZnCl_2 + H_2$
    c. $Zn + H_2$
    d. $ZnCl_2 + HCl$

24. Which equation correctly describes this reaction?
    a. $Zn + HCl \rightarrow ZnCl_2 + H_2$
    b. $ZnCl_2 + H_2 \rightarrow Zn + 2\ HCl$
    c. $Zn + 2HCl \rightarrow ZnCl_2 + H_2$
    d. $2\ Zn + 2\ HCl \rightarrow 2\ (ZnCl_2 + H_2)$

25. How should the assistant classify this reaction?
    a. synthesis
    b. decomposition
    c. replacement
    d. combustion

26. Which of the following actions would probably speed up the reaction between zinc and hydrochloric acid?
    a. making sure the masses of the reactants and the products are the same
    b. cooling down the reactants before combining them
    c. adding an inhibitor
    d. breaking up the zinc into smaller pieces

Program Resources

- ◆ **Inquiry Skills Activity Book** Provides teaching and review of all inquiry skills
- ◆ **Standardized Test Preparation Book** Provides standardized test practice
- ◆ **Reading in the Content Area** Provides strategies to improve science reading skills
- ◆ **Teacher's ELL Handbook** Provides multiple strategies for English language learners

CHAPTER 2 Atoms and Bonding

Sections	Time	Student Edition Activities	Other Activities
CHAPTER PROJECT 2 **Molecule Models** p. L49	Ongoing (3 weeks)	Check Your Progress, pp. L54, L64, L69 Project Wrap Up, p. L77	TE Chapter 2 Project Notes, pp. L48–49
1 Inside an Atom pp. L50–54 ◆ 2.1.1 Describe the structure of an atom and define protons, neutrons, and electrons. ◆ 2.1.2 Explain the role of valence electrons in forming chemical bonds.	$2\frac{1}{2}$ periods/ 1–2 blocks	**Discover** How Far Away Is the Electron?, p. L50	TE Demonstration, p. L51 TE Demonstration, p. L53
2 Atoms in the Periodic Table pp. L55–58 ◆ 2.2.1 Describe the organization of the periodic table. ◆ 2.2.2 Identify the groups within the periodic table and state what properties elements in a group have in common.	4 periods/ 2 blocks	**Discover** What Are the Trends in the Periodic Table?, p. L55 **Sharpen Your Skills** Classifying, p. L56 **Science at Home** p. L57 **Skills Lab: Making Models** Comparing Atom Sizes, p. L58	
3 Ionic Bonds pp. L59–64 ◆ 2.3.1 Explain the differences between an atom and an ion. ◆ 2.3.2 Describe how an ionic bond forms. ◆ 2.3.3 Identify the properties of ionic compounds.	3 periods/ $1\frac{1}{2}$ blocks	**Discover** How Do Ions Form?, p. L59 **Sharpen Your Skills** Interpreting Data, p. L62 **Try This** Crystal Clear, p. L63	TE Addressing Naive Conceptions, p. L60 TE Including All Students, p. L61 TE Inquiry Challenge, p. L62 TE Building Inquiry Skills: Observing, p. L63 TE Integrating Physics, p. L64
4 Covalent Bonds pp. L65–71 ◆ 2.4.1 Describe how covalent bonds form. ◆ 2.4.2 Identify the properties of molecular compounds. ◆ 2.4.3 Distinguish between polar and nonpolar bonds, and between polar and nonpolar compounds.	$3\frac{1}{2}$ periods/ 1–2 blocks	**Discover** Why Don't Water and Oil Mix?, p. L65 **Sharpen Your Skills** Designing Experiments, p. L67 **Skills Lab: Interpreting Data** Shedding Light on Chemical Bonds, pp. L70–71 (Probeware version available)	TE Building Inquiry Skills: Making Models, p. L66 TE Demonstration, p. L68 ISLM L-2, "Testing for Hard Water"
5 INTEGRATING EARTH SCIENCE Crystal Chemistry pp. L72–74 ◆ 2.5.1 Explain how the chemical bonds of a crystal determine the substance's properties. ◆ 2.5.2 Describe and give examples of mineral crystals.	$1\frac{1}{2}$ periods/ $\frac{1}{2}$–1 block	**Discover** How Small Do They Get?, p. L72 **Science at Home** p. L74	TE Inquiry Challenge, p. L73
Study Guide/Assessment pp. L75–77	1 period/ $\frac{1}{2}$ block	**PLM** Provides blackline masters for probeware labs	ISAB Provides teaching and review of all inquiry skills

For Standard or Block Schedule The Resource Pro® CD-ROM gives you maximum flexibility for planning your instruction for any type of schedule. Resource Pro® contains Planning Express®, an advanced scheduling program, as well as the entire contents of the Teaching Resources and the Computer Test Bank.

Key: **SE** Student Edition
PLM Probeware Lab Manual
ISAB Inquiry Skills Activity Book

CHAPTER PLANNING GUIDE

Program Resources	Assessment Strategies	Media and Technology
TR Chapter 2 Project Teacher Notes, pp. L34–35 **TR** Chapter 2 Project Overview and Worksheets, pp. L36–39	**TE** Check Your Progress, pp. L54, L64, L69 **TE** Performance Assessment: Chapter 2 Project Wrap Up, p. L77 **TR** Chapter 2 Project Scoring Rubric, p. L40	Science Explorer Internet Site Audio CDs and Audiotapes, English-Spanish Section Summaries
TR 2-1 Lesson Plan, p. L41 **TR** 2-1 Section Summary, p. L42 **TR** 2-1 Review and Reinforce, p. L43 **TR** 2-1 Enrich, p. L44	**SE** Section 1 Review, p. L54 **TE** Ongoing Assessment, pp. L51, L53 **TE** Performance Assessment, p. L54	Exploring Physical Science Videodisc, Unit 1 Side 1, "Rutherford's Experiment" Transparencies 7, "Model of a Carbon Atom"; 8, "Science and History—Models of the Atom"
TR 2-2 Lesson Plan, p. L45 **TR** 2-2 Section Summary, p. L46 **TR** 2-2 Review and Reinforce, p. L47 **TR** 2-2 Enrich, p. L48 **TR** Skills Lab blackline masters, pp. L61–62	**SE** Section 2 Review, p. L57 **SE** Analyze and Conclude, p. L58 **TE** Performance Assessment, p. L57	Exploring Physical Science Videodisc, Unit 1 Side 1, "Periodic Trends" Lab Activity Videotape, *Chemical Interactions*, 3 Transparency 9, "Electron Dot Diagrams of Period 2 Elements"
TR 2-3 Lesson Plan, p. L49 **TR** 2-3 Section Summary, p. L50 **TR** 2-3 Review and Reinforce, p. L51 **TR** 2-3 Enrich, p. L52 **SES** Book N, *Electricity and Magnetism*, Chapter 2	**SE** Section 3 Review, p. L64 **TE** Ongoing Assessment, pp. L61, L63 **TE** Performance Assessment, p. L64	Exploring Physical Science Videodisc, Unit 2 Side 2, "Ionic Bonding" Transparency 10, "Exploring an Ionic Bond"
TR 2-4 Lesson Plan, p. L53 **TR** 2-4 Section Summary, p. L54 **TR** 2-4 Review and Reinforce, p. L55 **TR** 2-4 Enrich, p. L56 **TR** Skills Lab blackline masters, pp. L63–65	**SE** Section 4 Review, p. L69 **SE** Analyze and Conclude, p. L71 **TE** Ongoing Assessment, p. L67 **TE** Performance Assessment, p. L69	Exploring Physical Science Videodisc, Unit 2 Side 2, "Bonding" Lab Activity Videotape, *Chemical Interactions*, 4 Transparency 11, "Electron Dot Diagrams of Atoms and Molecules"
TR 2-5 Lesson Plan, p. L57 **TR** 2-5 Section Summary, p. L58 **TR** 2-5 Review and Reinforce, p. L59 **TR** 2-5 Enrich, p. L60 **SES** Book F, *Inside Earth*, Chapter 4	**SE** Section 5 Review, p. L74 **TE** Ongoing Assessment, p. L73 **TE** Performance Assessment, p. L74	Interactive Student Tutorial CD-ROM, L-2
GSW Provides worksheets to promote student comprehension of content **RCA** Provides strategies to improve science reading skills **ELL** Provides multiple strategies for English language learners	**SE** Study Guide/Assessment, pp. L75–77 **TR** Performance Assessment, pp. L141–143 **TR** Chapter 2 Test, pp. L144–147 **CTB** *Chemical Interactions*, Chapter 2 Test **STP** Provides standardized test practice	Computer Test Bank, *Chemical Interactions*, Chapter 2 Test Interactive Student Tutorial CD-ROM, L-2

TE Teacher's Edition
RCA Reading in the Content Area
GSW Guided Study Workbook

TR Teaching Resources
ISLM Integrated Science Laboratory Manual
ELL Teacher's ELL Handbook

CTB Computer Test Bank
STP Standardized Test Preparation Book
SES Science Explorer Series Text

Meeting the National Science Education Standards and AAAS Benchmarks

National Science Education Standards	Benchmarks for Science Literacy	Unifying Themes
Science as Inquiry (Content Standard A) ◆ **Develop descriptions, explanations, predictions, and models using evidence** Students describe the structure of an atom and make models of atoms and of compounds. *(Sections 1, 2, 3, 4, 5; Skills Lab, Comparing Atom Sizes; Chapter Project)* **Physical Science** (Content Standard B) ◆ **Properties and changes of properties in matter** When atoms of different elements bond, some atoms form ionic bonds by transferring electrons and others form covalent bonds by sharing electrons. *(Sections 3, 4)* ◆ **Motions and forces** Charged particles attract other particles with opposite charges. Attractive forces between charged particles lead to the formation of ionic bonds. *(Section 3)* **Earth and Space Science** (Content Standard D) ◆ **Structure of the Earth system** The physical properties of the minerals that compose Earth are determined by their chemical compositions. *(Section 5)* **History and Nature of Science** (Content Standard G) ◆ **Nature of science** The periodic table is organized based on common properties of elements. *(Section 2)*	**2A Patterns and Relationships** The organization of the periodic table reveals patterns in chemical structure and describes how atoms of certain elements will combine to form bonds. *(Sections 2, 3, 4)* **4D The Structure of Matter** Atoms are composed of particles with definite properties. Atoms with similar structures have similar chemical properties. *(Sections 1, 2)* **4E Energy Transformations** Chemical reactions occur when bonds between atoms are formed or broken. These reactions, which always involve energy changes, involve the transfer or sharing of electrons. *(Sections 1, 2, 3, 4; Skills Lab, Shedding Light on Chemical Bonds)* **11B Models** Atoms and ions of different elements can be compared using models. Different models of the atom have been developed by scientists to reflect different understandings of the structure of the atom. *(Sections 1, 2, 3, 4, 5; Skills Lab, Comparing Atom Sizes; Chapter Project)*	◆ **Patterns of Change** Elements with similar properties are grouped together in the periodic table. These elements often form similar kinds of bonds. The properties of a compound depend on the types of bonds formed between the atoms. *(Sections 2, 3, 4, 5)* ◆ **Scale and Structure** Atoms are made of smaller particles called protons, electrons, and neutrons. The bonds between atoms depend on the structure of the atoms. Covalently bonded atoms form molecules. *(Sections 1, 2, 3, 4, 5; Skills Lab, Modeling Atom Sizes; Chapter Project)* ◆ **Unity and Diversity** All chemical bonds share certain characteristics. Different kinds of bonds between atoms can be identified and compared. *(Sections 1, 2, 3, 4, 5; Chapter Project)* ◆ **Systems and Interactions** The making and breaking of chemical bonds result from interactions between electrons in atoms. *(Sections 1, 3, 4; Skills Lab, Shedding Light on Chemical Bonds)* ◆ **Stability** The stability of an element depends on its number of valence electrons. The number and arrangement of the valence electrons in an atom determine what kind of bonds it will make with other atoms. Some atoms become more stable when they form bonds. *(Sections 1, 2, 3, 4)* ◆ **Modeling** Atoms, ions, and molecules can be compared using models. *(Sections 1, 2, 3, 4, 5; Skills Lab, Comparing Atom Sizes; Chapter Project)*

Take It to the Net

 Interactive text at www.phschool.com

Science Explorer comes alive with iText.

- **Complete student text** is accessible from any computer with Internet service or a CD-ROM drive.
- **Animations, simulations, and videos** enhance student understanding and retention of concepts.
- **Self-tests and online study tools** assess student understanding.
- **Teacher management tools** help you make the most of this valuable resource.

STAY CURRENT with **SCIENCE NEWS**®

Find out the latest research and information about chemical interactions at: **www.phschool.com**

Go to **www.phschool.com** and click on the Science icon. Then click on Science Explorer under PH@school.

Student Edition Activities Planner

ACTIVITY	Time (minutes)	Materials *Quantities for one work group*	Skills
Section 1			
Discover, p. 50	10	**Consumable** paper **Nonconsumable** pencil, metric ruler, dime or smaller circular item	Making Models
Section 2			
Discover, p. 55	15	**Nonconsumable** periodic table	Interpreting Data
Sharpen Your Skills, p. 56	15	**Nonconsumable** periodic table	Classifying
Science at Home, p. 57	home	No special materials are required.	Classifying
Skills Lab, p. 58	20	**Nonconsumable** drawing compass, calculator, periodic table of the elements (Appendix D)	Making Models
Section 3			
Discover, p. 59	15	**Nonconsumable** enough checkers for each team to have 12 red and black pairs of checkers, or a sufficient number of any objects in two colors	Making Models
Sharpen Your Skills, p. 62	15	**Consumable** No special materials are required.	Interpreting Data
Try This, p. 63	15 min setup, 3 min daily over a week	**Consumable** 15 cm thread, coarse salt such as kosher or sea salt, hot tap water **Nonconsumable** jar or cup, pencil, stirring rod or spoon	Observing
Section 4			
Discover, p. 65	10	**Consumable** water, vegetable oil, liquid soap **Nonconsumable** small jars with lids	Inferring
Sharpen Your Skills, p. 67	10	**Consumable** No special materials are required.	Designing Experiments
Skills Lab, pp. 70–71	50	**Consumable** sodium chloride, additional substances supplied by the teacher **Nonconsumable** 2 1.5-V dry cells, small beaker, plastic spoon, small light bulb and socket, 4 lengths of wire for connections with insulation scraped off ends, 100-mL graduated cylinder	Interpreting Data
Section 5			
Discover, p. 72	12	**Consumable** rock salt crystals, paper towels **Nonconsumable** metal spoons or small mallets, hand lenses	Predicting
Science at Home, p. 74	home	**Consumable** round objects of different sizes, such as grapes, raisins, clay balls, dried peas	Making Models

A list of all materials required for the Student Edition activities can be found beginning on page T15. You can obtain information about ordering materials by calling 1 800 848 0500 or by accessing the Science Explorer Internet site at: **www.phschool.com**

Molecule Models

The chemical bonds formed between atoms can be modeled to demonstrate the structure of chemical compounds.

Purpose In this project, students construct model atoms and use these models to demonstrate ionic and covalent bonds in compounds.

Skills Focus After completing the Chapter 2 Project, students will be able to

◆ make models of atoms and compounds;

◆ compare and contrast ionic and covalent bonds;

◆ communicate their findings about atoms to their classmates.

Project Time Line This project should take approximately one week to complete. Students should begin by deciding what materials they will use to construct their atoms. Once they have made their atoms, they should spend the next day or two working on their models of simple compounds. Allow an additional day for students to prepare for their class presentations. Before beginning the project, see Chapter 2 Project Teacher Notes on pages 34–35 in Teaching Resources for more details on carrying out the project. Also distribute to students the Chapter 2 Project Student Overview, Worksheets, and Scoring Rubric on pages 36–40 in Teaching Resources.

Possible Materials Provide a wide variety of materials from which students can choose. Some possibilities are listed below. Encourage students to suggest and use other materials as well.

◆ Fruits, vegetables, raisins, gumdrops, jellied fruit candies, marshmallows, jellybeans, and clay can be used for the atoms.

◆ Tape, toothpicks, pipe cleaners, or paper clips can be used to connect atoms.

◆ Permanent markers will be needed to illustrate valence electrons.

◆ A ball-and-stick modeling kit will be needed for the project launch.

Launching the Project Use a ball-and-stick modeling kit to demonstrate molecular modeling. Show students that

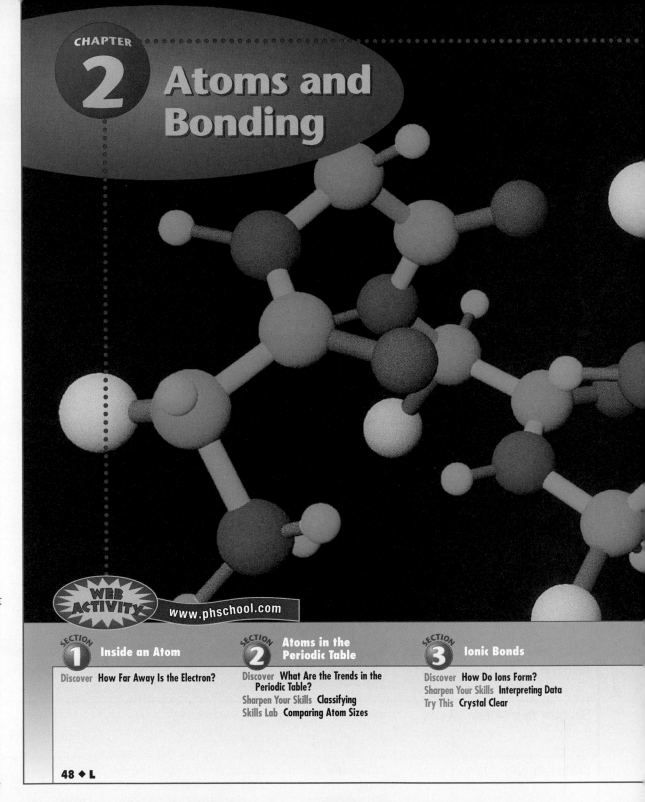

WEB ACTIVITY www.phschool.com

SECTION
1 **Inside an Atom**

Discover **How Far Away Is the Electron?**

SECTION
2 **Atoms in the Periodic Table**

Discover **What Are the Trends in the Periodic Table?**
Sharpen Your Skills **Classifying**
Skills Lab **Comparing Atom Sizes**

SECTION
3 **Ionic Bonds**

Discover **How Do Ions Form?**
Sharpen Your Skills **Interpreting Data**
Try This **Crystal Clear**

48 ◆ L

different colored balls represent different elements. Also show them how the chemical bonds are represented by wooden dowels. Point out how multiple bonds are modeled in this kit. Ask: **Using these models, how can you tell molecules of one compound from molecules of another compound?** (*By the different elements and types of bonds that they contain*) Point out that it is important for models to follow consistent rules of organization.

Allow time for students to read the description of the project in their text and the Chapter 2 Project Overview on pages 36–37 in Teaching Resources. Encourage students to discuss atoms and compounds. Answer any initial questions students may have.

Have students work in small groups as a cooperative learning task. To ensure that every student will have ample opportunity to participate in planning and building the models, each group should consist of no more than three students.

Molecule Models

With computer-made models like these, you can see molecules up close and personal. Many compounds are made of molecules—much tinier, of course, than these models.

In this chapter, you will learn why atoms react with one another. You will also learn about the different types of chemical bonds that can hold atoms together. In your project you can use fruits, vegetables, or other materials to make models of atoms and show the way they bond in compounds.

Your Goal To make models demonstrating how atoms bond in compounds that contain ionic and covalent bonds.

To complete the project you must
- ◆ select appropriate materials to make models of atoms
- ◆ design a way to tell the difference between the atoms of various elements
- ◆ indicate the correct number of bonds each atom forms
- ◆ use your model atoms to compare compounds that contain ionic and covalent bonds

Get Started Brainstorm with some your classmates about materials you can use to represent atoms and chemical bonds. You may want to look ahead in the chapter to preview covalent and ionic bonding.

Check Your Progress You'll be working on this project as you study this chapter. To keep your project on track, look for Check Your Progress boxes at the following points.
Section 1 Review, page 54: Make models of atoms.
Section 3 Review, page 64: Build models of ionic compounds.
Section 4 Review, page 69: Build models of compounds that contain covalent bonds.

Wrap Up At the end of the chapter (page 77), you will present and explain your models to the class.

A computer-made model of a protein shows the many atoms that are bonded together in the molecule.

SECTION 4 Covalent Bonds

Discover **Why Don't Water and Oil Mix?**
Sharpen Your Skills **Designing Experiments**
Skills Lab **Shedding Light on Chemical Bonds**

Integrating Earth Science
SECTION 5 Crystal Chemistry

Discover **How Small Do They Get?**

Program Resources

- ◆ **Teaching Resources** Chapter 2 Project Teacher Notes, pp. 34–35; Chapter 2 Project Overview and Worksheets, pp. 36–39; Chapter 2 Project Scoring Rubric, p. 40

Media and Technology

 Audio CDs and **Audiotapes** English-Spanish Section Summaries

 www.phschool.com

You will find an Internet activity, chapter self-tests for students, and links to other chapter topics at this site.

Performance Assessment

The Chapter 2 Project Scoring Rubric on page 40 of Teaching Resources will help you evaluate how well students complete the Chapter 2 Project. Students will be assessed on
- ◆ whether their models correctly represent individual and bonded atoms, including number of bonds formed;
- ◆ how well their model designs distinguish between the atoms of different elements;
- ◆ how accurately their models show the differences between ionic and covalent bonding in compounds;
- ◆ the thoroughness and organization of their presentations.

By sharing the Chapter 2 Scoring Rubric with students at the beginning of the project, you will make it clear to them what they are expected to do.

Objectives

After completing the lesson, students will be able to

◆ describe the structure of an atom and define protons, neutrons, and electrons;

◆ explain the role of valence electrons in forming chemical bonds.

Key Terms nucleus, proton, neutron, electron, valence electron, electron dot diagram

1 Engage/Explore

Activating Prior Knowledge

Give students two inflated rubber balloons, or have them blow up and tie two balloons themselves. Have students rub the balloons against their hair or against wool fabric. Ask: **After rubbing, what happens when a balloon is held near your hair? What happens when the two balloons are held near each other?** *(After rubbing, the balloon and hair are attracted to each other, but the two balloons move away from each other.)* Ask students to explain why this happens. *(Samples: The balloons are charged; static electricity)*

DISCOVER ACTIVITY

Skills Focus making models

Materials *pencil, paper, metric ruler, dime or smaller circular item*

Time 10 minutes

Tips Remind students that the diameter of a circle is represented by a line that passes through the center of the circle.

Expected Outcome Students will probably predict that the outer edge of the model atom will be near the edges of their papers or desks.

Think It Over Sample: The diameter of a dime is 1.75 cm. An atom with this size nucleus would be 1,750 meters in diameter—a little more than a mile. *(175,000 cm × 1 m/100 cm = 1,750 m)*

SECTION
1 Inside an Atom

DISCOVER ·········· ACTIVITY····

How Far Away Is the Electron?

1. On a piece of paper, make a small circle no bigger than a dime. The circle represents the nucleus, or center, of a model atom.

2. Measure the diameter of the circle in centimeters.

3. Now predict where you think the outer edge of this model atom will be. For example, will the outer edge be within the edges of the paper? Your desk? The classroom? The school building?

Think It Over

Making Models The diameter of an actual atom can be 100,000 times the diameter of its nucleus. Calculate the diameter of your model atom. How close was your prediction in Step 3 to your calculation? (*Hint:* To compare your result to the real world, change the units of your prediction from centimeters to meters.)

GUIDE FOR READING

◆ What is the structure of an atom?

◆ What role do valence electrons play in forming chemical bonds?

Reading Tip As you read, make a table listing the particles found in an atom. Include the name of each particle, its charge, and where in an atom the particle is located.

Picture this: It's –5°C, five degrees below the freezing temperature of water. Two white solids—ice and salt—are side by side. You begin to heat the materials to see how each one will change. As the temperature rises, the ice melts at 0°C, making liquid water. It then boils into a gas at 100°C. The water is long gone before you notice a change in the salt. Finally, at 801°C the salt begins to melt. It boils away when the temperature reaches 1,413°C.

Although these materials were both solids when you started heating them, they showed very different properties as conditions changed. These differences are caused in part by the kinds of chemical bonds that hold their atoms together. To understand how atoms bond, you first need to know more about atoms themselves.

▼ **Ice**   **Rock salt** ▼

Structure of an Atom

Ice, salt, and all other materials in your world are made of atoms. Atoms are so small it would take about two million to make a line across the period at the end of this sentence. It's amazing that things so tiny are the building blocks of all substances in the universe.

If you could look into a single atom, what might you see? Figuring out what atoms are made of hasn't been simple. Theories about their shape and structure have changed many times over the past 200 years and continue to change even now. But some properties of atoms are well understood. For one thing, scientists know atoms are made of even smaller particles.

READING STRATEGIES

Reading Tip Have students create tables such as the one below. Invite volunteers to give presentations based on the information in their tables.

Particle	Charge	Location
Proton	positive	inside nucleus
Neutron	neutral	inside nucleus
Electron	negative	outside nucleus

Vocabulary As students read, have them list the boldfaced terms in the section and write definitions for the terms in their own words.

Study and Comprehension Have students work alone or with partners to outline the information in the section. Suggest students use the major headings in the section as main topics in their outlines. You may want to outline the information under the first heading, *Structure of an Atom*, with the class.

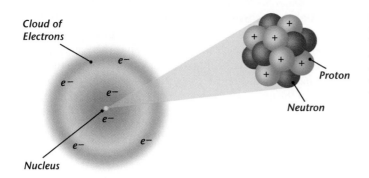

Cloud of Electrons

Nucleus

Figure 1 An atom's tiny nucleus contains protons and neutrons. The electrons move in the space around the nucleus.
Applying Concepts Is this carbon atom negatively charged, positively charged, or neutral overall?

Proton

Neutron

An atom consists of a nucleus surrounded by one or more electrons. The **nucleus** (NOO klee us) is the tiny, central core of an atom. It contains particles called protons and neutrons. **Protons** have a positive electric charge (indicated by a plus symbol, +). **Neutrons** have no charge. They are neutral. (Could you guess that from their name?) A third type of particle moves in the space around the outside of the nucleus. These very energetic particles, called **electrons,** move rapidly in all directions. Electrons carry a negative charge (indicated by a negative symbol, −).

Look at the carbon atom illustrated in Figure 1. If you count the number of protons and electrons, you'll see there are six of each. In an atom, the number of protons equals the number of electrons. As a result, the total positive charge and total negative charge balance each other, making the atom neutral. The number of neutrons in an atom may be the same as the number of protons, but not always.

Although the charges of a proton and an electron cancel each other out, the particles differ greatly in mass. A proton is almost 2,000 times as massive as an electron! Neutrons, however, have about the same mass as protons.

Checkpoint Which particles in an atom are in the nucleus?

Electrons in Atoms

Electrons move around the nucleus so fast that it is impossible to know exactly where any electron is at a particular time. Think about the blades of a fan that is turned on. They go too fast to be seen. As electrons move around the nucleus, the effect is like the fan blades, but in three dimensions. You can think of the space around the nucleus as a spherical cloud of negatively charged electrons.

Figure 2 When a fan is turned on, you see a blur instead of separate blades. A fan is a model for the way electrons fill the space around the nucleus of an atom.

Program Resources

◆ **Teaching Resources** 2-1 Lesson Plan, p. 41; 2-1 Section Summary, p. 42
◆ **Guided Reading and Study Workbook** Section 2-1

Media and Technology

 Transparencies "Model of a Carbon Atom," Transparency 7

Answers to Self-Assessment
Caption Question
Figure 1 An atom is neutral overall.
Checkpoint
Protons and neutrons

2 *Facilitate*

Structure of an Atom

Including All Students
Students who have weak math skills may be confused by the way the + and − symbols are used to describe electric charge and the way they are used in mathematics. Explain that positive charges are not necessarily greater than negative charges; the charges are simply opposites. **learning modality: logical/mathematical**

Using the Visuals: Figure 1
Help students understand the charges on atoms by asking: **How many protons are shown in this atom?** *(six)* **If the atom has no electric charge, how many electrons does this atom have?** *(six)* Ask students to explain how the neutrons affect the charge on the atom. *(Not at all; neutrons have no electric charge.)* **learning modality: visual**

Electrons in Atoms

Demonstration
Materials *small battery-operated fan*
Time 5 minutes

ACTIVITY

Show students that when the fan is off, they can distinctly see each blade. Turn the fan on and ask students to describe the position of each blade. Ask: **How does this demonstration model the meaning of a "cloud" of electrons?** *(Just like the fan blades, the electrons are present, but they are moving too fast to be visible individually.)* **learning modality: visual**

Ongoing Assessment
Oral Presentation Ask students to identify the charge on each particle within an atom.

Electrons in Atoms, continued

SCIENCE & History

Remind students that captions and labels on the time line contain valuable information about the changing ideas about the atom. Point out that each atomic model relied upon information in the previous models as well as new information. Ask: **What was the difference between the Dalton model of the atom and the Rutherford model?** *(Dalton thought of the atom as a tiny solid ball; Rutherford's atom was mostly empty space with a tiny nucleus and electrons orbiting it.)* **What did Chadwick discover? What did his model explain?** *(Neutrons. The model explained why atoms were heavier than the total mass of their protons and electrons.)*

Extend Suggest that students use simple materials such as clay and synthetic pillow stuffing to make a three-dimensional version of each model described.

In Your Journal Students' interviews should include questions such as, "What evidence did you find that led you to propose a different model of the atom?" and "Do you think the current model of the atom is completely accurate, or do you think it might be changed in the future?" Encourage students to research answers supported by the scientist's work. **learning modality: verbal**

 Students can save their interviews in their portfolios.

Little Particles, Big Spaces Most of an atom's mass comes from its protons and neutrons. But most of an atom's volume is the space in which the electrons move. That space is huge compared to the space occupied by the nucleus. To picture the difference, imagine standing at the pitcher's mound in a baseball stadium. If the nucleus were the size of a pencil eraser, the electrons could be in the outfield or as far away as the top row of seats!

☑ *Checkpoint* Where are the electrons in an atom?

Models of Atoms

For over two centuries, scientists have worked on models of atoms in an effort to understand why matter behaves as it does. As scientists have learned more, the model of the atom has changed.

1808
Dalton Model

British chemist John Dalton published his *New System of Chemical Philosophy*, explaining that each element is made of small atoms and that different elements have atoms of different mass. Dalton imagined atoms as tiny, solid balls.

1897
Thomson Model

British scientist J. J. Thomson proposed a new model. He suggested that an atom is a positively charged sphere with electrons embedded in it. His model could be described as looking like a muffin with berries scattered through it.

1800

For almost 100 years, not much ▲ new information was learned about atoms.

1900

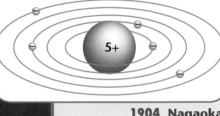

1904 Nagaoka Model

Japanese physicist Hantaro Nagaoka proposed a model of the atom that had a large sphere in the center with a positive charge. His model showed the electrons revolving around this sphere like the planets around the sun.

Background

Facts and Figures The following table gives the atomic mass and atomic radius compared to hydrogen for selected elements. Even though atoms are mostly empty space, comparing the radii of single atoms provides a glimpse into their densities.

For example, an atom of uranium has a radius only 7 times that of hydrogen, but the atomic mass of uranium is 238 times the atomic mass of hydrogen.

Element	Atomic Mass	Radius Compared to H Radius
hydrogen	1	1
osmium	190	5.2
lead	207	7.2
uranium	238	7

Valence Electrons An atom's electrons are not all the same distance from the nucleus. Nor are they held to the atom with equal strength. Those farthest away or most loosely held are called **valence electrons** (VAY luns). The number of valence electrons in an atom determines many properties of the atom, and therefore, of an element. For example, only valence electrons are involved in chemical bonding.

In Your Journal

Find out more about one of the scientists who worked on models of the atom. Write an imaginary interview with this person in which you discuss his work with him.

5+

1911
Rutherford Model

British physicist Ernest Rutherford concluded that the atom is mostly empty space. Electrons orbit randomly around a small, positively charged nucleus.

1932
Chadwick Model

British physicist James Chadwick discovered the neutron, a particle having about the same mass as the proton but with no electrical charge. The existence of the neutron explained why atoms were heavier than the total mass of their protons and electrons.

| 1910 | 1920 | 1930 | 1940 | 1950 |

1913
Bohr Model

Danish physicist Niels Bohr determined that electrons aren't randomly located around the nucleus. His model showed electrons moving in specific layers, or shells. He said that atoms absorb or give off energy when the electrons move from one shell to another.

Cloud of electrons

1920s to Present
Modern Model

The current model of the atom came from the work of many scientists from the 1920s to the present. It shows the electrons as forming a negatively charged cloud around the nucleus. It is impossible to determine exactly where an electron is at any given time.

Chapter 2 **L ◆ 53**

Answers to Self-Assessment

✓ *Checkpoint*
The electrons are in a spherical cloud around the nucleus.

Language Arts Connection
Inform students that the word *valence* comes from the Latin word *valere*, which means "to be strong." Point out that the word *equivalent* is based on the same word and that the prefix *equi-* means "equal or similar." Suggest students use this to remember that atoms with the same number of valence electrons have the same combining power. **learning modality: verbal**

Demonstration

Materials *2 small button magnets, iron filings, overhead projector, sheet of transparency paper*

ACTIVITY

Time 10 minutes

Place the transparency paper on the overhead projector and set one magnet near its center. Sprinkle the filings on the paper, then move the magnet around until the filings are evenly distributed in a cloud around the magnet. Tell students the magnet represents the positively charged nucleus of an atom, and the iron filings represent the negatively charged electrons. Ask: **Which filings in the cloud do you think would react with another atom?** (*The filings farthest away from the magnet*) Place the second magnet a short distance away from the filings. Move this magnet closer to the first until some filings begin to move away from the first magnet and toward the second. Make sure students realize that these filings represent the valence electrons. Encourage students to think about why these filings move. (*Sample: The filings on the edge are less attracted to the first magnet because they are farther away.*) **learning modality: visual**

Ongoing Assessment

Oral Presentation Have students describe three models of the atom. Students should name the parts of each atom and explain how one model differs from another.

Why Atoms Form Bonds

Building Inquiry Skills: Making Models

Encourage students to use Figure 3 as a guide for drawing dot diagrams. Give students the number of valence electrons for other elements and have them practice drawing dot diagrams on their own. **learning modality: visual**

3 Assess

Section 1 Review Answers

1. Nucleus, found in the center of an atom; neutrons, uncharged particles found within the nucleus; protons, positively charged particles found within the nucleus; electrons, negatively charged particles found moving rapidly in the space around the nucleus
2. The number of electrons (negative charges) in an atom equals the number of protons (positive charges).
3. Valence electrons are transferred or shared between atoms during the formation of chemical bonds.
4. Electrons are much less massive than protons and neutrons, but the space in which electrons move is much larger than the nucleus.
5. The symbol for the element, the number of valence electrons

Check Your Progress
CHAPTER PROJECT 2

Check students' choices of model-building materials to make sure they are appropriate and easy to use. If students cannot decide what to use to connect their atoms to form compounds, suggest they use soft materials such as soft candy as their atoms, and toothpicks to demonstrate the chemical bonds.

Performance Assessment

Drawing Inform students that a helium atom has 2 protons, 2 neutrons, and 2 valence electrons. Direct students to draw a model of a helium atom and a dot diagram for helium.

Figure 3 In electron dot diagrams, each dot represents one outer, or valence, electron of an atom. *Interpreting Diagrams Each hydrogen atom has only one electron, but an argon atom has 18 electrons. How many of argon's electrons are valence electrons?*

Hydrogen   Argon

One way to show the number of valence electrons that an atom has is with an **electron dot diagram.** It includes the symbol for an element surrounded by dots. Each dot stands for one valence electron.

Why Atoms Form Bonds

A neutral atom never has more than eight valence electrons. Most kinds of atoms have fewer. When atoms form bonds with each other, one of two things usually happens. Either the number of valence electrons increases to a total of eight, or all the valence electrons are given up. When atoms end up with eight or zero valence electrons, they become less reactive than they were before. Chemists say that such atoms are more chemically stable.

A chemical bond forms between two atoms when valence electrons move between them. Electrons may be transferred from one atom to another, or they may be shared between the atoms. In either case, the change causes the atoms to become connected, or bonded. Chemical reactions occur when bonds between atoms form. Reactions also occur when bonds are broken. Each time, electrons are moved around. The result is the formation of new substances.

Section 1 Review

1. Describe the parts of an atom and tell where each is found.
2. Explain why the electrical charge on an atom is zero, or neutral.
3. What happens to valence electrons during the formation of chemical bonds?
4. Explain why electrons make up much of an atom's volume but not much of its mass.
5. **Thinking Critically Applying Concepts** What information can you get from an electron dot diagram?

Check Your Progress
CHAPTER PROJECT 2

Select materials to use to build your models. Start by making models of several common elements such as hydrogen, oxygen, nitrogen, carbon, chlorine, sodium, potassium, and sulfur. (*Hint:* You will need to represent the valence electrons on each atom.) Make several atoms of each element and save them. Select materials to represent the chemical bonds.

Program Resources

◆ **Teaching Resources** 2-1 Review and Reinforce, p. 43; 2-1 Enrich, p. 44

Answers to Self-Assessment

Caption Question

Figure 3 Eight of argon's electrons are valence electrons.

SECTION
2 Atoms in the Periodic Table

DISCOVER

What Are the Trends in the Periodic Table?

1. Examine closely the periodic table of the elements your teacher provides. Each square shows the chemical symbol for an element plus information about the element.
2. Look in each square for the whole number located above the symbol of the element. As you read across a row from left to right, what trend do you see?
3. Now look at a column from top to bottom. What pattern do you see in these numbers?

Think It Over

Interpreting Data Are the elements organized in alphabetical order? Can you explain why one row ends and a new row starts? Why do you think certain elements are in the same column? What questions would you need to ask in order to understand how the elements are organized?

M ix some elements together and nothing happens. Mix other elements together and they react as explosively as the sodium and bromine in Figure 4. Other combinations of elements react either slowly or only when heated. Recall that atoms react with each other as a result of how many valence electrons each has. Therefore, knowing the number of valence electrons in atoms is a clue to which elements combine, and how. But where do you look for this information? You can look in the periodic table of the elements.

Organizing the Elements

The periodic table is a system used worldwide for organizing elements into categories based on how they react. The way the elements are organized in the periodic table also tells you something about their protons and electrons.

All the atoms of one kind of element have the same number of protons. For example, all carbon atoms have six protons, and all hydrogen atoms have only one. The **atomic number** is the number of protons in the nucleus of an atom. **Look at any periodic table and you will see that elements are arranged from left to right and top to bottom in order of increasing atomic number.** Remember that if you know the number of protons in an atom, you also know the number of electrons.

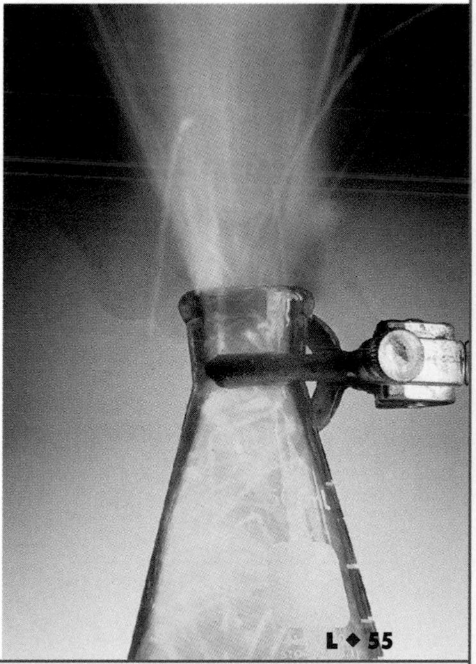

GUIDE FOR READING

- How is the periodic table organized?
- What do elements in a family have in common?

Reading Tip As you read, use the periodic table in Appendix D for reference. Look for repeating patterns.

Figure 4 The elements sodium and bromine react with an explosion.

L ◆ 55

Objectives

After completing the lesson, students will be able to
- ◆ describe the organization of the periodic table;
- ◆ identify the groups within the periodic table and state what properties elements in a group have in common.

Key Terms atomic number, group, family, period, halogen

1 Engage/Explore

Activating Prior Knowledge

Ask students: **If you go into a music store, how do you find a particular CD you're looking for?** *(You find the section for that type of music and then search for the artist and title.)* Ask students to give reasons why they think music stores organize CDs into categories such as jazz or rock. *(It makes it easier to find specific CDs; if you're looking for a particular type of music, you can browse in that section.)* Tell students that in this section they learn how the periodic table is organized and how the elements are grouped.

DISCOVER

Skills Focus interpreting data
Materials *periodic table*
Time 15 minutes
Tips Encourage students to find patterns to support their opinions on how the periodic table is organized.
Think It Over Students should recognize that the numbers in the element squares are arranged in increasing order. They may even know the term *atomic number*. Students may state that they would need to know more about the properties of the elements to understand how the table is organized.

2 Facilitate

Organizing the Elements

Using the Visuals: Figure 5

Have students locate the symbol H for hydrogen. Then draw their attention to the number above the symbol. Point out that this number is the atomic number of the element. Ask: **Which element has atomic number 2?** *(He, helium)* **Atomic number 4?** *(Be, beryllium)* **What is the atomic number of O, oxygen?** *(8)* Ask: **What pattern do you see in the atomic numbers in the table?** *(They increase from left to right.)* **learning modality: visual**

Comparing Families of Elements

Sharpen your Skills

Classifying

Materials *periodic table*
Time 15 minutes
Tips Remind students that the chemical properties of elements are related to the number of valence electrons.
Expected Outcome Students should recognize that elements in the same chemical family have similar chemical properties, so students should match elements by family, or group.
Answers krypton—neon; phosphorous—nitrogen; potassium—sodium; magnesium—calcium; silicon—carbon; oxygen—sulfur **learning modality: logical/mathematical**

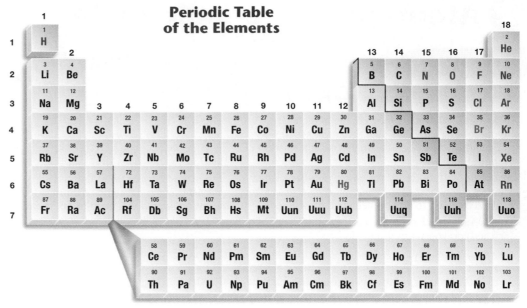

Figure 5 The periodic table organizes the elements into rows and columns.

Sharpen your Skills

Classifying

Match each element on the left with the element on the right that has the most similar chemical properties. Use the periodic table to help you.

Krypton (Kr)	Sodium (Na)
Phosphorus (P)	Neon (Ne)
Potassium (K)	Calcium (Ca)
Magnesium (Mg)	Sulfur (S)
Silicon (Si)	Nitrogen (N)
Oxygen (O)	Carbon (C)

Why did you match the pairs as you did?

Elements in the same column, up and down, are called a **group,** or **family.** Notice the numbers 1 through 18 across the tops of the columns in Figure 5. These numbers identify the group to which an element belongs. For example, carbon (C) is in Group 14 and oxygen (O) is in Group 16.

A row across the table is called a **period.** Hydrogen and helium make up the first period. The second period starts with lithium (Li) and continues across to neon (Ne). Notice that the atomic number increases one at a time from left to right across the periodic table. The number of valence electrons increases from left to right, too. Figure 6 shows the electron dot diagrams for the elements in the second period of the table.

Checkpoint *What is the difference betweeen a group and a period in the periodic table?*

Comparing Families of Elements

If you saw a flock of ducks on a pond, would you notice any similarities among the birds? Would they share characteristics that would set them apart from crows or robins on the nearby shore? **Each family in the periodic table has its own characteristic properties based on its number of valence electrons.**

Background

Facts and Figures The gases in Group 18 are called noble because they do not combine with oxygen, a designation also given to noble metals such as gold and platinum. Sir William Ramsay discovered the noble gases in the years 1892–1910. He was awarded the Nobel Prize for chemistry in 1904 for the discovery of four of the noble gases—neon, argon, krypton, and xenon.

Krypton was discovered in 1898. Its name comes from the Greek word for "hidden," and it is characterized by brilliant orange and green spectral lines.

Another noble gas, radon, was isolated in 1910. Ramsay named it *niton* (from a Latin word for "shining"), but it was renamed radon in 1923 because it comes from radium.

Noble Gases Group 18 at the far right side of the table is a good place to start learning about the characteristics of the families. Except for helium, atoms of these elements have eight valence electrons. (Look at the electron dot diagram for neon at right, as an example.) The Group 18 elements are known as the noble gases or inert gases. *Inert* means "inactive." Since they already have the maximum number of valence electrons, noble gas atoms don't react very easily with other atoms. Helium, which is as unreactive as the other noble gases, is stable with only two valence electrons.

Reactive Nonmetals Now look at the column to the left of the noble gases. The elements in Group 17, also called the **halogen** family, are very reactive. Atoms of these elements have seven valence electrons, as illustrated by flourine in Figure 6. A gain of just one electron leads to the more stable number of eight. As a result, elements in the halogen family react easily with other elements whose atoms can give up electrons.

Reactive Metals At the far left side of the periodic table is Group 1, the elements of the alkali metal family. If alkali metals lose one electron, the atoms are left with zero valence electrons. They become more chemically stable. This property makes the alkali metals very reactive elements. If the alkali metals lose electrons easily and the halogens gain electrons easily, what happens when they come in contact with each other? They react violently! This explains the explosive reaction between sodium and bromine shown at the beginning of this section. These two elements form the compound sodium bromide.

Hydrogen is located above Group 1 on the periodic table because it has only one valence electron. Like the alkali metal elements, hydrogen is extremely reactive.

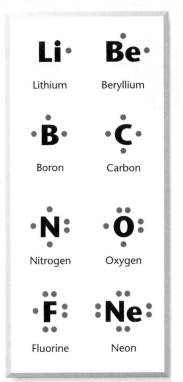

Figure 6 These eight elements make up the second period.
Calculating What is the trend in number of valence electrons from lithium to neon?

Section 2 Review

1. What is the basis for arranging the elements in the periodic table?
2. Why are the elements in each group in the periodic table considered a family?
3. What properties are shared by the noble gases?
4. **Thinking Critically Applying Concepts** How can you use the arrangement of elements in the periodic table to predict how they will react with other elements to form compounds?

Science at Home

People use many organization systems. Think of tools in a workshop or baseball cards in a collection. Look around your home for as many different systems of organization you can find. Check out drawers and cabinets. Look for things lined up in rows. Then discuss with your family how these systems of organization compare with the periodic table of the elements.

Program Resources

◆ **Teaching Resources** 2-2 Review and Reinforce, p. 47; 2-2 Enrich, p. 48

Media and Technology

Transparencies "Electron Dot Diagrams of Period 2 Elements," Transparency 9

Answers to Self-Assessment

Caption Question

Figure 6 The number of valence electrons increases from lithium to neon.

✓ Checkpoint

A group is a column in the periodic table, containing elements with the same number of valence electrons. A period is a row, in which the number of valence electrons increases from left to right.

Building Inquiry Skills: Interpreting Diagrams

On the board, draw the electron dot diagrams in Figure 6 from left to right as they would appear in the periodic table. Then write the symbols for the elements in period 3 on a line below the elements from Figure 6. Challenge students to draw electron dot diagrams for the period 3 elements. *(Each diagram will be the same as the one directly above it.)* Ask students if they notice a pattern in the dot diagrams. *(The number of valence electrons repeats each period.)* Tell students that the word *period* refers to a repeating pattern. **limited English proficiency**

3 Assess

Section 2 Review Answers

1. In order of increasing atomic number
2. Elements in the same group (family) have similar chemical properties and the same number of valence electrons.
3. Noble gases have the maximum number of valence electrons and are therefore unreactive.
4. Elements in the same group will react similarly. Those elements that can lose electrons will react with elements that can gain electrons.

Science at Home

Point out that there can be many ways to organize the same collection of items. For example, a baseball-card collection may be organized by year, or alphabetically by player name or team. Indicate that most organization systems will be arrangements that help people locate an item quickly.

Performance Assessment

Writing Ask students to briefly describe the information found in the periodic table. *(The atomic number, or the number of protons in the nucleus; the number of valence electrons, which indicates which elements may combine and how they will react)*

Comparing Atom Sizes

Preparing for Inquiry

Key Concept The periodic table reveals trends in the properties of elements.

Skills Objectives Students will be able to
- model the relative sizes of atoms;
- graph data showing the trend in size as atomic number increases in a group;
- predict the positions of elements on the periodic table.

Time 20 minutes

Guiding Inquiry

Invitation Ask students to compare and contrast a model car or ship and the real thing. (*Differences—size, model motor does not work, model wheels may not turn; Similarities—shape, scale, structure, color*)

Introducing the Procedure

Have students think of using the smallest value in a series as the basis for measuring other values. (*Millimeters as the basis for centimeters and meters*)

Troubleshooting the Experiment

Have students round the ratios to the nearest tenth. Remind students that the ratios are comparisons. For example, magnesium has an atomic radius about 1.4 times that of beryllium.

Expected Outcome

Students' graphs should show that atomic size increases with atomic number.

Analyze and Conclude

1. Answers will depend on predictions.
2. Make sure students have set up and labeled their graphs correctly.
3. On a curve; the radius increases as the atomic number increases.
4. At the bottom of the table; values for the atomic radii of other families.
5. Atoms are too small to be seen, but the same ratios hold when using larger units.

Extending the Inquiry

More to Explore Students should use small objects of the appropriate relative radii to make their models.

Comparing Atom Sizes

In this lab, you will be using models to compare the sizes of atoms in one family of elements in the periodic table.

Problem

How is the radius of an atom related to its atomic number?

Materials

drawing compass
calculator
periodic table of the elements (Appendix D)

Procedure

1. Using the periodic table as a reference, predict whether the size (radius) of atoms will increase, remain the same, or decrease as you go from the top to the bottom of a chemical family.
2. Look at the table on this page that lists each element in Group 2 and its atomic radius. Copy the table into your notebook.
3. Calculate the relative radius of each atom compared to beryllium, the smallest atom listed. Do this by dividing each radius in the table by the value for beryllium. (*Hint:* The relative radius of magnesium would be 160 divided by 112, or 1.4.) Record these values, rounded to the nearest tenth, in your data table.
4. Using a compass, draw a circle for each element with a radius that corresponds to the relative radius you calculated in Step 3. Use centimeters as your unit for the radius of each of these circles. **CAUTION:** *Do not push the sharp point of the compass against your skin.*
5. Label each model with the symbol of the element it represents.

DATA TABLE			
Atomic Number	Element	Radius (pm)*	Relative Radius
4	Be	112	1
12	Mg	160	
20	Ca	197	
38	Sr	215	
56	Ba	222	

*A picometer (pm) is one billionth of a millimeter.

Analyze and Conclude

1. Based on your models, was your prediction in Step 1 correct? Explain your answer.
2. Make a graph of the data given in the first and third columns of your table. Label the horizontal axis Atomic Number. Mark the divisions from 0 to 60. Then label the vertical axis Radius and mark its divisions from 0 to 300 picometers.
3. Do your points fall on a straight line or on a curve? What pattern does your graph show?
4. Predict where you would find the largest atom in any chemical family. What evidence would you need to tell if your prediction is correct?
5. **Think About It** If an atom has an actual radius of 100 to 200 picometers, why would drawing a model with a radius of about one to two centimeters be useful?

More to Explore

Look up the atomic masses for the Group 2 elements. Devise a plan to model their relative atomic masses using real-world objects.

Sample Data Table

Atomic Number	Element	Radius (pm)	Relative Radius
4	Be	112	1
12	Mg	160	1.4
20	Ca	197	1.8
38	Sr	215	1.9
56	Ba	222	2.0

Program Resources

- **Teaching Resources** Skills Lab blackline masters, pp. 61–62

Media and Technology

 Lab Activity Videotape
Chemical Interactions, 3

SECTION 3 Ionic Bonds

DISCOVER ••••••••••••••••••••••••••••• ACTIVITY ••••

How Do Ions Form?

1. Place three pairs of checkers (three red and three black) on your desk. The red represent electrons and the black represent protons.

2. Place nine pairs of checkers (nine red and nine black) in a separate group on your desk.

3. Move a red checker from the smaller group to the larger group.

4. Count the number of positive charges (protons) and negative charges (electrons) in each group.

5. Now sort the checkers into a group of four pairs and a group of eight pairs. Repeat Steps 3 and 4, this time moving two red checkers from the smaller group to the larger group.

Think It Over

Modeling What is the total charge on each group before you moved the red checkers (electrons)? What is the charge on each group after you moved the checkers? Based on this activity, what do you think happens to the charge of an atom when it loses electrons? When it gains electrons?

I magine you are walking down the street with your best friend. A market has a bin of apples for sale. A sign says that they cost 40 cents each. You both want an apple, but your friend has only 35 cents while you have 45 cents. What can you do? It doesn't take you long to figure out that if you give your friend a nickel, you can each buy an apple. Transferring the nickel to your friend gets both of you what you want. Your actions model, in a simple way, what can happen between atoms.

Electron Transfer

Like your friend with not quite enough money to buy an apple, an atom with five, six, or seven valence electrons has not quite enough to total the more stable number of eight. On the other hand, an atom with one, two, or three valence electrons can lose a few and become stable. When atoms have fewer than four valence electrons, they can transfer these to other atoms that have more than four. In this way, atoms either gain electrons or lose electrons, becoming more stable.

GUIDE FOR READING

◆ How does an atom become an ion?

◆ What are the characteristic properties of ionic compounds?

◆ How are the ions in an ionic compound held together?

Reading Tip As you read, make an outline describing the characteristics of compounds containing ionic bonds.

L ◆ 59

SECTION 3 Ionic Bonds

Objectives

After completing the lesson, students will be able to
◆ explain the differences between an atom and an ion;
◆ describe how an ionic bond forms;
◆ identify the properties of ionic compounds.

Key Terms ion, ionic bond, polyatomic ion, crystal

1 Engage/Explore

Activating Prior Knowledge

Ask students: **Suppose you have too much food in your lunch and a friend has too little. How could you both have the right amount to eat?** (*Give your friend some of your food.*) Remind students that some atoms form bonds by giving electrons to other atoms.

•••••••• DISCOVER ••••••••

Skills Focus modeling
Materials *enough* *checkers for each team to have 12 red and black pairs of checkers, or a sufficient number of any objects in two colors*
Time 15 minutes
Tips Ask: **What is the total number of red checkers? Black checkers?** (*Twelve of each*) **What is the total charge on the entire set of all the checkers?** (*No charge*)
Think It Over Before the transfers, each group had a neutral charge. After the transfers, the group receiving red checkers had one or two negative charges, and the group giving up the checkers had one or two positive charges. An atom becomes positively charged when it loses electrons and negatively charged when it gains electrons.

2 Facilitate

Electron Transfer

Addressing Naive Conceptions

Materials *iron nail or pin, magnet*
Time 5 minutes

Students may be surprised that an atom can be more stable when it carries a charge than it is when it is neutral. Use the magnet and an iron nail or pin to demonstrate that, when the magnet and the magnetically charged objects are together, they are both charged and stable. **learning modality: visual**

Forming an Ionic Bond

Building Inquiry Skills: Inferring

Have students use the information in Figure 8 to make inferences about the numbers of ions that combine to form compounds. Ask: **How many ions of magnesium and oxygen would you need to make an electrically neutral compound?** *(One of each)* **What is the formula of the compound?** *(MgO)* Then have students consider making an ionic compound containing magnesium and iodine. Then ask: **How many magnesium ions and iodine ions would you need to make an electrically neutral compound?** *(One magnesium ion and two iodine ions)* **What would be this compound's formula?** *(MgI₂)* **learning modality: logical/mathematical**

Including All Students

Allow students who need additional help distinguishing atoms from ions to make flowcharts to describe how an atom becomes an ion. Prompt students by asking them to explain why atoms do not have a charge but ions do. *(An atom has an equal number of electrons and protons; ions have an unequal number.)* **learning modality: verbal**

Figure 7 When an atom loses one of its negatively charged electrons, it becomes a positively charged ion.

Figure 8 Positively charged ions have lost one or more electrons. Negatively charged ions have gained one or more electrons. *Classifying Which ions in the table are positively charged and which are negatively charged?*

Ions and Their Charges

Name	Charge	Symbol or Formula
Lithium	1+	Li^+
Sodium	1+	Na^+
Potassium	1+	K^+
Ammonium	1+	NH_4^+
Calcium	2+	Ca^{2+}
Magnesium	2+	Mg^{2+}
Aluminum	3+	Al^{3+}
Fluoride	1–	F^-
Chloride	1–	Cl^-
Iodide	1–	I^-
Bicarbonate	1–	HCO_3^-
Nitrate	1–	NO_3^-
Oxide	2–	O^{2-}
Sulfide	2–	S^{2-}
Carbonate	2–	CO_3^{2-}
Sulfate	2–	SO_4^{2-}
Phosphate	3–	PO_4^{3-}

An **ion** (EYE ahn) is an atom or group of atoms that has become electrically charged. **When an atom loses an electron, it loses a negative charge and becomes a positive ion. When an atom gains an electron, it gains a negative charge and becomes a negative ion.**

Forming an Ionic Bond

Consider what can happen if sodium and chlorine atoms combine. Sodium has one valence electron and chlorine has seven. Suppose sodium's valence electron is transferred to chlorine. Then both atoms become ions. The sodium atom becomes a positive ion (Na^+). The chlorine atom becomes a negative ion (Cl^-). Negative and positive electric charges attract each other, so the oppositely charged Na^+ and Cl^- ions come together. They form sodium chloride, which you know as table salt.

An **ionic bond** is the attraction between two oppositely charged ions. This attraction is similar to the attraction between the opposite poles of two magnets. When the two ions come together, the opposite charges cancel out. Every sodium ion (with a charge written as 1+) is balanced by a chloride ion (with a charge written as 1–). The formula for sodium chloride, NaCl, shows you this 1 : 1 ratio.

Compounds are electrically neutral. When ions come together, they do so in a way that balances out the charges on the ions. Figure 8 lists some common ions. Look at the charge of the magnesium ion. How many chloride ions would be needed to cancel out the 2+ charge of magnesium in the compound magnesium chloride? The formula for magnesium chloride, $MgCl_2$, tells you the answer is two.

☑ *Checkpoint* What effect does gaining an electron have on the charge of an atom?

Background

History of Science In the 1830s, the English chemist Michael Faraday performed many experiments to determine the relationship between electricity and chemical bonds. He discovered that a certain amount of electrical current could cause a chemical reaction in which atoms of an element came out of solution. He also discovered that a certain amount of charge could convert an ion of an element into a neutral atom of the element.

Faraday was the first scientist to reveal electrical forces on the atomic level. His work led to the discovery of subatomic particles and the value of the positive and negative charges on protons and electrons. Faraday wrote, "The atoms of matter are in some way endowed or associated with electrical powers, to which they owe their most striking qualities, amongst them their mutual chemical affinity."

EXPLORING Ionic Bonds

Reactions between metals and nonmetals often form ionic compounds. These reactions occur easily between the metals in Group 1 and the halogens in Group 17. Here you can see what happens when an ionic bond forms between a sodium atom and a chlorine atom.

Sodium metal

Sodium atoms have one valence electron. When the electron is lost, the atoms become more stable.

Na·

1 valence electron

Chlorine gas

Chlorine atoms become more stable when they gain just one electron.

·Cl:

7 valence electrons

One electron is transferred from the sodium atom to the chlorine atom.

Sodium loses 1 electron   Chlorine gains 1 electron

After losing an electron, the sodium atom becomes a sodium ion with a 1+ charge.

Sodium ion   Chloride ion

After gaining an electron, the chlorine atom becomes a chloride ion with a 1– charge.

Oppositely charged ions attract each other. This attractive force is an ionic bond. In sodium chloride, each sodium ion balances the charge of one chloride ion. Overall, the compound sodium chloride is electrically neutral.

Sodium chloride

Media and Technology

 Transparencies "Exploring an Ionic Bond," Transparency 10

Answers to Self-Assessment

Caption Question

Figure 8 Positively charged ions: lithium, sodium, potassium, ammonium, calcium, magnesium, and aluminum; the rest are negatively charged.

✓ Checkpoint

An atom that gains an electron becomes a negatively charged ion.

Polyatomic Ions

Figure 9 What do seashells, chalk, limestone, and eggshells have in common? They all contain calcium carbonate, which is an ionic compound made of Ca^{2+} and CO_3^{2-} ions.

Polyatomic Ions

Some ions are made of more than one atom. Ions that are made of more than one atom are examples of **polyatomic ions** (pahl ee uh TAHM ik). The prefix *poly* means "many," so the word *polyatomic* means "many atoms." You can think of a polyatomic ion as a group of atoms that react as one. Each polyatomic ion has an overall positive or negative charge. If a polyatomic ion combines with another ion of opposite charge, an ionic compound forms. Think, for example, about the carbonate ion (CO_3^{2-}). It is made of one carbon atom and three oxygen atoms and has an overall charge of 2–. This ion can combine with a calcium ion (Ca^{2+}), forming calcium carbonate ($CaCO_3$). Calcium carbonate is the main compound in limestone.

Naming Ionic Compounds

Magnesium chloride, sodium bicarbonate, sodium oxide—where do these names come from? For an ionic compound, the name of the positive ion comes first, followed by the name of the negative ion. The name of the positive ion is usually the name of a metal. It may also be the name of a positive polyatomic ion, such as ammonium. If the negative ion is an element, the end of its name changes to *-ide*. For example, MgO is magnesium oxide. If the negative ion is polyatomic, its name remains unchanged. For example, the chemical name for washing soda (Na_2CO_3) is sodium carbonate.

☑ *Checkpoint* What kind of atom has a name change when it becomes an ion?

Properties of Ionic Compounds

Do you think table salt, iron rust, baking soda, and limestone are very much alike? If you answer no, you're right. If you answer yes, you're right, too! You wouldn't want to season your food with rust, or construct a building out of baking soda. But despite their differences, these compounds share some similarities because they all contain ionic bonds. **The characteristic properties of ionic compounds include crystal shape, high melting points, and electrical conductivity.**

Crystal Shape The object in Figure 10 that looks like a glass sculpture is really a chunk of halite, or table salt. Halite is an ionic compound. All samples of halite have sharp edges, corners, and flat surfaces. The shapes result from how the ions are arranged. In solid sodium chloride, the Na^+ and Cl^- ions come together in an alternating pattern, as shown in the diagram. The ions form an orderly, three-dimensional arrangement called a **crystal.**

In an ionic compound, every ion is attracted to ions near it that have an opposite charge. Positive ions tend to be near negative ions and farther from other positive ions. As a result, a positive sodium ion isn't attracted to just one negative chloride ion. It is attracted to ions above, below, and to all sides. Because chloride ions are attracted to sodium ions in the same way, a crystal forms. This pattern holds true no matter what the size of the crystal. In a single grain of salt, the crystal can extend for millions of ions in every direction. The number of sodium ions and chloride ions in the crystal is equal. The formula for sodium chloride, $NaCl$, represents this 1 : 1 ratio.

Na^+
Cl^-

Figure 10 A halite crystal contains sodium and chloride ions in an alternating pattern.
Making Generalizations What general characteristics of crystals can you observe in the photograph of halite?

Crystal Clear

Can you grow a salt crystal?

 ACTIVITY

1. Add salt to a jar containing about 200 mL of hot tap water, and stir. Keep adding salt until no more dissolves and it settles out when you stop stirring.
2. Tie a large crystal of coarse salt into the middle of a piece of thread.
3. Tie one end of the thread to the middle of a pencil.
4. Suspend the other end of the thread in the solution by laying the pencil across the mouth of the jar. Do not allow the crystal to touch the solution.
5. Place the jar in a quiet, undisturbed area. Check the size of the crystal over the next few days.

Observing Does the salt crystal change size over time? What is its shape? What do you think is happening to the salt in the solution?

Properties of Ionic Compounds

TRY THIS

Skills Focus observing **ACTIVITY**
Materials *15 cm thread, coarse salt such as kosher or sea salt, jar or cup, pencil, hot tap water, stirring rod or spoon*
Time 15 minutes for setup, 3 minutes observation time daily over a week
Tips The higher the temperature of the water, the more salt will dissolve.
Expected Outcome The crystal will increase in size as sodium and chloride ions in the solution wick up the thread and join the crystal.
Extend Allow students to examine salt crystals under a microscope and compare the shape of the crystals to the large crystal produced in this lab.
learning modality: visual

Building Inquiry Skills: Observing

Materials *magnesium sulfate, alum, hand lenses* **ACTIVITY**
Time 15 minutes

Tell students they will work in pairs to examine magnesium sulfate and alum with a hand lens. Ask students to describe the crystal shape of each of these ionic compounds. (*Magnesium sulfate has a needlelike rod shape and alum an octagonal shape.*) Suggest that students make drawings of the crystal shapes and label them with descriptions. **learning modality: visual**

Portfolio Students can save their drawings in their portfolios.

Answers to Self-Assessment

Caption Question
Figure 10 Sharp edges, corners, and flat surfaces

 Checkpoint
The name changes for single atoms that become negative ions.

Ongoing Assessment

Writing Ask students to describe how ions are arranged in crystals made of ionic compounds. (*When ions combine, they form alternating patterns and bond with each other on all sides. This makes crystals, orderly, three-dimensional patterns.*)

Properties of Ionic Compounds, continued

Integrating Physics

Materials *switch, light bulb, 9-V battery, insulated wires, 2 iron nails, 500-mL cup, 250 mL salt, 100 mL water*

ACTIVITY

Time 15 minutes

Assemble a circuit by connecting, in order, one nail, the battery, an open switch, light bulb, and the second nail. With the switch open, place salt in the cup and insert the two nails into the salt. CAUTION: *Make sure the nails do not touch each other.* Briefly close the switch. Open the switch. Carefully add water to the salt. Make sure the nails do not touch. Briefly close the switch. Ask: **What could explain the flow of electricity through the salt water?** *(The ions in the salt were free to move.)* **learning modality: visual**

3 Assess

Section 3 Review Answers

1. The atom gains or loses electrons.
2. Crystal shape, high melting points, electrical conductivity
3. They are oppositely charged.
4. Sodium fluoride, beryllium iodide, potassium sulfate, calcium oxide, hydrogen sulfide, magnesium carbonate
5. Water breaks the sodium chloride ions apart, allowing the ions to move freely.
6. ScI_3

Check Your Progress

CHAPTER PROJECT 2

Make sure students' models take the shape of crystals with indefinite boundaries, not as individual molecules.

Performance Assessment

Writing Have students describe tests to determine whether an unknown compound contains ionic bonds. *(Look for regular crystal structure, test the melting point, dissolve the compound in water and test for electrical conductivity.)*

Figure 11 A conductivity tester shows that a solution of salt in water conducts electricity. The bulb lights up because the ions in the salt solution complete the circuit for the flow of electricity.

High Melting Points What happens when you heat an ionic compound such as table salt? Remember, the ions are held together in a crystal by attractions between oppositely charged particles. When the particles have enough energy to overcome the attractive forces between them, they break away from each other. It takes a temperature of 801°C to reach this energy for table salt. Ionic bonds are strong enough to cause all ionic compounds to be solids at room temperature.

Electrical Conductivity When ionic compounds dissolve in water, the solution conducts electricity. Electricity is the flow of electric charge, and ions have electric charges. However, if you connect wires from a salt crystal to a battery and a light bulb, don't expect anything to happen. A solid ionic compound does not conduct electricity very well. The ions in the crystal are tightly bound to each other. If the charged particles do not move, electricity does not flow. But what if the ions are broken apart? When ionic compounds dissolve in water, the ions separate. These ions then move freely, and the solution conducts electricity.

Melting ionic compounds also allows them to conduct electricity. Can you figure out why? Think about the difference between the particles in a solid and a liquid. In a solid, the particles do not move from place to place. But in a liquid, the particles slip and slide past each other. As long as the ions can move around, electricity can flow.

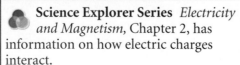

Section 3 Review

1. How does an ion form from an atom?
2. What properties may be used to identify ionic compounds?
3. Why are ions in an ionic compound attracted to each other?
4. Name these compounds: NaF, BeI_2, K_2SO_4, CaO, H_2S, $MgCO_3$.
5. Solid salt does not conduct electricity. How does dissolving salt in water allow electricity to flow?
6. **Thinking Critically Problem Solving** The metal scandium (Sc) has three valence electrons. What is the formula of the ionic compound formed when scandium reacts with iodine?

Check Your Progress

CHAPTER PROJECT 2

Use your materials to make models of compounds containing ionic bonds, such as sodium chloride (NaCl), magnesium chloride ($MgCl_2$), or potassium oxide (K_2O). (*Hint:* Figure out whether each atom forms a positive or negative ion. Then use combinations that result in a neutral compound.)

Program Resources

Science Explorer Series *Electricity and Magnetism*, Chapter 2, has information on how electric charges interact.

◆ **Teaching Resources** 2-3 Review and Reinforce, p. 51; 2-3 Enrich, p. 52

SECTION 4 Covalent Bonds

DISCOVER

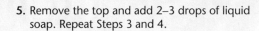

Why Don't Water and Oil Mix?

1. Pour water into a small jar that has a tight-fitting top until the jar is about a third full.

2. Add an equal amount of vegetable oil to the water and cover the jar tightly.

3. Shake the jar vigorously for approximately 15–20 seconds. Observe the contents.

4. Allow the jar to sit undisturbed for about 1 minute. Observe the contents again.

5. Remove the top and add 2–3 drops of liquid soap. Repeat Steps 3 and 4.

Think It Over

Inferring Describe how adding soap affected the mixing of the oil and water. How might your observations depend on chemical bonds in the soap, oil, and water molecules?

Remember the market with apples selling for 40 cents each? On another day, the apples are also on sale at two for 70 cents. You and your friend check your pockets and find 35 cents each. What can you do? You could give your friend a nickel to make enough money for one apple. Then you would have only 30 cents, not enough to get one for yourself. But if you share your money, together you can buy two apples.

Electron Sharing

Just as you and your friend can buy apples by sharing money, atoms can become more stable by sharing valence electrons. A chemical bond formed when two atoms share electrons is called a **covalent bond.**

Unlike ionic bonds, which form between metals and nonmetals, covalent bonds often form between two or more nonmetals. Oxygen, carbon, nitrogen, and the halogens are examples of atoms that frequently bond to other nonmetals by sharing electrons.

The element fluorine forms molecules made of two fluorine atoms. Each fluorine atom shares one of its seven valence electrons with the other atom. When you count the number of electrons on one atom, you count the shared pair each time. By sharing, both atoms have eight valence electrons. **In a covalent bond, both atoms attract the two shared electrons at the same time.**

GUIDE FOR READING

◆ How do electrons allow covalent bonds to form?

◆ Why do some atoms in covalent bonds have slight negative or positive charges?

◆ How are polar and nonpolar compounds different?

Reading Tip Before you read, preview the illustrations in the section. Predict how covalent bonds differ from ionic bonds.

Figure 12 The shared pair of electrons in a molecule of fluorine is a single covalent bond.

Shared pair of electrons

Chapter 2 **L ◆ 65**

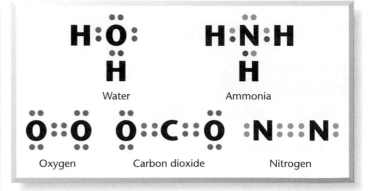

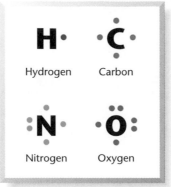

Figure 13 The electron dot diagrams for hydrogen, carbon, nitrogen, and oxygen (left) show the number of valence electrons for each. The diagrams of molecules (right) show how the electrons are shared in covalent bonds. *Interpreting Diagrams How many bonds does each nitrogen atom form?*

2 Facilitate

Electron Sharing

Using the Visuals: Figure 12

Ask a volunteer to count the number of valence electrons surrounding the fluorine atom on the left of the pair. *(eight)* Ask another volunteer to count the number of valence electrons surrounding the fluorine atom on the right of the pair. *(eight)* Point out that shared electrons are counted as valence electrons for each atom. **learning modality: visual**

How Many Bonds?

Building Inquiry Skills: Applying Concepts

Have students look at the dot diagrams in Figure 13. Point out that the oxygen atom does not remove the electron from either hydrogen atom in a water molecule. Therefore, the hydrogen atoms *share* rather than *lose* their electrons. Neither the hydrogen nor the oxygen becomes an ion. Ask: **How many valence electrons does nitrogen have?** *(five)* **How many does it need to be more stable?** *(three)* Ask students to explain how nitrogen and hydrogen combine to form ammonia, NH_3. *(A single nitrogen atom shares electrons with three hydrogen atoms. That way the nitrogen atom has eight valence electrons.)* **learning modality: visual**

Building Inquiry Skills: Making Models

Materials *modeling clay*
Time 15 minutes

Suggest students use clay to create three-dimensional models of the dot diagram for a molecule of oxygen. Students can use one clay ball to represent oxygen nuclei, and smaller clay balls to represent valence electrons. Ask: **If two atoms share two pairs of electrons, how many electrons are shared?** *(four)* Challenge students to model carbon dioxide, a molecule with four pairs of shared electrons. **learning modality: kinesthetic**

How Many Bonds?

Look at the electron dot diagrams for oxygen, nitrogen, and carbon atoms in Figure 13. Count the dots around each atom. The number of bonds these atoms can form equals the number of valence electrons needed to make a total of eight.

For example, oxygen has six valence electrons, so it can form two covalent bonds. In a water molecule, oxygen forms one covalent bond with each hydrogen atom. Since nitrogen has five valence electrons, it can form three bonds. In ammonia (NH_3), a nitrogen atom bonds with three hydrogen atoms.

Next, look at the diagram of a molecule of oxygen. Do you see something different? This time *two* pairs of electrons are shared between the oxygen atoms, forming a **double bond.** In a carbon dioxide molecule, carbon forms a double bond with each oxygen atom. Elements such as nitrogen and carbon can even form triple bonds in which three pairs of electrons are shared.

Count the electrons around any atom in the molecules in Figure 13. Remember that shared pairs count for both atoms forming a bond. You'll find that each atom has eight valence electrons. The exception is hydrogen, which can have no more than two electrons and forms one bond.

Properties of Molecular Compounds

Molecular compounds consist of molecules having covalently bonded atoms. Such compounds have very different properties from ionic compounds.

Look at Figure 14, which lists the melting and boiling points for some molecular compounds. There's quite a difference

Figure 14 Molecular compounds have much lower melting points than ionic compounds.

Melting and Boiling Points of Some Molecular Compounds			
Compound	Formula	Melting Point (°C)	Boiling Point (°C)
Water	H_2O	0	100
Methane	CH_4	–182	–164
Carbon dioxide	CO_2	—	–78.6*
Ammonia	NH_3	–77.7	–33.6
Rubbing alcohol	C_3H_8O	–89.5	82.4
Table sugar	$C_{12}H_{22}O_{11}$	185–186	(decomposes)

*Carbon dioxide changes directly from a solid to a gas.

Background

History of Science Most chemists used to think that all bonds were ionic. Beginning about 1916, however, Gilbert Newton Lewis proposed that chemical bonds could also be formed by the sharing of valence electrons; that is, by "co-valent" bonds.

In his theory, Lewis described how two atoms can each contribute one electron when they bond, so that they share a pair of electrons. He developed electron dot diagrams, also called Lewis structures, to help advance his theory.

Lewis published his views in 1923 in *Valence and the Structure of Atoms and Molecules*, a classic book in the field of physical chemistry and the first work to describe covalent bonding.

between these melting points and the 801°C described earlier for table salt! In molecular solids, the molecules are held close to each other. But the forces holding them are much weaker than those holding ions together in an ionic solid. Less heat is needed to separate molecules than is needed to separate ions. Some molecular compounds, such as table sugar and water, do form crystals. But these compounds, like other molecular solids, melt and boil at much lower temperatures than ionic compounds do.

Most molecular compounds are poor conductors of electricity. No charged particles are available to move, and electricity does not flow. That's why molecular compounds, such as plastic and rubber, are used to insulate electric wires. Even as liquids, molecular compounds are poor conductors. Pure water, for example, does not conduct electricity. Neither does water with table sugar dissolved in it.

✓ *Checkpoint* *Why are molecular compounds poor conductors?*

Unequal Sharing of Electrons

Have you ever played tug of war? If you have, you know that if both teams have equal strength, the contest is a tie. But what if the teams pull on the rope with unequal force? Then the rope moves closer to one side or the other. The same is true of electrons in a covalent bond. **Some atoms pull more strongly on the shared electrons than other atoms do. As a result, the electrons move closer to one atom, causing the atoms to have slight electrical charges.** These charges are not as strong as the charges on ions. But the unequal sharing is enough to make one atom slightly negative and the other atom slightly positive. A covalent bond in which electrons are shared unequally is **polar.**

Sharpen your Skills

Designing Experiments

Suppose you have samples **ACTIVITY** of two colorless, odorless gases. You are told that one gas is methane (CH_4) and the other is carbon dioxide (CO_2). How could you use the information in Figure 14 to find out which gas is which? Describe the experiment you would set up. Tell what conditions you would control and what you would change. What result would you look for to get an answer?

Figure 15 The unequal sharing of the electrons in a polar covalent bond is like a tug of war in which one atom is slightly stronger than the other atom.

Answers to Self-Assessment

Caption Question

Figure 13 Three

✓ *Checkpoint*

Molecular compounds are poor conductors because they do not contain any charged particles that are available to move.

Properties of Molecular Compounds

Sharpen your Skills

Designing Experiments

Time 10 minutes

Tips Review changes of **ACTIVITY** state and what happens to substances at their melting and boiling points. Point out that carbon dioxide ordinarily changes directly from a solid to a gas without passing through a liquid phase.

Expected Outcome Students may suggest that they would cool each gas and record the temperature at which a change in state occurs and the nature of the change (gas to solid, or gas to liquid and then to solid). The manipulated variable is the temperature; variables such as pressure and amount of gas should be kept constant. The gas that turns to a solid at −78.6°C is carbon dioxide.

Extend Have students describe an experiment to distinguish between solid carbon dioxide and solid ammonia.

Unequal Sharing of Electrons

Language Arts Connection

Have students look up the word *polar* to help them understand how it applies to the charge on atoms in covalent bonds. Encourage students to write descriptions of the charges on atoms in their own words. **learning modality: verbal**

Language Arts CONNECTION

Remind students that the word *valence* originally meant "strength." Help students realize that the word *covalent* can also be remembered as describing atoms that combine to share their strength, or their hold on the electrons.

In Your Journal Students should list words and describe them using the meaning of "together" for the prefix *co-*. Students' sentences should use the words correctly. (*Samples: copilot, coeducational, costar, coordinate, coproducer*) **learning modality: verbal**

Attractions Between Molecules

Demonstration

Materials *disposable petri dish with the top and bottom halves separated, 50 cm string, tape, water* **ACTIVITY**
Time 15 minutes

Tape one end of the string to the inside of one half of the petri dish. Place the other half of the dish on the desktop, inside down. Then place the two halves back to back. Slowly lift the top dish with the string. Ask students for their observations. (*The top half of the dish moves upward.*) Now place several drops of water on the surface of the dish still resting on the tabletop. Press the two halves together, back to back. Press to squeeze out as much air as possible. Slowly pull up on the string. Ask students for their observations. (*The halves stick together and move up as one.*) Ask students to explain why this happens. (*Because the water molecules are polar, they attract each other and "stick together."*) **learning modality: visual**

Figure 16 In the nonpolar bond in F_2, the two fluorine atoms pull equally on the shared electrons. In the polar bond in HF, fluorine pulls more strongly on the shared electrons than hydrogen does.

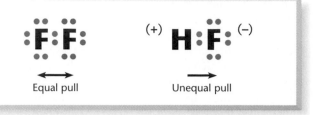

Equal pull   Unequal pull

If two atoms pull equally on the electrons, neither atom becomes charged. This is the case when the two atoms are identical, as in fluorine gas (F_2). The valence electrons are shared equally and the bond is **nonpolar.** Compare the bond in F_2 with the polar bond in hydrogen fluoride (HF) in Figure 16.

Nonpolar Molecules Keep tug of war in mind as you look at the carbon dioxide (CO_2) molecule in Figure 17. Oxygen attracts electrons much more strongly than carbon, so bonds between oxygen and carbon are polar. But the two oxygen atoms are pulling with equal strength in opposite directions. In a sense, they cancel each other out. Overall, a carbon dioxide molecule is nonpolar even though it has polar bonds. A molecule is nonpolar if it contains polar bonds that cancel each other. As you might guess, molecules that contain only nonpolar bonds are also nonpolar.

Polar Molecules Water molecules are polar. As you can see in Figure 17, the shape of the molecule leaves the two hydrogen atoms more to one end and the oxygen atom toward the other. The oxygen atom pulls electrons closer to it from both hydrogen atoms. Overall, the molecule is polar. It has a slightly negative charge at the oxygen end and a slightly positive charge near the hydrogen atoms.

☑ *Checkpoint* *What makes a covalent bond polar?*

Attractions Between Molecules

If you could shrink small enough to move among a bunch of water molecules, what would you find? The negatively charged oxygen ends and positively charged hydrogen ends behave like poles of a bar magnet. They attract the opposite ends of other water molecules. These attractions between positive and negative ends pull water molecules toward each other.

What about carbon dioxide? There is no pulling between these molecules. Remember, carbon dioxide molecules are nonpolar. No oppositely charged ends means there are no strong attractions between the molecules.

Language Arts CONNECTION

Breaking a word into its parts can help you understand its meaning. Take *covalent,* for example. The prefix *co-* means "together." The *-valent* part comes from "valence electrons." So "valence electrons together" can remind you that in a covalent bond, valence electrons are shared.

In Your Journal

The prefix *co-* is used in many other words—*coauthor, coexist,* and *cooperate* are just a few. Add five more *co-* words to this list and try to define them all without looking them up. Then check their meanings in a dictionary and write sentences that use each one.

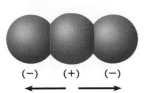

CO₂ molecule (nonpolar)

(−) (+) (−)

Opposite pulling cancels

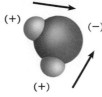

H₂O molecule (polar)

(+)

(+)

(−)

Electrons pulled toward oxygen

Figure 17 CO_2 molecules are nonpolar, and H_2O molecules are polar. Attractions between the slightly positive and slightly negative ends of water molecules pull the molecules toward each other (below).

Differences in the attractions between molecules lead to different properties in polar and nonpolar compounds. For example, water and vegetable oil don't mix. Oil is nonpolar, and nonpolar compounds do not dissolve well in water. The polar water molecules are attracted more strongly to each other than to the molecules of oil. Water stays with water and oil stays with oil.

 INTEGRATING TECHNOLOGY These differences in attractions come in handy when you wash laundry. Many kinds of dirt—for example, grease—are nonpolar compounds. Their molecules won't mix well with plain water. So how can you wash dirt out of your clothes?

If you did the Discover activity, you found that adding soap helped the oil and water to mix. When you do laundry, detergent causes the nonpolar dirt to mix with the polar water. Soaps and detergents have long molecules. One end of a soap molecule is polar, and the other end is nonpolar. Soaps and detergents dissolve in water because the polar ends of their molecules are attracted to water molecules. Meanwhile, their nonpolar ends mix easily with the dirt. When the water washes down the drain, the soap and the dirt go with it.

Section 4 Review

1. How are valence electrons involved in the formation of a covalent bond?
2. How do atoms in covalent bonds become slightly negative or slightly positive?
3. Explain how attractions between molecules could cause polar water to have a higher boiling point than nonpolar carbon dioxide.
4. **Thinking Critically Comparing and Contrasting** In terms of electrons, how is a covalent bond different from an ionic bond?

Check Your Progress

CHAPTER PROJECT 2

Use your materials to build molecules with single covalent bonds. Also make models of molecules containing double or triple bonds. (*Hint:* After you make bonds, each atom should have a total of eight valence electrons or, in the case of hydrogen, two valence electrons.)

Chapter 2 **L ◆ 69**

Answers to Self-Assessment

☑ *Checkpoint*

A covalent bond is polar when the electrons in the bond are shared unequally.

Program Resources

◆ **Teaching Resources** 2-4 Review and Reinforce, p. 55; 2-4 Enrich, p. 56

 Integrating Technology

Inform students that substances such as soap and detergent that have polar and nonpolar ends are called emulsifying agents. Emulsifying agents are common in prepared foods. For example, lecithin from soybeans is often added to oil-and-vinegar salad dressings. The lecithin acts as a bridge between the oil and the vinegar to make them mix, and keeps them from separating as they would without lecithin. **learning modality: verbal**

3 Assess

Section 4 Review Answers

1. They are shared by two atoms.
2. One atom pulls electrons closer to it than the other atom. This makes the atom slightly negative, while the other atom becomes slightly positive.
3. Attractions between polar water molecules are stronger than attractions between nonpolar CO_2 molecules. More energy (a higher temperature) is needed to overcome the strong attractions and change water into a gas.
4. Covalent bonds—electrons are shared between atoms; ionic bonds— electrons are transferred from one atom to another.

Check Your Progress

CHAPTER PROJECT 2

Make sure students model the simpler covalent compounds correctly before they go on to model the more complicated molecules. Again, be sure all models have the correct number of bonds for each atom. Students' models should include single, double, and triple bonds.

Performance Assessment

Skills Check Have students draw dot diagrams for two compounds that contain ionic bonds and two that contain covalent bonds.

 Portfolio Students can save their dot diagrams in their portfolios.

L ◆ 69

Shedding Light on Chemical Bonds

Preparing for Inquiry

Key Concept Compounds that contain moving ions can conduct electricity.

Skills Objectives Students will be able to

◆ conduct experiments to determine whether certain substances conduct electricity;

◆ analyze the results of the tests;

◆ draw conclusions regarding the nature of the bonds in each compound.

Time Up to 50 minutes, depending on the number of substances tested

Advance Planning

◆ Suggested substances to be tested include: vegetable oil, hydrogen peroxide, orange juice, vinegar, sugar, baking soda, Epsom salts, powdered skim milk.

◆ Use 16- or 18-gauge wire. The resistance in 22-gauge wire is too high. Cut the wire into lengths of about 25–30 cm. Use wire strippers to remove about 2 cm of insulation from the ends of the wires.

◆ Use fresh batteries and 2.2-volt bulbs. If using probeware, refer to the *Probeware Lab Manual.*

Suggested Shortcuts To save time, perform the lab as a demonstration.

Guiding Inquiry

Invitation Ask students if they think water is a good conductor of electricity. *(Most will say yes.)* Place the leads of a conductivity tester into a beaker of distilled water. The bulb will not light up. Tell students there are very few impurities that are present as ions in distilled water to carry the charge. Then add some salt to the water until the tester starts to glow. Ask students to explain what is happening. *(Salt ionizes when it dissolves in water, providing ions to the solution.)* Make sure students understand that most water, such as tap water, conducts electricity because it contains ions in solution.

SHEDDING LIGHT ON CHEMICAL BONDS

Electricity is the flow of electric charges. In this lab, you will interpret data about which compounds conduct electricity in order to determine the nature of their bonds.

Problem

How can you use a conductivity tester to determine whether a compound contains ionic or covalent bonds?

Materials

2 dry cells, 1.5-V

small light bulb and socket

4 lengths of wire with insulation scraped off the ends

} or conductivity probe

small beaker

small plastic spoon

sodium chloride

100-mL graduated cylinder

additional substances supplied by your teacher

DATA TABLE	
Sample	Observations
Water	
Sodium chloride in water	

Procedure

1. Make a conductivity tester as described below or, if you are using a conductivity probe, see your teacher for instructions. Then make a data table in your notebook similar to the one above.

2. Pour about 50 mL of water into a small beaker. Place the free ends of the two wires of the conductivity tester into the water. Be sure the ends are close but not touching each other. Record your observations.

MAKING A CONDUCTIVITY TESTER

A. Use wire to connect the positive terminal of a dry cell to a lamp socket. **CAUTION:** *The bulb is fragile and can break.*

B. Use another wire to connect the negative terminal to the positive terminal of a second dry cell.

C. Connect a third wire to the negative terminal of the second dry cell.

D. Connect a fourth wire to the other terminal of the lamp socket.

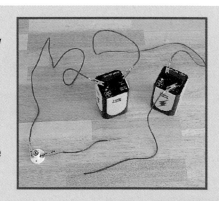

Introducing the Procedure

Before students assemble their conductivity testers, have them test the bulbs using a single battery and wires to be sure the bulbs work. Demonstrate this test if necessary.

Troubleshooting the Experiment

◆ Students should use equal amounts of solids in equal volumes of water to make a valid comparison between substances. Suggest they measure the masses of the solutes.

◆ The two wires should be close together in solution, but they should not be touching.

◆ The light may flicker on and off. Students should count the presence of light as evidence that the substance conducts.

Expected Outcome

Most substances containing ionic bonds will conduct electricity fairly well when dissolved in water. Molecular compounds do not conduct electricity well, either as pure liquids or as water solutions.

3. Remove the conductivity tester and add a small sample (about 3 spoonfuls) of sodium chloride to the water in the small beaker. Stir with the spoon until mixed.

4. Repeat the conductivity test and record your observations in your data table.

5. Rinse the beaker, spoon, and wire ends with clear water. Then repeat Steps 3 and 4 for each substance provided by your teacher.
   ◆ If the substance is a solid, mix 1 to 3 spoonfuls of it with about 50 mL of fresh water. Test the resulting mixture.
   ◆ If the substance is a liquid, simply pour about 50 mL into the beaker. Test it as you did the solutions.

Analyze and Conclude

1. Why did you test plain water first?
2. Based on your observations, add a column to your chart indicating whether each substance tested contained ionic or covalent bonds.
3. Explain why one substance is a better conductor of electricity than another.
4. Did all the substances that conducted electricity show the same amount of conductivity? How do you know?
5. **Think About It** How might varying the amount of each substance added to the water have affected your results? How could you better control the amount of each substance?

Design an Experiment

Design another experiment to compare a different property of compounds containing ionic and covalent bonds. You might want to examine properties such as the ability to dissolve in water or in some other liquid. Present your experimental plan to your teacher before proceeding.

Analyze and Conclude

1. Plain water was tested as a control and to show that a water solution can conduct electricity only with the presence of an added substance.
2. Sample chart:

Sample	Type of Bond
water	covalent
sodium chloride in water	ionic
sugar in water	covalent
vegetable oil	covalent
Epsom salts in water	ionic

3. Compounds containing ionic bonds are better conductors of electricity. When they dissolve, the ions are free to move within a solution. Compounds containing covalent bonds separate into neutral molecules that do not carry electrical charge.
4. Electrical conductivity is indicated by the brightness of the light bulb. Not all substances showed the same brightness, therefore not all showed the same amount of electrical conductivity.
5. Using different amounts would not change whether a substance conducted electricity, but it might change the amount of conductivity. Using the same mass of each substance in the same volume of water would help control the experiment.

Extending the Inquiry

Design an Experiment Review students' plans for safety and thoroughness before allowing them to conduct tests. Tests of whether substances dissolve in water and another liquid should use the same volume of liquid and the same mass of each substance. CAUTION: *Liquids that dissolve substances with covalent bonds are often poisonous and flammable. Appropriate ventilation and fire prevention procedures should be followed.*

Program Resources

◆ **Teaching Resources** Skills Lab blackline masters, pp. 63–65
◆ **Integrated Science Laboratory Manual** L-2, "Testing for Hard Water"
◆ **Probeware Lab Manual** Blackline masters

Safety

Make sure students wear goggles and lab aprons during the lab. Caution students to handle the glass beakers with care. Review the safety guidelines in Appendix A.

Media and Technology

 Lab Activity Videotape
Chemical Interactions, 4

SECTION 5 Crystal Chemistry

Objectives

After completing the lesson, students will be able to
◆ explain how the chemical bonds of a crystal determine the substance's properties;
◆ describe and give examples of mineral crystals.

Key Term mineral

1 Engage/Explore

Activating Prior Knowledge

Ask students: **What crystals do you know about?** (*Students may know about quartz, salt, sugar crystals, and crystals grown with kits.*) Then ask students to describe characteristics these crystals share. (*Regular shape, relatively hard*)

········· **DISCOVER** ·········

Skills Focus predicting
Materials *rock salt crystals, metal spoons or small mallets, paper towels, hand lenses, safety goggles*
Time 12 minutes
Tips Small wooden mallets may work better than spoons for crushing larger crystals.
Expected Outcome When crystals are broken or crushed, smaller crystals with the same shape are formed.
Think It Over The crystals would be shaped the same, like a cube, only much smaller.

SECTION 5 Crystal Chemistry

DISCOVER ···························· ACTIVITY

How Small Do They Get?

1. Place a piece of rock salt on a hard surface. Make a rough sketch of the shape of your sample.

2. Put on your goggles. Cover the salt with a paper towel. Use the back of a metal spoon or a rock hammer to break the salt into smaller pieces.

3. Look at these smaller pieces with a hand lens. Then draw a picture of the shapes you see.

4. Crush a few of these smaller pieces with the spoon. Repeat Step 3.

Think It Over
Predicting What do you think the crystals would look like if you crushed them into such small pieces that you needed a microscope to see them?

GUIDE FOR READING

◆ How are the properties of a mineral related to chemical bonds?

Reading Tip As you read, make a list of the ways in which a mineral can be described or identified.

A class of earth science students gathers rock samples on a field trip. They want to know whether the rocks contain any of the minerals they have been studying. The teacher takes a hammer and strikes one rock. It cracks open to reveal a few small crystals peeking out of the new surface. The crystals are mostly the same shape and have a metallic shine. The teacher tries to scratch one crystal, first with her fingernail and then with a copper penny. Only the penny leaves a mark. By now, the students have enough information to make an inference about the identity of the crystals. They'll do more tests back in their classroom to be sure the mineral is what they think it is.

Properties of Minerals

A **mineral** is a naturally occurring solid that has a crystal structure and a definite chemical composition. A few minerals, such as sulfur and gold, are pure elements. But most minerals are compounds.

Mineralogists, scientists who study minerals, identify minerals by looking at certain properties. These properties include color, shininess, density, crystal shape, hardness, and magnetism. Color and shininess can be judged just by looking at a mineral. Other properties, however, require measurements or testing. For example, scientists rate a mineral's hardness by comparing it with something harder or softer. You can scratch the softest mineral, talc, with your fingernail. Diamond is the hardest mineral. Other minerals are somewhere in between.

Figure 18 The mineral sulfur (above) is a pure element. The mineral galena (right) is a compound of sulfur and lead.

READING STRATEGIES

Reading Tip After students list ways in which a mineral can be described or identified, invite a volunteer to write the list on the board. Have students give examples of, or additional information about, each property.

Study and Comprehension After students read the section, have them organize the information in concept maps.

Program Resources

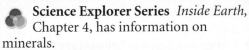

Science Explorer Series *Inside Earth*, Chapter 4, has information on minerals.
◆ **Teaching Resources** 2-5 Lesson Plan, p. 57; 2-5 Section Summary, p. 58
◆ **Guided Reading and Study Workbook** Section 2-5

Another key property is the way a mineral breaks apart. Some minerals break into regular shapes. Mica, for example, splits easily along flat surfaces and at sharp angles. Crystals also grow in characteristic shapes. All the properties of a mineral depend on its chemical composition. Since each mineral has a different composition, its properties will not be exactly like those of any other mineral.

☑ *Checkpoint* What is a mineral?

Bonding in Mineral Crystals

Every mineral has a crystal structure. The repeating pattern of particles creates a shape that may be visible to your eye. Or, you may have to look under a microscope to see it. Either way, the structure of the crystal is a characteristic property of the mineral.

Mineral crystals may be made of ions, or they may contain atoms that are covalently bonded together. **The arrangement of particles in a mineral and the kind of bonds holding them together determine properties such as crystal shape, hardness, and the way the crystal breaks apart.**

An Ionic Crystal In Section 3, you read about halite, a mineral made of sodium chloride (NaCl). You can easily scratch halite with a steel knife. If you put a crystal of halite into water, it would dissolve. The oppositely charged sodium and chloride ions in a halite crystal alternate in every direction, making a pattern something like a three-dimensional checkerboard. This arrangement affects the shape in which halite crystals grow.

If you break a piece of halite, the smaller pieces of halite have the same shape as the bigger piece. When bonds in an ionic crystal break, they break along a face of ions. A blow or crushing action shifts the ions slightly so that positive ions are next to other positive ions and negative ions are next to other negative ions. The effect is the same as bringing the

Figure 19 Mica's flakes **(A)** are a result of how the mineral splits when it breaks. The crystals of fluorite **(B)** and tourmaline **(C)** grew in the shapes you see. *Observing* How do the shapes of fluorite crystals and tourmaline crystals differ?

Figure 20 The particles in an ionic crystal such as halite can shift because of a blow or pressure.

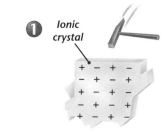

① Ionic crystal

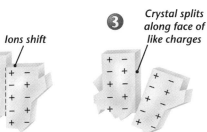

② Ions shift

③ Crystal splits along face of like charges

Chapter 2 **L ◆ 73**

Answers to Self-Assessment

Caption Question

Figure 19 Fluorite crystals have a cubic structure and are shaped like diamonds. Tourmaline crystals have a hexagonal structure and appear long and spiky.

☑ *Checkpoint*

A mineral is a naturally occurring solid that has a crystal structure and a definite chemical composition.

Properties of Minerals

Inquiry Challenge

Materials *minerals such as talc, mica, rock salt, quartz, asphalt, graphite, calcite; copper penny; iron nail; steel file; small piece of glass*

ACTIVITY

Time 25 minutes

Have students work in pairs or small groups to rank the mineral samples from softest to hardest. (*Students should try to scratch each mineral with their fingernails, then with the other tools and minerals. Students should see which minerals scratch the glass. Rankings should coincide with the Mohs scale, with graphite the softest and quartz the hardest of the samples listed here.*) **learning modality: kinesthetic**

Bonding in Mineral Crystals

Using the Visuals: Figure 20

Invite students to look at Figure 20. Point out that the diagram shows only a portion of the charges in the crystal. Note that the blow from the hammer shifts ions in the crystal. The third and fourth columns shift one spot downward so that a positive ion shifts next to another positive ion, a negative next to another negative, and so on down the face of ions. Ask: **What happens when like charges come close to each other?** (*They repel.*) Ask students to track the change in positions of the charges near the split, noting that the crystal weakens and splits apart at these points. **learning modality: visual**

Ongoing Assessment

Writing Ask students to list five properties or characteristics they could use to distinguish one mineral from another. (*Color, shininess, density, crystal shape, hardness, the way it breaks apart*)

Comparing Crystals

Using the Visuals:
Figures 19 and 21

Have students compare the mica crystals in Figure 19 with the quartz crystals in Figure 21. Point out that both compounds contain silicon and oxygen. Ask: **Why do these minerals have different crystal shapes?** (*They have different chemical bonds.*) **learning modality: visual**

3 Assess

Section 5 Review Answers

1. Any two: Crystal structure, hardness, and the way the crystals break or grow

2. Hardness

3. The way a crystal breaks depends on the type and strength of the chemical bonds.

4. Any three: Halite crystals contain ionic bonds; quartz contains covalent bonds. Halite is softer than quartz. Halite will dissolve in water, quartz will not. Halite breaks into smaller crystals of the same shape, quartz does not.

Science at Home

Materials *round objects of different sizes, such as grapes, raisins, clay balls, dried peas*

ACTIVITY

Clay balls work well because they will stick together to stabilize the structure. Students should show their family members that the model has characteristics in common with actual ionic crystals. It can extend indefinitely in all directions, it consists of an array of alternating positive and negative ions, and the ratio of positive to negative ions is constant (1 : 1 in this case).

Performance Assessment

Writing Ask students to compare covalent and ionic crystals. Suggest they name an example of each type of crystal.

Figure 21 The uneven surfaces on this crystal are typical of broken quartz.
Comparing and Contrasting
How does the way quartz breaks compare to the way mica breaks?

north ends of two magnets together. It creates a weakness in the crystal. The ions push each other away, breaking bonds along a flat surface or face. The result is that the smaller crystals retain the cube shape that is characteristic of halite.

A Covalent Crystal If you picked up a handful of sand, most likely you would be holding some quartz. Quartz is a compound made of silicon and oxygen atoms covalently bonded together to form the compound silicon dioxide (SiO_2). The covalent bonds in quartz are much stronger than the ionic bonds in halite. Quartz won't dissolve in water. You can't scratch it with a knife. In fact, you could use quartz to scratch steel! Because of its strong bonds, a quartz crystal doesn't have clear lines of weakness. You can't crush it into predictable shapes with a hammer. Instead, it breaks into smaller pieces with irregular shapes. The broken surfaces have shell-like ridges similar to chipped glass. These features help identify the mineral as quartz.

Comparing Crystals

Not all mineral crystals made of ions have the same properties as halite. Similarly, not all minerals made of covalently bonded atoms are like quartz. Properties such as hardness, for example, depend on the strength of the bonds in a crystal. The stronger bonds of quartz make it harder than halite. But other crystals with covalently bonded atoms are stronger than quartz. Still others have weaknesses in their bonds that cause the minerals to break apart the same way every time.

Experienced mineralogists can usually identify a mineral just by looking at it. But when there is a question, they test the sample for characteristics such as hardness and the way the crystals break. The results give the answer.

 Section 5 Review

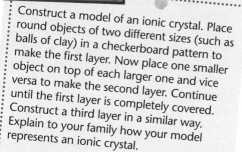

Science at Home

1. Name two properties of minerals that depend on chemical bonds.

2. What property of a mineral can be determined by scratching it?

3. How does the way in which a mineral crystal breaks apart help to identify it?

4. Thinking Critically Comparing and Contrasting Name three ways in which a halite crystal differs from a quartz crystal.

Construct a model of an ionic crystal. Place round objects of two different sizes (such as balls of clay) in a checkerboard pattern to make the first layer. Now place one smaller object on top of each larger one and vice versa to make the second layer. Continue until the first layer is completely covered. Construct a third layer in a similar way. Explain to your family how your model represents an ionic crystal.

Answers to Self-Assessment

Caption Question

Figure 21 Quartz breaks unevenly into smaller pieces with irregular shapes, while mica splits along flat surfaces and at sharp angles.

Program Resources

◆ **Teaching Resources** 2-5 Review and Reinforce, p. 59; 2-5 Enrich, p. 60

SECTION 1 Inside an Atom

Key Ideas

◆ An atom consists of a nucleus of protons and neutrons, surrounded by rapidly moving electrons.

◆ Chemical reactions involve the valence electrons of atoms. Chemical bonds form when electrons are transferred or shared between atoms.

Key Terms

nucleus   electron
proton   valence electron
neutron   electron dot diagram

SECTION 2 Atoms in the Periodic Table

Key Ideas

◆ The periodic table organizes the elements according to atomic number.

◆ Families of elements have similar chemical properties.

◆ The noble gases (Group 18) are the least reactive elements. Elements in groups 1 and 17 are highly reactive.

Key Terms

atomic number   period
group   halogen
family

SECTION 3 Ionic Bonds

Key Ideas

◆ Ions form when atoms become charged after gaining or losing electrons.

◆ Ionic compounds exist in the form of crystals made of many ions, each attracted to all the surrounding ions of opposite charge.

◆ Ionic compounds have high melting and boiling points. They conduct electricity when dissolved in water.

Key Terms

ion   polyatomic ion
ionic bond   crystal

SECTION 4 Covalent Bonds

Key Ideas

◆ In covalent bonds, pairs of electrons are shared between atoms.

◆ In polar covalent bonds, the shared electrons are attracted more to one atom than the other.

◆ Attractions between polar molecules are stronger than attractions between nonpolar molecules, leading to differences in properties.

Key Terms

covalent bond   molecular   polar
double bond   compound   nonpolar

SECTION 5 Crystal Chemistry

INTEGRATING EARTH SCIENCE

Key Ideas

◆ Minerals have characteristic properties, such as hardness, density, color, crystal shape, and the way the crystal breaks and grows.

◆ The properties of a mineral depend on its chemical composition and its bonding.

◆ The stronger the chemical bonds in a mineral crystal, the harder the crystal is.

Key Term

mineral

Organizing Information

Venn Diagram Copy and complete the diagram, and add a title.

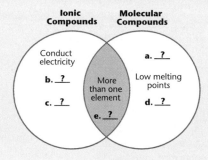

Organizing Information

Venn Diagram Sample title: Comparing Ionic and Molecular Compounds

a. Do not conduct electricity **b.** High melting points **c.** Form when electrons are transferred **d.** Form when electrons are shared **e.** Electrically neutral

Program Resources

◆ **Teaching Resources** Chapter 2 Project Scoring Rubric, p. 40; Chapter 2 Performance Assessment Teacher Notes, pp. 141–142; Chapter 2 Performance Assessment Student Worksheet, p. 143; Chapter 2 Test, pp. 144–147

Media and Technology

Interactive Student Tutorial CD-ROM L-2

Computer Test Bank *Chemical Interactions*, Chapter 2 Test

Reviewing Content
Multiple Choice
1. a 2. c 3. b 4. c 5. b

True or False
6. true 7. negative ion 8. true
9. stronger 10. true

Checking Concepts
11. Beryllium (Be), magnesium (Mg), calcium (Ca), barium (Ba), radium (Ra)
12. Ionic, covalent, covalent, ionic. Bonds between metals and nonmetals (Na and F, Mg and S) are usually ionic. Bonds between nonmetals (N and O, C and Br) are usually covalent.
13. If the electrons are attracted equally, they are shared equally by the two atoms and the bond is nonpolar.
14. polar
15. Students should describe gaining an electron from sodium and becoming a negative ion (with a charge of 1−), and being attracted to the positive sodium. Students should describe sharing electrons equally in reactions with other chlorine atoms.

Thinking Critically
16. Elements in Groups 1 and 17 are the most reactive. Elements in Group 18 are the least reactive. The location of an element in the periodic table also tells you how many valence electrons its atoms have. In general, atoms with very few or almost 8 valence electrons are the most reactive.
17. CaO, AlI_3, Rb_2S, Al_2O_3
18. Covalent bonds. Compounds containing ionic bonds have higher melting points, and they conduct electricity.
19. Test each mineral for hardness, how it breaks, melting point, solubility in water, and its ability to conduct electricity. Compare the results with data about known minerals.

Reviewing Content

 For more review of key concepts, see the Interactive Student Tutorial CD-ROM.

Multiple Choice
Choose the letter of the best answer.

1. The atomic number of an atom is determined by the number of
   a. protons.   b. electrons.
   c. neutrons.   d. valence electrons.
2. The vertical columns on the periodic table organize elements by
   a. periods.   b. metals.
   c. families.   d. nonmetals.
3. When an atom loses an electron, it
   a. becomes a negative ion.
   b. becomes a positive ion.
   c. forms a covalent bond.
   d. gains protons.
4. Which of these is a property of an ionic compound?
   a. low melting point
   b. poor conductor of electricity
   c. crystal shape
   d. shared electrons
5. A chemical bond in which a pair of electrons is shared between two atoms is called
   a. ionic.   b. covalent.
   c. polyatomic.   d. triple.

True or False
If the statement is true, write true. If it is false, change the underlined word or words to make the statement true.

6. Using the periodic table, you can determine that a potassium atom has <u>one</u> valence electron.
7. When a chlorine atom gains an electron, it becomes a <u>positive ion</u>.
8. When atoms share electrons unequally, a <u>polar</u> bond forms.
9. Two polar molecules have <u>weaker</u> attractions between them than two nonpolar molecules do.
10. <u>Hardness</u> is determined by how easily a mineral can be scratched.

Applying Skills
20. Group 16
21. Six
22. Two sodium atoms; Na_2X
23. Two
24. Sample questions: Is it a solid, a liquid, or a gas at room temperature? What kind of chemical reactions does it undergo?

Checking Concepts
11. Strontium is classified as an alkaline earth metal. Look at the periodic table and name the other elements that are alkaline earth metals.
12. Use the periodic table to identify what type of chemical bond is involved in each of these compounds: NaF, NO_2, CBr_4, MgS. Explain your reasoning.
13. How is a covalent bond between two atoms affected when each atom attracts electrons equally?
14. Of all the elements, fluorine atoms attract electrons most strongly. When fluorine atoms form covalent bonds with other kinds of atoms, are the bonds polar or nonpolar?
15. **Writing to Learn** Imagine you are a chlorine atom. Write a first-person description of the changes you undergo when forming an ionic bond with sodium. Compare these with what happens when you form a covalent bond with another chlorine atom.

Thinking Critically
16. **Making Generalizations** How does the location of an element on the periodic table help you determine how reactive that element might be?
17. **Applying Concepts** Use the periodic table to find the number of valence electrons for calcium (Ca), aluminum (Al), rubidium (Rb), oxygen (O), sulfur (S), and iodine (I). Then use that information to predict the formula for each of the following compounds: calcium oxide, aluminum iodide, rubidium sulfide, and aluminum oxide.
18. **Inferring** Element Z is a yellow solid that melts at about 100°C and does not conduct electricity. What type of bond holds the element's atoms together? Explain the reasoning for your answer.
19. **Problem Solving** Suppose you were given two mineral crystals that looked alike. How would you determine the identity of each?

Applying Skills

Element X exists as a nonpolar molecule made of two identical atoms. When individual atoms of element X react with sodium, they form ions with a 2– charge. Use the periodic table in Appendix D to answer Questions 20–24.

20. **Classifying** To what group of elements does element *X* belong?
21. **Inferring** How many valence electrons does an atom of element *X* have?
22. **Predicting** Sodium can react with element *X* to form a compound. How many atoms of sodium are needed for each atom of element *X*? Write the formula for the compound.
23. **Calculating** How many covalent bonds can element *X* form?
24. **Posing Questions** In order to identify element *X*, what additional questions would you need to ask?

Performance Assessment
CHAPTER PROJECT 2

Project Wrap Up Before you present your models to the class, use an index card for each model to make a key telling what each part of the model represents. Explain why you chose particular items to model the atoms and the chemical bonds. How are your models alike or different from models of the same compounds made by other students?

Reflect and Record In your journal, compare your models containing ionic bonds with those containing covalent bonds. Which were easier to show? Why? What more would you like to know about bonding that could help improve your models?

Performance Assessment
CHAPTER PROJECT 2

Project Wrap Up Students should have made index cards for each of their models. Make sure they describe the atoms and the chemical bonds between the atoms. The index cards should also contain a brief discussion of why particular materials were chosen. During the class presentations, students should discuss their models. Encourage classmates to ask questions about particular aspects of each model, including choice of materials.
Reflect and Record Students should discuss any difficulties they had modeling different bonds. Encourage students to come up with three or four questions about atoms, and help them use resource books or the Internet to answer their questions and revise their models.

Test Preparation

Use these questions to prepare for standardized tests.

Use the diagram to answer Questions 25–28.

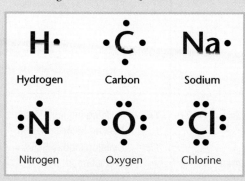

25. When one nitrogen atom joins with another nitrogen atom forming a molecule of nitrogen gas, the atoms are held together by a(n)
    a. single bond   **b.** double bond
    c. triple bond   **d.** ionic bond

26. When nitrogen and hydrogen combine, the ratio of hydrogen atoms to nitrogen atoms in a molecule of the resulting compound is
    a. 2 to 1
    b. 3 to 1
    c. 1 to 3
    d. 1 to 1

27. Atoms of which pair of elements are most likely to form a polar covalent bond?
    a. H and O
    b. C and O
    c. Na and Cl
    d. Cl and Cl

28. The correct symbol for an ion of oxygen is
    a. O^+
    b. O^{2+}
    c. O^-
    d. O^{2-}

Test Preparation

25. c 26. b 27. a 28. d

Program Resources

- **Inquiry Skills Activity Book** Provides teaching and review of all inquiry skills
- **Standardized Test Preparation Book** Provides standardized test practice
- **Reading in the Content Area** Provides strategies to improve science reading skills
- **Teacher's ELL Handbook** Provides multiple strategies for English language learners

3 Acids, Bases, and Solutions

Sections	Time	Student Edition Activities	Other Activities
CHAPTER PROJECT 3 **Make Your Own Indicator** p. L79	Ongoing (2–3 weeks)	Check Your Progress, pp. L95, L101, L106 Project Wrap Up, p. L109	**TE** Chapter 3 Project Notes, pp. L78–79
1 Working With Solutions pp. L80–89 ◆ 3.1.1 Define and compare solutions and suspensions. ◆ 3.1.2 Explain what happens to particles of a solute when a solution forms. ◆ 3.1.3 Identify the factors that affect solubility of a substance. ◆ 3.1.4 Describe how solutes affect the freezing and boiling points of solvents.	5 periods/ 2½ blocks	**Discover** What Makes a Mixture a Solution?, p. L80 **Try This** Does It Dissolve?, p. L83 **Sharpen Your Skills** Graphing, p. L85 **Sharpen Your Skills** Controlling Variables, p. L86 **Science at Home** p. L87 **Skills Lab: Designing Experiments** Speedy Solutions, pp. L88–89	**TE** Inquiry Challenge, pp. L81, L84 **TE** Integrating Life Science, p. L81 **TE** Real-Life Learning, p. L82 **TE** Demonstration, p. L83 **TE** Including All Students, p. L84 **TE** Building Inquiry Skills: Measuring, p. L85; Inferring, p. L86 **ISLM** L-3, "Determining Solubility"
2 Describing Acids and Bases pp. L90–95 ◆ 3.2.1 Identify and describe the properties of acids and give examples. ◆ 3.2.2 Identify and describe the properties of bases and give examples.	3 periods/ 1½ blocks	**Discover** What Colors Does Litmus Paper Turn?, p. L90	**TE** Integrating Earth Science, p. L92
3 Acids and Bases in Solution pp. L96–103 ◆ 3.3.1 Describe the ions formed when acids and bases are dissolved in water. ◆ 3.3.2 Describe the pH scale and tell how it is used. ◆ 3.3.3 Explain what happens in a neutralization reaction.	4 periods/ 2 blocks	**Discover** What Can Cabbage Juice Tell You?, p. L96 **Try This** pHone Home, p. L98 **Real-World Lab: You, the Consumer** The Antacid Test, pp. L102–103	**TE** Building Inquiry Skills: Making Models, p. L98 **TE** Building Inquiry Skills: Predicting, p. L99 **TE** Inquiry Challenge, p. L99 **TE** Integrating Environmental Science, p. L100
4 *INTEGRATING LIFE SCIENCE* **Digestion and pH** pp. L104–106 ◆ 3.4.1 Distinguish between mechanical and chemical digestion, and tell the importance of each. ◆ 3.4.2 Explain how pH affects digestion.	1½ periods/ 2 blocks	**Discover** Where Does Digestion Begin?, p. L104	
Study Guide/Assessment pp. L107–109	1 period/ ½ block		**ISAB** Provides teaching and review of all inquiry skills

For Standard or Block Schedule The Resource Pro® CD-ROM gives you maximum flexibility for planning your instruction for any type of schedule. Resource Pro® contains Planning Express®, an advanced scheduling program, as well as the entire contents of the Teaching Resources and the Computer Test Bank.

Key: **SE** Student Edition
PLM Probeware Lab Manual
ISAB Inquiry Skills Activity Book

CHAPTER PLANNING GUIDE

Program Resources	Assessment Strategies	Media and Technology
TR Chapter 3 Project Teacher Notes, pp. L66–67 **TR** Chapter 3 Project Overview and Worksheets, pp. L68–71	**TE** Check Your Progress, pp. L95, L101, L106 **TE** Performance Assessment: Chapter 3 Project Wrap Up, p. L109 **TR** Chapter 3 Project Scoring Rubric, p. L72	Science Explorer Internet Site Audio CDs and Audiotapes, English-Spanish Section Summaries
TR 3-1 Lesson Plan, p. L73 **TR** 3-1 Section Summary, p. L74 **TR** 3-1 Review and Reinforce, p. L75 **TR** 3-1 Enrich, p. L76 **TR** Skills Lab blackline masters, pp. L89–90 **SES** Book M, *Motion, Forces, and Energy,* Chapter 4	**SE** Section 1 Review, p. L87 **SE** Analyze and Conclude, p. L89 **TE** Ongoing Assessment, pp. L81, L83, L85 **TE** Performance Assessment, p. L87	Exploring Earth Science Videodisc, Unit 2 Side 2, "Opposites Attract" Transparencies 12, "Solution of an Ionic Solid"; 13, "Effect of Solutes on Freezing and Boiling" Lab Activity Videotape, *Chemical Interactions,* 5
TR 3-2 Lesson Plan, p. L77 **TR** 3-2 Section Summary, p. L78 **TR** 3-2 Review and Reinforce, p. L79 **TR** 3-2 Enrich, p. L80 **SES** Book K, *Chemical Building Blocks,* Chapter 3 **SES** Book F, *Inside Earth,* Chapter 5	**SE** Section 2 Review, p. L95 **TE** Ongoing Assessment, pp. L91, L93 **TE** Performance Assessment, p. L95	Interactive Student Tutorial CD-ROM, L-3
TR 3-3 Lesson Plan, p. L81 **TR** 3-3 Section Summary, p. L82 **TR** 3-3 Review and Reinforce, p. L83 **TR** 3-3 Enrich, p. L84 **TR** Real-World Lab blackline masters, pp. L91–93 **SES** Book E, *Environmental Science,* Chapter 5	**SE** Section 3 Review, p. L101 **SE** Analyze and Conclude, p. L103 **TE** Ongoing Assessment, pp. L97, L99 **TE** Performance Assessment, p. L101	Exploring Physical Science Videodisc, Unit 2 Side 2, "Food From the 'Hood'"; Exploring Life Science Videodisc, Unit 3 Side 2, "pH in Aquaria" Lab Activity Videotape, *Chemical Interactions,* 6 Transparencies 14, "Strong and Weak Acids in Solution"; 15, "pH Scale"
TR 3-4 Lesson Plan, p. L85 **TR** 3-4 Section Summary, p. L86 **TR** 3-4 Review and Reinforce, p. L87 **TR** 3-4 Enrich, p. L88 **SES** Book D, *Human Biology and Health,* Chapter 3	**SE** Section 4 Review, p. L106 **TE** Ongoing Assessment, p. L105 **TE** Performance Assessment, p. L106	Interactive Student Tutorial CD-ROM, L-3
GSW Provides worksheets to promote student comprehension of content **RCA** Provides strategies to improve science reading skills **ELL** Provides multiple strategies for English language learners	**SE** Study Guide/Assessment, pp. L107–109 **TR** Performance Assessment, pp. L148–150 **TR** Chapter 3 Test, pp. L151–154 **CTB** *Chemical Interactions,* Chapter 3 Test **STP** Provides standardized test practice	Computer Test Bank, *Chemical Interactions,* Chapter 3 Test Interactive Student Tutorial CD-ROM, L-3

TE Teacher's Edition
RCA Reading in the Content Area
GSW Guided Study Workbook

TR Teaching Resources
ISLM Integrated Science Laboratory Manual
ELL Teacher's ELL Handbook

CTB Computer Test Bank
STP Standardized Test Preparation Book
SES Science Explorer Series Text

Meeting the National Science Education Standards and AAAS Benchmarks

National Science Education Standards	Benchmarks for Science Literacy	Unifying Themes
Science as Inquiry (Content Standard A) ◆ **Design and conduct a scientific investigation** Students design an experiment to find how a single variable affects solubility of salt in water. *(Skills Lab)* **Physical Science** (Content Standard B) ◆ **Properties and changes of properties in matter** Substances that dissolve in a solvent are soluble. Solubility varies with conditions, such as temperature. Different substances have different solubilities. *(Section 1)* Acids have a sour taste, react with some metals and carbonates, and turn litmus red. Bases have a bitter taste, feel slippery, do not react with metals or carbonates, and turn litmus blue. *(Section 2)* When acids and bases mix, they neutralize and form a salt and water. *(Section 3; Real-World Lab)* **Life Science** (Content Standard C) ◆ **Structure and function in living systems** The digestive system breaks down food using mechanical digestion and chemical digestion. Different enzymes in the digestive system require environments with different pH values. *(Section 4)* **Science and Technology** (Content Standard E) ◆ **Design a solution or product** Students create their own acid-base indicators and test it. *(Chapter Project)* ◆ **Evaluate completed technological designs or products** Students evaluate the effectiveness of different antacids. *(Real-World Lab)*	**1B Scientific Inquiry** Students design an experiment to test how altering one variable can affect the solubility of salt. *(Skills Lab)* **4D The Structure of Matter** The pH of a solution varies based on the properties of compounds in the solution. Acidic solutions have hydrogen ions present, while basic solutions have hydroxide ions present. *(Sections 1, 2, 3; Chapter Project)* **5E Flow of Matter and Energy** Mechanical action and chemical digestion by enzymes cause food to break down in the digestive system into simpler molecules. *(Section 4)* **6C Basic Functions** The mouth is neutral, the stomach is acidic, and the small intestine is slightly basic; these different levels of acidity allow enzymes to efficiently digest food. *(Section 4)* **11C Constancy and Change** Solutions may be molecular or ionic. Solubility varies with conditions, such as temperature and the nature of the solvent. When acids and bases are mixed, they produce water and a salt, and the pH of the solution moves closer to 7. *(Sections 1, 2, 3)* **12A Values and Attitudes** Students keep accurate records as they evaluate the solubility of salt and form judgments about the effectiveness of antacids. *(Skills Lab; Real-World Lab)*	◆ **Patterns of Change** Litmus paper and other indicators cause predictable color changes when in contact with acids or bases. When acids and bases react together, they form salts. In the digestive system, food is broken down into smaller particles through mechanical and chemical digestion. *(Sections 2, 3, 4; Chapter Project; Real-World Lab)* ◆ **Systems and Interactions** Solutions are made up of solutes and solvents. The particles of a solute separate into ions or molecules as they are surrounded by solvent particles in a solution. Solutes vary in solubility, and factors such as temperature affect solubility. *(Section 1; Skills Lab)* ◆ **Unity and Diversity** All solutions are made up of solutes and solvents. Solutions can be unsaturated or saturated. Acids form hydrogen ions in water. Bases form hydroxide ions in water. Weak acids and bases in solution break into ions to a lesser degree than strong acids and bases do. *(Section 3; Skills Lab)*

Take It to the Net

 Interactive text at www.phschool.com

Science Explorer comes alive with iText.

- **Complete student text** is accessible from any computer with Internet service or a CD-ROM drive.
- **Animations, simulations, and videos** enhance student understanding and retention of concepts.
- **Self-tests and online study tools** assess student understanding.
- **Teacher management tools** help you make the most of this valuable resource.

STAY CURRENT with **SCIENCE NEWS** ®

Find out the latest research and information about chemical interactions at: **www.phschool.com**

Go to **www.phschool.com** and click on the Science icon. Then click on <u>Science Explorer</u> under PH@school.

ACTIVITY	Time (minutes)	Materials Quantities for one work group	Skills
Section 1			
Discover, p. 80	80	**Consumable** 2 plastic cups, water, pepper, salt **Nonconsumable** plastic spoon	Observing
Try This, p. 83	20	**Consumable** solids and liquids that dissolve in water, including soap flakes, salt, sugar, vinegar, rubbing alcohol; solids and liquids that do not dissolve in water, including pepper, powdered chalk, corn starch, vegetable oil, baby oil **Nonconsumable** plastic cups, plastic spoons	Creating Data Tables
Sharpen Your Skills, p. 85	10	**Consumable** graph paper **Nonconsumable** ruler	Graphing
Sharpen Your Skills, p. 86	10	**Consumable** Various substances to use as solutes, such as table salt, sugar, baking soda; water **Nonconsumable** balance, hot plate, thermometer, beakers, stirring rod or spoon	Controlling Variables
Science at Home, p. 87	home	**Consumable** baking soda, water **Nonconsumable** cup, small spoon	Predicting
Skills Lab p. 88–89	30 min– several days	**Consumable** ice; coarse, rock, and table salt **Nonconsumable** spoon; solid stoppers, #4; thermometers; hot plate; balance; stirring rods; timer or watch; test tube rack; test tubes, 25 x 150 mm; graduated cylinders and beakers, various sizes	Designing Experiments
Section 2			
Discover, p. 90	15	**Consumable** red and blue litmus papers, lemon juice, orange juice, tap water, baking soda, soap, ammonia cleaner, vinegar, salt, or other acids or bases **Nonconsumable** plastic dropper, plastic cups	Classifying
Section 3			
Discover, p. 96	15	**Consumable** red cabbage juice, lemon juice, ammonia **Nonconsumable** 3 plastic droppers, 3 plastic cups	Forming Operational Definitions
Try This, p. 98		**Consumable** variety of household materials, universal pH indicator paper **Nonconsumable** plastic droppers, plastic cups	Interpreting Data
Real-World Lab, pp. 102–103	30–45	**Consumable** small plastic cups; dilute HCl, 50 mL; methyl orange solution, 1 mL; liquid antacid, 30 mL of each brand tested **Nonconsumable** 3 plastic droppers	Designing Experiments, Measuring, Interpreting Data
Section 4			
Discover, p. 104	5	**Consumable** piece of crusty bread	Inferring

A list of all materials required for the Student Edition activities can be found beginning on page T15. You can obtain information about ordering materials by calling 1-800-848-9500 or by accessing the Science Explorer Internet site at: **www.phschool.com**

CHAPTER PROJECT 3

Make Your Own Indicator

Many natural substances can be used as acid-base indicators because they change colors when they react with an acid or a base.

Purpose In this project, students make their own indicator dyes from foods, plants, or other materials and use them to test readily available acids and bases.

Skills Focus After completing the Chapter 3 Project, students will be able to
◆ design experiments to determine which common plant materials are acid-base indicators;
◆ control variables to test several substances with acid-base indicators;
◆ compare and contrast their experimental results with results obtained from using a standard pH scale;
◆ communicate their findings about the acid-base indicators to their classmates.

Project Time Line This project will take approximately two weeks to complete. During the first week, students select materials from which to make their indicators and extract the dye from these materials. During the second week, students use their indicators to test a variety of substances. They should also test several substances with pH test paper. Allow one or two days for testing. When all tests are complete, students should rank their findings and prepare their presentations. Before beginning the project, see Chapter 3 Project Teacher Notes on pages 66–67 in Teaching Resources for more details on carrying out the project. Also distribute to students the Chapter 3 Project Overview, Worksheets, and Scoring Rubric on pages 68–72 in Teaching Resources.

Suggested Shortcuts The time required for this project can be reduced by decreasing the number of indicators to prepare and/or the number of substances students should test. Alternatively, you can have each student prepare a class batch of a different indicator that can then be distributed among their classmates.

CHAPTER 3 Acids, Bases, and Solutions

WEB ACTIVITY www.phschool.com

SECTION **1** Working With Solutions
Discover What Makes a Mixture a Solution?
Try This Does It Dissolve?
Sharpen Your Skills Graphing
Sharpen Your Skills Controlling Variables
Skills Lab Speedy Solutions

SECTION **2** Describing Acids and Bases
Discover What Colors Does Litmus Paper Turn?

SECTION **3** Acids and Bases in Solution
Discover What Can Cabbage Juice Tell You?
Try This pHone Home
Real-World Lab The Antacid Test

78 ◆ L

Possible Materials Provide a wide variety of materials from which students can choose. Some possibilities are listed below. Encourage students to suggest and use other materials as well.
◆ Substances that would make good indicators include: red cabbage, tea (flavored or unflavored), beets, rose petals, rhubarb, red grapes, red onion skin, blueberries, tomato skin, grass, and greens (such as collard, kale, spinach, mustard).

◆ Substances for students to test include: vinegar, milk, lemon juice, apple juice, carbonated drinks, soapy water, salt water (35 g NaCl to 1,000 mL H_2O), ammonia, bleach, household cleaners, and shampoo.
◆ Students will need equipment such as electric blenders, mortars and pestles, cheesecloth, and strainers for extracting dye. They will also need empty bottles with screw-top lids for storing their indicator juices once they have been made.

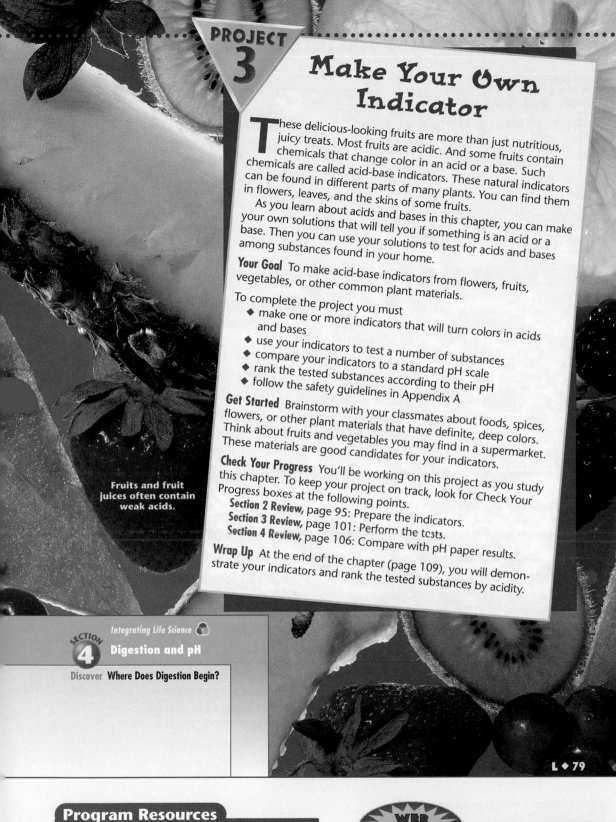

PROJECT 3

Make Your Own Indicator

These delicious-looking fruits are more than just nutritious, juicy treats. Most fruits are acidic. And some fruits contain chemicals that change color in an acid or a base. Such chemicals are called acid-base indicators. These natural indicators can be found in different parts of many plants. You can find them in flowers, leaves, and the skins of some fruits.

As you learn about acids and bases in this chapter, you can make your own solutions that will tell you if something is an acid or a base. Then you can use your solutions to test for acids and bases among substances found in your home.

Your Goal To make acid-base indicators from flowers, fruits, vegetables, or other common plant materials.

To complete the project you must
◆ make one or more indicators that will turn colors in acids and bases
◆ use your indicators to test a number of substances
◆ compare your indicators to a standard pH scale
◆ rank the tested substances according to their pH
◆ follow the safety guidelines in Appendix A

Get Started Brainstorm with your classmates about foods, spices, flowers, or other plant materials that have definite, deep colors. Think about fruits and vegetables you may find in a supermarket. These materials are good candidates for your indicators.

Check Your Progress You'll be working on this project as you study this chapter. To keep your project on track, look for Check Your Progress boxes at the following points.

Section 2 Review, page 95: Prepare the indicators.
Section 3 Review, page 101: Perform the tests.
Section 4 Review, page 106: Compare with pH paper results.

Wrap Up At the end of the chapter (page 109), you will demonstrate your indicators and rank the tested substances by acidity.

Fruits and fruit juices often contain weak acids.

SECTION 4 *Integrating Life Science*

Digestion and pH

Discover **Where Does Digestion Begin?**

L ◆ 79

Program Resources

◆ **Teaching Resources** Chapter 3 Project Teacher Notes, pp. 66–67; Chapter 3 Project Overview and Worksheets, pp. 68–71; Chapter 3 Project Scoring Rubric, p. 72

Media and Technology

 Audio CDs and **Audiotapes**
English-Spanish Section Summaries

WEB ACTIVITY **www.phschool.com**

You will find an Internet activity, chapter self-tests for students, and links to other chapter topics at this site.

Launching the Project Show students a glass of tea. Explain to them that many naturally occurring colored compounds, such as the tea, can be used to identify substances as acids or bases. Have test tubes of vinegar and ammonia solutions prepared in advance. Add two drops of the tea to each test tube so students can see the changes. Finally, use pH test paper to find the actual pH of untested vinegar and ammonia.

Allow time for students to read the description of the project in their text and the Chapter Project Overview on pages 68–69 in Teaching Resources. Then encourage discussions about acid and base indicators, materials that could be used, and any initial questions students may have. Caution students that many of the materials that will work as indicators may stain their skin or clothes, so they should wear lab aprons and old clothes and clean up all spills immediately.

Performance Assessment

The Chapter 3 Project Scoring Rubric on page 72 of Teaching Resources will help you evaluate how well students complete the Chapter 3 Project. Students will be assessed on
◆ their thoroughness in preparation and extraction of substances that indicate acids and bases;
◆ the organization of their data tables and the completeness of their observation entries, including color changes and actual pH values;
◆ how well they analyze their experiments and observations;
◆ the thoroughness and organization of their presentations.
By sharing the Chapter 3 Scoring Rubric with students at the beginning of the project, you will make it clear to them what they are expected to do.

Objectives

After completing the lesson, students will be able to
◆ define and compare solutions and suspensions;
◆ explain what happens to particles of a solute when a solution forms;
◆ identify the factors that affect solubility of a substance;
◆ describe how solutes affect the freezing and boiling points of solvents.

Key Terms suspension, solution, solvent, solute, dilute solution, concentrated solution, solubility, saturated solution, unsaturated solution

1 Engage/Explore

Activating Prior Knowledge

Show students containers of water, water and sugar solution, and salt water. Ask students to compare the three containers and tell you if they can detect the difference just by looking. Have students discuss how they could distinguish between the solutions.

········ **DISCOVER** ········

Skills Focus observing
Materials *2 paper cups, water, small spoon, graduated cylinder, pepper, table salt*
Time 10 minutes
Tips Remind students to wash the spoon before making their second mixture.
Expected Outcome The pepper will not dissolve in the water, but the salt will.
Think It Over First mixture: the pepper is visible; second mixture: the salt dissolves and forms a clear mixture. Students may recall that sand and water resemble pepper and water and that sugar and water resemble salt and water. Accept other answers that demonstrate the same concepts.

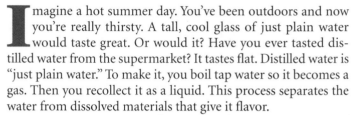

DISCOVER ··· ACTIVITY

What Makes a Mixture a Solution?

1. Put about 50 mL of water into a plastic cup. Add a spoonful of pepper and stir well.
2. To a second cup of water, add a spoonful of salt. Stir well.
3. Compare the appearance of the two mixtures.

Think It Over
Observing What is the difference between the two mixtures? What other mixtures have you seen that are similar to pepper and water? That are similar to salt and water?

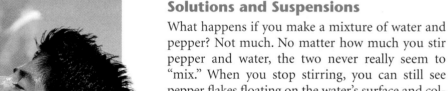

GUIDE FOR READING

◆ What happens to the particles of a solute when a solution forms?
◆ What factors affect the solubility of a substance?
◆ How do solutes affect the freezing point and boiling point of a solvent?

Reading Tip As you read, make a list of main ideas about solutions.

Imagine a hot summer day. You've been outdoors and now you're really thirsty. A tall, cool glass of just plain water would taste great. Or would it? Have you ever tasted distilled water from the supermarket? It tastes flat. Distilled water is "just plain water." To make it, you boil tap water so it becomes a gas. Then you recollect it as a liquid. This process separates the water from dissolved materials that give it flavor.

Tap water is a mixture of pure water (H_2O) and a variety of other substances, such as chlorine, fluoride, and metallic ions. Gases, such as oxygen and carbon dioxide, are also dissolved in water. Like all mixtures, the composition of tap water can vary. Tap water can differ from one home to the next, across a town, or from state to state. Tap water is an example of a kind of mixture called a solution.

Solutions and Suspensions

What happens if you make a mixture of water and pepper? Not much. No matter how much you stir pepper and water, the two never really seem to "mix." When you stop stirring, you can still see pepper flakes floating on the water's surface and collecting at the bottom of the cup. You could scoop them out if you wanted to. Pepper and water make a suspension. A **suspension** (suh SPEN shun) is a mixture in which particles can be seen and easily separated by settling or filtration. If you tasted the pepper suspension, you might find that one mouthful of it tastes peppery, but another mouthful does not. Such a mixture is not evenly mixed.

READING STRATEGIES

Reading Tip Suggest that as students read through the section, they list the main headings and subheadings, leaving several lines of space between each heading. Then have students write one sentence describing what each subsection is about. Have students rewrite the information in the boldfaced sentences in their own words.

Vocabulary Have students list these boldfaced words on a sheet of paper, giving at least one example for each term:
◆ suspension *(pepper and water)*
◆ solution *(salt and water)*
◆ solvent *(water)*
◆ solute *(salt)*
◆ dilute solution *(weak tea)*
◆ concentrated solution *(strong tea)*

On the other hand, if you stir table salt into water, the salt disappears. Water and table salt form a **solution,** a well-mixed mixture. If you taste a salt solution, any sip tastes just as salty as the next. A solution has the same properties throughout. Solutions and suspensions differ in other ways, too. The particles of a solution—too small to see—are much smaller than those of a suspension. Solutions and suspensions differ in the way the parts of the mixture can be separated. You cannot separate table salt from water by filtering it or by letting it settle. Boiling the water away, however, will work. Letting the water evaporate will also separate the salt.

Solvents and Solutes

All solutions have at least two parts: the solvent and the solute. The **solvent** is the part of a solution present in the largest amount. It dissolves the other substances. A substance that is present in a solution in a smaller amount and dissolved by the solvent is the **solute.** In salt water, the solvent is water and the solute is salt.

Water as a Solvent In many common solutions, the solvent is water. Sugar in water, for example, is the starting solution for flavored soft drinks. Adding food coloring gives the drink color. Dissolving carbon dioxide gas in the mixture produces a soda. Water dissolves so many substances that it is often called the "universal solvent."

 INTEGRATING LIFE SCIENCE Life depends on water solutions. Nutrients used by plants are dissolved in water in the soil. Sap is a solution that carries sugar to tree cells. Water is the solvent in blood, saliva, and tears. Reactions in cells take place in solution. To keep cells working, you must replace the water you lose in sweat and urine—two other water solutions.

Figure 1 Glitter mixes with the water when you shake the paperweight, but settles out later. *Classifying Are the glitter particles in solution or in suspension?*

Figure 2 When air bubbles are blown through a fish tank, oxygen gas dissolves in the water. Fish take in this oxygen through their gills. Without oxygen, the fish would die.

Chapter 3 **L ◆ 81**

2 Facilitate

Solutions and Suspensions

Inquiry Challenge

Materials *2 coffee filters, 500 mL water, 50 g sugar crystals, 50 g sand, 2 stirrer sticks, four 500-mL beakers*

Have students predict how they can separate mixtures of sand and water and sugar and water. If possible, use turbinado sugar, which looks like sand. After approving students' plans, have them carry out their experiments. *(Sample experiment: Prepare two identical sugar and water solutions and two identical mixtures of sand and water; filter one sand mixture and one sugar mixture, and allow the other two to sit for a day or so. Sand will remain in the filter and quickly settle out from the mixture. Dissolved sugar will pass through the filter but will form small crystals as the water evaporates.)*
learning modality: kinesthetic

Solvents and Solutes

Integrating Life Science

Materials *slice of fresh onion skin, slice of dried onion skin, hand lens*
Time 15 minutes

Allow students to compare slices of cells of the two onion skins and note how water affects the appearance of living cells. **learning modality: visual**

Answers to Self-Assessment
Caption Question
Figure 1 The glitter particles are in suspension because the particles can be seen and easily separated, and they settle out.

Ongoing Assessment

Oral Presentation Ask students to name some common water solutions and identify the solvent and the solute in each. *(Sample: Soft drinks are water solutions. Water is the solvent; sugar, food coloring, and carbon dioxide gas are the solutes.)*

Solvents and Solutes, continued

Real-Life Learning

Materials *labels from items such as soup, juice, salad dressing, ketchup, mustard, soft drinks, shampoo*
Time 15 minutes

ACTIVITY

Ask each student to examine the ingredients on one label. Challenge students to determine if the product is a solution or a suspension and then identify the solvent and solutes. Ask: **How can you tell which ingredient is a solvent?** *(It is present in the largest quantity, so it is listed first on the product label.)* **learning modality: verbal**

Particles in a Solution

Addressing Naive Conceptions

Students may think that a chemical change occurs when ionic solids dissolve in water because the ions separate from each other. Remind students that ions form when atoms gain or lose electrons. When the compounds dissolve in water, no electrons are transferred. The ions do not become atoms again. No new substances have formed; therefore, no chemical change has occurred. **learning modality: verbal**

Using the Visuals: Figure 4

Have students identify the sodium ions and the chloride ions in the first diagram. Ask students to describe what situation the diagram could represent. *(Sample: A visible piece of table salt is placed in a container of water.)* Then have students use their own words to describe what is happening in the second diagram. *(Sample: The salt is dissolving as water molecules surround the positive and negative ions.)* Ask students to describe what is happening in the third diagram. *(All the ions in the salt have been surrounded by water molecules and the salt is completely dissolved.)* **learning modality: visual**

Figure 3 Solutions can be made from any combination of the three states of matter. *Interpreting Tables In which of these solutions is the solvent a substance other than water?*

Examples of Common Solutions		
Solute	**Solvent**	**Solution**
Gas	Gas	Air (oxygen and other gases in nitrogen)
Gas	Liquid	Soda water (carbon dioxide in water)
Liquid	Liquid	Antifreeze (ethylene glycol in water)
Solid	Liquid	Dental filling (silver in mercury)
Solid	Liquid	Ocean water (sodium chloride and other compounds in water)
Solid	Solid	Brass (zinc and copper)

Solutions Without Water Many solutions are made with solvents other than water. For example, gasoline is a solution of several different liquid fuels. You don't even need a liquid solvent to make solutions. Solutions can be made of various combinations of gases, liquids, and solids.

Particles in a Solution

Why do solutes seem to disappear when you mix them with water? If you had a microscope powerful enough to look at the particles in the mixture, what would you see? **Whenever a solution forms, particles of the solute leave each other and become surrounded by particles of the solvent.**

Ionic Solids in Water Figure 4 shows what happens when an ionic solid mixes with water. The positive and negative ions are attracted to polar water molecules. Water molecules surround each ion as it leaves the surface of the crystal. As each layer of the solid is exposed, more ions can dissolve.

Figure 4 Water molecules surround and separate positive and negative ions as an ionic solid dissolves. Notice that sodium ions attract the oxygen ends of the water molecules.

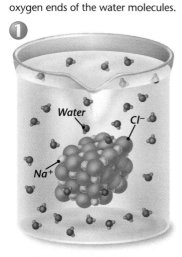
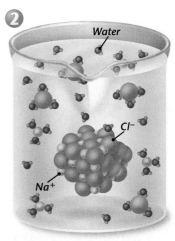
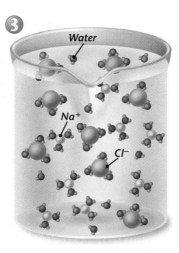

82 ◆ L

Background

Facts and Figures Almost everything you eat or drink is a mixture. Drinks like iced tea are uniform, or homogeneous, mixtures called solutions. Foods like fruit salad are nonuniform, or heterogeneous, mixtures.

Mixtures of solids and liquids form solutions, suspensions, or gels. Sports drinks are solutions of solids (sugar and other substances) in a liquid (water). Stirring flour into water creates a suspension: the flour eventually settles out. Gels, such as gelatin, form when a solid traps a liquid in a network so that the liquid cannot move freely.

When two liquids are mixed, they may dissolve in each other, as water and honey do. Or they may form separate layers, such as oil and water. When oil and water are thoroughly mixed, tiny oil droplets may be suspended indefinitely in the water to form emulsions like milk or mayonnaise.

Molecular Solids in Water Not every substance breaks into ions when it dissolves in water. A molecular solid, such as sugar, breaks up into individual neutral molecules. The polar water molecules attract the slightly polar sugar molecules. This causes the sugar molecules to move away from each other. But covalent bonds within the molecules are undisturbed. Like ions, the sugar molecules become surrounded by water.

Solutions and Conductivity You have a solution, but you don't know if it was made with salt or sugar in water. How could you use what you know about particles to find out? (Remember, a smart scientist never tastes chemicals!) Think about what you learned about the electrical conductivity of compounds. Ionic compounds dissolved in water conduct electricity, but molecular compounds do not. You could test the conductivity of the solution. If no ions were present (as in a sugar solution), electricity would not flow.

☑ *Checkpoint* How do ionic and molecular solids differ from each other in solution?

Concentration

Suppose you make two cups of hot herbal tea. You leave a tea bag in the first cup for fifteen seconds. You put another tea bag in the second cup for a few minutes. When you're done, the tea in the second cup is darker than the tea in the first cup.

The two cups of tea differ in their concentrations. That is, they differ in the amount of solute (tea) dissolved in a certain amount of solvent (water). Chemists describe the first mixture as a **dilute solution** because only a little solute is dissolved in the water. By comparison, the darker tea is a **concentrated solution** because it has more solute dissolved in the water.

Does It Dissolve?

Compare how well a few common substances dissolve in water. **ACTIVITY**

1. Put on your safety goggles.
2. Put half a spoonful of soap flakes into a small plastic cup. Add about 50 mL of water and stir. Did the soap flakes mix with water?
3. Clean out the cup and repeat the test for each of several other solids and liquids, such as baking soda, chalk dust, hand cream, and fruit juice. Decide which materials are soluble in water and which are not.

Creating Data Tables Make a table and record your results. Which dissolve more easily, solids or liquids?

Figure 5 Tea is made of several solutes dissolved in water. "Weak" tea is a dilute solution of these solutes. "Strong" tea is a more concentrated solution.

TRY THIS

Skills Focus creating data tables

Materials *plastic cups; plastic spoons; solids and liquids that dissolve in water, including soap flakes, salt, sugar, vinegar, rubbing alcohol; solids and liquids that do not dissolve in water, including pepper, powdered chalk, corn starch, vegetable oil, baby oil*

Time 20 minutes

Tips Label the materials and set them out for students to use. Make powdered chalk by putting a few chalk pieces in a plastic bag and crushing them with a rubber mallet.

Creating Data Tables Soap flakes, salt, sugar, vinegar, and rubbing alcohol dissolve easily. Pepper, chalk, and vegetable oil do not. The ability to dissolve is not related to whether a substance is a solid or a liquid.

Extend Have students compare how materials dissolve in tap and distilled water. **learning modality: visual**

Concentration

Demonstration

Materials *thawed grape or berry juice concentrate, water, large container, mixing spoon* **ACTIVITY**

Time 10 minutes

This demonstration will help students who are still mastering English. Allow students to compare the color of concentrated juice as you add first one, then two, cans of water to the concentrate in the container. Ask: **How can you make the juice more dilute?** (*Add more water.*) Then ask: **As you add water, do you change the amount of solute or solvent?** (*solvent*) **limited English proficiency**

Program Resources

 Science Explorer Series *Motion, Forces, and Energy,* Chapter 4

Media and Technology

Transparencies "Solution of an Ionic Solid," Transparency 12

Answers to Self-Assessment

Caption Question

Figure 3 In air the solvent is nitrogen gas, in dental fillings the solvent is mercury, and in brass the solvent is a solid metal.

☑ *Checkpoint*

In solution, ionic solids conduct electricity because they form ions in the water. Molecular solids do not form ions; they dissolve into separate molecules.

Ongoing Assessment

Drawing Have students make diagrams that show how a dilute solution differs from a concentrated solution.

 Students can save their diagrams in their portfolios.

Solubility

Inquiry Challenge

Materials *large beaker, 250 mL water, 25 g*  *unlabeled sample of powdered sugar or baking soda, stirring stick, stopwatch*
Time 20 minutes

Group students and have them design experiments to determine if a white powder is baking soda or powdered sugar. Assign each student a specific task, such as mixer, measurer and materials manager, and timer. Ask: **What do you hypothesize will happen if the sample is powdered sugar? If it is baking soda?** Check students' designs and allow groups to carry out their experiments. Conclude by asking: **How did you use solubility to infer the identity of your substance?** *(If the substance dissolved easily, it was sugar because sugar is more soluble than baking soda. If the substance did not dissolve or dissolved slowly, then it was baking soda.)*
cooperative learning

Including All Students

Materials *dry sponge, bowl, water, graduated cylinder*
Time 15 minutes

This activity will help students who are visually impaired. Place the sponge in the bowl. Slowly add water to the sponge in 10-mL increments. After the third addition of water, allow visually impaired students to feel the sponge. Then ask: **Can the sponge hold any more water?** *(yes)* Explain that the sponge is not yet saturated. Ask: **What do you predict you will see or feel in the bowl when the sponge is saturated?** *(Water that the sponge cannot absorb)* Allow students to continue adding water to the sponge until it is completely saturated.
learning modality: kinesthetic

Solubility in 100 g Water at 0°C	
Compound	**Solubility (g)**
Salt (NaCl)	35.7
Baking soda ($NaHCO_3$)	6.9
Carbon dioxide (CO_2)	0.348
Sugar ($C_{12}H_{22}O_{11}$)	180

Figure 6 Each compound listed in the table dissolves in water, but they have different solubilities. *Comparing and Contrasting Which compound is the most soluble? Which is the least soluble?*

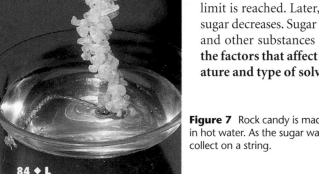

84 ◆ L

Solubility

If a substance dissolves in water, a question you might ask is, "How well does it dissolve?" Suppose you add sugar to a glass of iced tea. You could add half a spoonful to make it taste slightly sweet. Or, you could add two spoonfuls to make it sweeter. Is there a limit to how "sweet" you can make the tea? Yes. At the temperature of iced tea, several spoonfuls of sugar are about all you can add. No matter how much you stir the tea, no more sugar will dissolve. **Solubility** is a measure of how well a solute can dissolve in a solvent at a given temperature.

When you've added so much solute that no more dissolves, you have a **saturated solution.** Any more sugar would just fall to the bottom of the glass and not make the tea any sweeter. On the other hand, if you can continue to dissolve more solute, you still have an **unsaturated solution.**

The solubility of a substance tells you the limit on how much you can add before you make a saturated solution. Because solubility is a characteristic property of matter, you can use it to help identify a compound. The solubility of a substance is usually described for a specific solvent (such as water) and under certain conditions (such as temperature). Figure 6 compares the solubilities of some familiar compounds when they dissolve in water.

From the table you can see that 35.7 g of salt will dissolve in 100 g of water at 0°C. But the same quantity (mass) of water at the same temperature will dissolve 180 g of sugar! If you had two white solids, you could use solubility to tell the difference without tasting them.

Checkpoint Why doesn't solute added to a saturated solution dissolve?

Changing Solubility

Which holds more sugar, iced tea or hot tea? You have already read that there is a limit on solubility. An iced tea and sugar solution quickly becomes saturated. Yet a hot, steaming cup of the same tea can hold several more spoonfuls of sugar before the limit is reached. Later, if the solution is cooled, the solubility of sugar decreases. Sugar crystals will form. The solubilities of sugar and other substances change when conditions change. **Among the factors that affect the solubility of a substance are temperature and type of solvent.**

Figure 7 Rock candy is made by dissolving sugar in hot water. As the sugar water cools, sugar crystals collect on a string.

Background

Facts and Figures Hard water, a solution of calcium and magnesium ions, is responsible for problems such as soap scum and hard-water spots in sinks and on fixtures. Hard water combines with soap or other detergents to form a residue that cannot be rinsed away. This residue remains in clothes and on people's skin and hair. In addition, hard water deposits mineral scale inside pipes and appliances and reduces their effectiveness.

Water becomes hard when rainwater, which is usually slightly acidic, filters through rock and reacts with metals such as calcium and magnesium. Most soft water comes from treated hard water. Water softeners pass water over beads that hold salts such as sodium chloride or potassium chloride. The beads attract the calcium and magnesium and release the sodium or potassium into the water.

Figure 8 Has this ever happened to you? Opening a bottle of soda water can sometimes produce quite a spray as dissolved gas comes out of solution. *Relating Cause and Effect* Why does more gas escape from a warm bottle of soda water than from a cold bottle?

Temperature Sugar is one of many solids that dissolve better when the temperature of the solvent increases. Cooks apply this principle to prepare certain foods. A cook cannot dissolve enough sugar at room temperature to make candy or fudge. The cook must heat the liquid mixture to dissolve the sugar. Later, when the food cools, it will taste sweeter than if it were made at room temperature.

Unlike most solids, gases become less soluble when the temperature goes up. For example, more carbon dioxide will dissolve in cold water than in hot water. Carbon dioxide makes soda water fizzy when you pour it into a glass. If you open a warm bottle of soda water, carbon dioxide escapes the liquid in greater amounts than if the soda water had been chilled. Why does warm soda taste "flat"? It contains less gas. If you like soda water that's very fizzy, open it when it's cold!

Solvents If you've ever shaken a bottle of salad dressing, you've seen how quickly water and oil separate. This is because water is polar and oil is nonpolar. Polar compounds and nonpolar compounds do not mix very well. For liquid solutions, the solvent affects how well a solute dissolves. The expression "like dissolves like" gives you a clue to which solutes are soluble in which solvents. Ionic and polar compounds dissolve in polar solvents. Nonpolar compounds do not dissolve in polar solvents. If you work with paints, you know that water-based (latex) paints can be cleaned up with just soap and water. But oil-based paints may require cleanup with a nonpolar solvent, such as turpentine.

Graphing

The table below shows how many grams of potassium nitrate (KNO_3) can dissolve in 100 g of water at different temperatures. Use the data to make a graph. Label the horizontal axis *Temperature* and the vertical axis *Solubility.*

Temperature (°C)	Solubility (g/100g H_2O)
0	13
20	31
40	65
60	108
80	164
100	247

What does the graph show?

Program Resources

◆ **Intregrated Science Laboratory Manual**
   L-3, "Determining Solubility"

Media and Technology

 Exploring Earth Science Videodisc
Unit 2, Side 2,
"Opposites Attract"   Chapter 6

Answers to Self-Assessment

Caption Questions

Figure 6 Sugar is the most soluble; carbon dioxide is the least soluble.
Figure 8 The solubility of the dissolved gas decreases as the temperature rises.

☑ *Checkpoint*

In a saturated solution, the limit of the solubility of the solute has been reached.

Changing Solubility

Building Inquiry Skills: Measuring

Materials *100 mL water, salt, balance, ice, beaker*
Time 20 minutes

Help students visualize the amount of salt that will dissolve in 100 mL of water at room temperature by adding salt to the water in 5-g increments up to 35 g, then in 1-g increments until the water is saturated. Ask: **What do you predict will happen if you lower the temperature of the water by adding ice to the beaker?** *(The solubility will decrease, so some salt will fall out of solution.)* Allow students to test their predictions. **learning modality: visual**

Sharpen your *Skills*

Graphing

Materials *graph paper, ruler*
Time 10 minutes

Tips Suggest students set up their graphs so that the horizontal and vertical axes are labeled 0–100°C in 20-degree increments and 0–250 g/100 g water in 50-g increments, respectively.

Graphing Students' graphs should show a straight line going up from left to right (a positive slope), indicating that the solubility of KNO_3 increases with increasing temperature.

Extend Ask students to use the graph to determine the temperatures at which 50 g and 100 g of potassium nitrate can dissolve in 100 g of water. *(50 g at around 30°C; 100 g at around 50°C)*

Ongoing Assessment

Writing Have students contrast the effect of temperature on the solubility of solids and gases in liquids.

Effects of Solutes on Solutions

Building Inquiry Skills: Inferring

Materials *very cold distilled, tap, and salt water; stainless steel bowls; small paper cups; ice; salt; marker*

Time 15 minutes for setup, 1 hour for observation

Prepare the solutions. Also make several cold salt-water baths by placing ice, water, and salt in the bowls. Have students work in small groups to add a small amount of each solution to each of three paper cups. Ask students: **Which solution will freeze first?** To test their predictions, students can float the cups in the salt-water baths, then check the cups every 10 minutes. Ask: **What do your observations tell you about distilled water?** *(Its freezing point is higher, so it must contain fewer or no solutes.)* **cooperative learning**

Sharpen your Skills

Controlling Variables

Time 10 minutes

Tips Constant variables—quantity of water, type of solute; manipulated variable—mass of the solute; responding variable—temperature at which water boils

Expected Outcome Increasing the mass of the solute raises the boiling temperature of water.

Extend Challenge students to determine whether different solutes cause water to boil at different temperatures.

Sharpen your Skills

Controlling Variables

How does the quantity (mass) of a solute affect the boiling temperature of water? Design an experiment using a solute, water, a balance, a hot plate, and a thermometer.

What variables should remain constant in your experiment? What is the manipulated variable? What will be the responding variable?

With approval from your teacher, do the experiment. Report on your results.

Figure 9 The freezing point and boiling point of water are affected by the presence of solute particles. Solute particles interfere with the change of state.

Effects of Solutes on Solutions

Have you ever made ice cream? First you mix cream, sugar, and other ingredients. Then you freeze the mixture by packing it in ice and water. But ice water by itself is not cold enough to do the job. Cream freezes at a temperature lower than the freezing point of water (0°C). Adding salt to the ice water creates a mixture that is several degrees cooler. This salty ice water is cold enough to freeze the cream. Mmm!

You can use salt to affect boiling, too. When cooking spaghetti, people often add table salt to the water. As a result, the water boils at a temperature higher than 100°C, the boiling point of water. One small spoonful of salt in about a liter of water will raise the boiling point about 0.25 degrees. A few large spoonfuls of salt in a pot of water could increase the boiling temperature by about 0.5 degrees. This change is enough to cook the spaghetti faster.

Why does salt make cold water colder when it freezes and hot water hotter when it boils? The answer to both parts of this question depends on solute particles.

Lower Freezing Points **Solutes lower the freezing point of a solvent.** When liquid water freezes, the molecules stop moving about. Instead, they form crystals of solid ice. Look at Figure 9 to compare the particles in pure water with those in a saltwater solution. Notice that pure water is made only of water molecules. In the salt solution, solute particles are present, too. In fact, they're in the way. The solute particles make it harder for the water molecules to form crystals. The temperature must drop lower than 0°C for a solid to form.

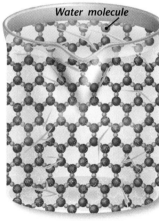

Pure liquid water — Water molecule

Ice — Water molecule

Salt water — Water molecule — Solute particles

Background

History of Science The discovery that water solutions freeze at lower temperatures than pure water led to advances in food preparation and storage. Pure water freezes at 0°C, but foods must be colder because they are composed of different solutes dissolved in water.

People have been eating frozen ices for at least 2,000 years, but they were difficult to make until people learned to use salt to lower the temperature of ice. Soon people were able to make ice cream at home. A Baltimore company produced the first commercially made ice cream in 1851.

Solutions of salt and water were also used to freeze fish and chicken. In the 1920s, Clarence Birdseye received a patent for a method of freezing fish between two metal plates cooled by a solution of calcium chloride. This allowed fish to cool to –40°C.

Higher Boiling Points Solutes raise the boiling point of a solvent. To see why, think about the difference between the molecules of a liquid and those of a gas. In a liquid, molecules are moving close to each other. In a gas, they are far apart and moving much more rapidly. As the temperature of a liquid rises, the molecules gain energy and escape into the air. Now compare the left and right solutions in Figure 9 again. In pure water, all the molecules are water. In the solution, however, some of the particles are water molecules and others are particles of solute. The presence of the solute makes it harder for the water molecules to escape, so more energy is needed. The temperature must go higher than 100°C for the water to boil.

Figure 10 The coolant in a car radiator is a solution.
Predicting On a very cold day, what might happen to a car that had only water in the radiator?

 INTEGRATING TECHNOLOGY Car manufacturers make use of the effects of solutes to protect engines from heat and cold. The coolant in a car radiator is a solution of water and another liquid called antifreeze. Often the antifreeze is ethylene glycol, which freezes at –13°C and boils at 176°C. The mixture of the two liquids has a lower freezing point and higher boiling point than either liquid alone. This solution safely absorbs heat given off by the running engine. Risk of damage to the car from overheating is greatly reduced. So is the risk of damage from freezing in very cold weather.

Section 1 Review

1. Describe what happens to the molecules of a solid, such as a sugar cube, when it dissolves in water. How does the process differ for an ionic compound, such as table salt?
2. Why would an ionic compound be more likely to dissolve in water than in oil?
3. Would you expect a concentrated solution of sugar in water to boil at 100°C? Explain.
4. **Thinking Critically Relating Cause and Effect** Why is the temperature needed to freeze ocean water lower than the temperature needed to freeze the surface of a freshwater lake?

Science at Home

With your family, make a saturated solution of baking soda in water. Add one small spoonful of baking soda to about 250 mL of cool water. Stir until the baking soda dissolves. Continue adding baking soda in this manner until no more dissolves. Keep track of how much baking soda you use. Then ask your family to predict what would happen if you used warm water instead. Test their predictions and compare the results with those of the first test.

Chapter 3 **L ◆ 87**

Program Resources

◆ **Teaching Resources** 3-1 Review and Reinforce, p. 75; 3-1 Enrich, p. 76

Media and Technology

Transparencies "Effect of Solutes on Freezing and Boiling," Transparency 13

Answers to Self-Assessment

Caption Question

Figure 10 The car's engine might be damaged because the water inside the radiator could freeze on a very cold day.

 Integrating Technology

Challenge students to infer whether a car would be better protected by pure antifreeze or a mixture of half antifreeze and half water. Ask students to explain their inferences. *(Half antifreeze and half water, because the mixture has a lower freezing point and a higher boiling point than either water or antifreeze)* **learning modality: verbal**

3 Assess

Section 1 Review Answers

1. The molecules of sugar separate from each other and become surrounded by water molecules, but the molecules do not separate into ions or atoms. When an ionic compound dissolves, it breaks up into ions, which are surrounded by water molecules.
2. Polar water molecules attract the positive and negative ions. Nonpolar oil molecules do not.
3. Adding salt to ice makes a salt and water solution, which has a freezing point lower than that of water alone.
4. Ocean water is a solution of salt and water. The salt lowers the freezing point of water below that of fresh water.

Science at Home

Materials *cup, baking soda, cool water, warm water, small spoon*
Suggest students use warm tap water to demonstrate that more baking soda will dissolve at higher temperatures of water than at lower temperatures. A greater effect will be observed if the temperature difference is greater. Therefore, students should start with ice-cold water and finish with warmer water.

Performance Assessment

Oral Presentation Have groups of students prepare demonstrations to show the amount of solute a solvent can hold at three distinct temperatures.

L ◆ 87

Speedy Solutions

Preparing for Inquiry

Key Concept The rate at which salt dissolves in water depends on variables such as water temperature, rate of stirring, salt grain size, and volume of water.

Skills Objective Students will design experiments to determine how a chosen variable affects the rate at which salt dissolves.

Time This lab could take anywhere from 30 minutes to several days. (See "Helping Design a Plan" and "Troubleshooting the Experiment" sections, below.)

Advance Planning

◆ Provide alcohol thermometers, not those made with mercury.

◆ Remind students not to use thermometers as stirring rods.

◆ Provide mitts and insulated pads for students to use when handling hot plates and other heated materials.

Guiding Inquiry

Invitation Show students a test tube containing some water. Drop a few grains of salt into the tube and swirl. Ask: **How do you know when the salt is completely dissolved?** (*No more crystals appear in the bottom of the tube.*) Ask: **How could you change the amount of time it takes to dissolve the salt?** (*Sample responses: change the temperature of the water, shake the tube more vigorously, use more water.*) Then ask students how they could measure the factors they mentioned. (*With thermometers, by counting the number of shakes in a given time period, by measuring the volume of water added*)

Helping Design a Plan

◆ Students should state which variable, such as temperature or volume of water, they wish to test.

◆ Have students formulate hypotheses regarding their variable. For example, if students choose to test rate of stirring, ask: **What do you think will happen if you do not stir, or if you stir three times every second?** Have

---

Speedy Solutions

In this lab, you will design an experiment to find out how a chosen variable affects the speed at which salt dissolves in water.

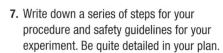

Problem

How can you control the rate at which salt dissolves in water?

Materials

spoon	solid stoppers, #4
thermometers	hot plate
balance	stirring rods
ice	timer or watch
test tube rack	test tubes, 25×150 mm
coarse, rock, and table salt	
graduated cylinders and beakers, various sizes	

Design a Plan

1. Make a list of all the variables you can think of that could affect the speed with which salt dissolves in water.

2. Compare your list with your classmates' lists, and add other variables.

3. Choose one variable from your list to test.

4. Write a hypothesis predicting the effect of your chosen variable on the speed of dissolving.

5. Decide how to work with your choice.
   ◆ If you choose temperature, you might perform tests at 10°C, 20°C, 30°C, 40°C, and 50°C.
   ◆ If you choose stirring, you might stir for various amounts of time.

6. Plan at least three tests for whichever variable you choose. Remember to control all other variables.

7. Write down a series of steps for your procedure and safety guidelines for your experiment. Be quite detailed in your plan.

8. As part of your procedure, prepare a data table in which to record your results. Fill in the headings on your table that identify your manipulated variable and the responding variable. (*Hint:* Remember to include units.)

9. Have your teacher approve your procedure, safety guidelines, and data table.

10. Perform the experiment.

DATA TABLE

Manipulated Variable	Dissolving Time		
	Test 1	Test 2	Test 3

---

students express their hypotheses as "If . . . then . . ." statements.

◆ Have students explain how they will manipulate the variables they will test. Encourage them to determine specific levels or amounts that they will test.

◆ Ask students: **How will you measure the responding variable?** (*By measuring how long it takes all the salt to dissolve.*)

Evaluating Student Plans

Make sure students describe their plans clearly. Their procedures should be arranged in logical order. Evaluate all plans for safety, especially if students plan to test temperature or stirring. Make sure students' materials lists include safety items such as goggles and stirring rods.

Troubleshooting the Experiment

◆ Students should limit the quantity of salt to less than 35g/100 mL water, or approximately the solubility of salt at 0°C.

◆ Students can measure the volume of water in a container by filling it with water from a graduated cylinder.

Analyze and Conclude

1. Which is the manipulated variable in your experiment? Which is the responding variable? How do you know which is which?
2. List three variables you held constant in your procedure. Explain why controlling these variables makes your data more reliable.
3. Make a line graph of your data. Label the horizontal axis with the manipulated variable. Label the vertical axis with the responding variable. Use an appropriate scale for each axis and label the units.
4. Study the shape of your graph. Write a conclusion about the effect of the variable you tested on the speed of salt dissolving in water.
5. Does your conclusion support the hypothesis you wrote in Step 4? Explain.
6. How do your results relate to what you have learned about particles and solubility?
7. What advantage would there be in running your tests a second or third time?
8. **Think About It** If you switched procedures with another student who tested the same variable as you, do you think you would get the same results? Explain why or why not.

More to Explore

Choose another variable from the list you made in Steps 1 and 2. Repeat the process with that variable. Of the two variables you chose, which was easier to work with? Explain.

L ◆ 89

Safety

Remind students not to use thermometers as stirring rods. Caution them to use mitts or insulated pads when handling hot plates and other heated materials. Students should take care when handling glassware, and wipe up any spilled liquids immediately. Review the safety guidelines in Appendix A.

Program Resources

◆ **Teaching Resources** Skills Lab blackline masters, pp. 89–90
◆ **Inquiry Skills Activity Book** Provides teaching and review of all inquiry skills

Media and Technology

 Lab Activity Videotape
Chemical Interactions, 5

Expected Outcome

Results will vary, but most students will find that salt dissolves more quickly under the following conditions: at higher temperatures, with finer grains of salt, with more stirring or shaking.

Analyze and Conclude

1. Manipulated variable—chosen by student; responding variable—time it takes for salt to dissolve. The manipulated variable is changed by the student and the responding variable is what is measured as a result.
2. Students should correctly identify at least three variables and explain that using controls allows them to avoid confusion about which factor is causing an observed effect.
3. Graphs should accurately reflect data collected. All graphs should have the time that it took for the salt to dissolve on the *y*-axis.
4. Answers will vary. Samples: increase in water temperature, decrease in grain size, and more rapid stirring will all result in more rapid dissolving.
5. Answers will depend on the hypothesis stated. Make sure students correctly interpret conclusions with respect to their hypotheses.
6. Sample: Water molecules have to surround the sodium and chloride ions to dissolve the salt. At higher temperatures, water molecules are moving faster and will come in contact with the salt crystals more often. If the container is shaken, the particles come in contact more often. Smaller grains have a greater surface area, so more ions are in contact with water molecules.
7. More than one trial provides evidence that the data is accurate and procedures are being followed consistently.
8. Answers will vary. Students should realize that valid procedures should result in the same or similar data.

Extending the Inquiry

More to Explore Answers will vary depending on which variables were chosen. If they chose temperature for their first variable and size of grains as their second variable, students may have found it easier to control the water temperature than to differentiate between the sizes of salt grains. Accept logical explanations.

Objectives

After completing the lesson, students will be able to

◆ identify and describe the properties of acids and give examples;

◆ identify and describe the properties of bases and give examples.

Key Terms acid, corrosive, indicator, base

1 Engage/Explore

Activating Prior Knowledge

Show students a package of commercial batteries. Have students examine the warning or caution label. Ask: **Why must you be careful when handling a leaking battery?** *(Batteries contain substances that can cause burns.)*

DISCOVER

Skills Focus classifying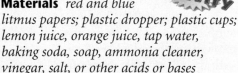
Materials *red and blue litmus papers; plastic dropper; plastic cups; lemon juice, orange juice, tap water, baking soda, soap, ammonia cleaner, vinegar, salt, or other acids or bases*
Time 15 minutes
Tips Set out samples in labeled plastic cups. Each group needs about one-third cup of each test substance. Remind students to rinse their droppers after each test. Caution students not to taste any of the substances.
Think It Over Turn blue litmus paper red —acids such as lemon juice, orange juice, tea, and vinegar; turn red litmus paper blue—bases such as baking soda, soap, and ammonia cleaner; do not change color of litmus paper—distilled water, salt water. Students may know that lemon juice, orange juice, and vinegar taste sour. Soap and ammonia cleaner feel slippery.

SECTION 2 Describing Acids and Bases

DISCOVER ACTIVITY

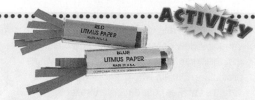

What Colors Does Litmus Paper Turn?

1. Use a plastic dropper to put a drop of lemon juice on a clean piece of red litmus paper. Put another drop on a clean piece of blue litmus paper. Observe.

2. Rinse your dropper with water. Then test other substances the same way. You might test orange juice, ammonia cleaner, tap water, vinegar, and solutions of soap, baking soda, and table salt. Record all your observations.

3. Wash your hands when you are finished.

Think It Over
Classifying Group the substances based on how they make the litmus paper change color. Do you notice any other characteristics that the members of each group have in common?

GUIDE FOR READING

◆ What properties can you use to identify acids?

◆ What properties can you use to identify bases?

Reading Tip Before you read, preview *Exploring Uses of Acids* and *Exploring Uses of Bases*. List examples of acids and bases you are already familiar with.

Did you eat any fruit for breakfast today—perhaps an orange, an apple, or fruit juice? If so, an acid was part of your meal. The last time you washed your hair, did you use shampoo? If your answer is yes, then you may have used a base.

You use many products that contain acids and bases. Manufacturers, farmers, and builders depend on acids and bases in their work. The chemical reactions of acids and bases even keep you alive! What are acids and bases? How do they react, and what are their uses? In this section you will start to find out.

Properties of Acids

What is an acid and how do you know when you have one? Test its properties. **Acids** are compounds that share some characteristic properties. **An acid is a substance that tastes sour, reacts with metals and carbonates, and turns blue litmus paper red.**

Sour Taste If you've ever tasted a lemon, you've had firsthand experience with the sour taste of acids. Can you think of other foods that sometimes taste sour, or tart? Citrus fruits—lemons, grapefruits, oranges, and limes—are acidic. They all contain citric acid. Other fruits (cherries, tomatoes, apples) contain acids also. The vinegar used in salad dressing is made from a solution of water and acetic acid. Tea is acidic, too. So is spoiled milk, but you might not want to drink it!

Although sour taste is a property of many acids, it is not one you would use to identify a compound as

Figure 11 A sour taste often means that food is acidic.

90 ◆ L

---

an acid. Scientists never taste chemicals in order to identify them. Though acids in sour foods may be safe to eat, many other acids are not.

Reactions With Metals   Do you notice bubbles in Figure 13? Acids react with certain metals to produce hydrogen gas. Not all metals react this way, but magnesium, zinc, and iron do. When they react, the metals seem to disappear in the solution. This observation is one reason acids are described as **corrosive,** meaning they "eat away" at other materials.

 INTEGRATING TECHNOLOGY   The metal plate in Figure 13 is being etched with acid. Etching is one method of making printing plates that are then used to print works of art on paper. To make an etching, an artist first coats a metal plate with an acid-resistant material—often beeswax. Then the design is cut into the beeswax with a sharp tool, exposing some of the metal. When the plate is treated with acid, the acid eats away the design in the exposed metal. Later, ink applied to the plate collects in the grooves made by the acid. The ink is transferred to the paper when the etching is printed.

Some Important Acids	
Acid	**Formula**
Hydrochloric acid	HCl
Nitric acid	HNO_3
Sulfuric acid	H_2SO_4
Carbonic acid	H_2CO_3
Acetic acid	$HC_2H_3O_2$
Phosphoric acid	H_3PO_4

Figure 12   The table lists the names and formulas of some common acids.

Figure 13   Metal etching takes advantage of the reaction of an acid with a metal. Lines are cut in a wax coating on a plate. Here, hydrochloric acid eats away at the exposed zinc metal, forming bubbles you can see in the close-up. *Applying Concepts* *What gas forms in this reaction?*

Program Resources

◆ **Teaching Resources**   3-2 Lesson Plan, p. 77; 3-2 Section Summary, p. 78
◆ **Guided Reading and Study Workbook** Section 3-2

Answers to Self-Assessment

Caption Question
Figure 13   Hydrogen gas forms in the reaction of zinc with hydrochloric acid.

---

2 Facilitate

Properties of Acids

Including All Students

For students who need help organizing information, provide a reminder that acids turn blue litmus paper red. Then ask: **Based on how acids affect litmus, what substances from the Discover activity would you classify as acids?** *(Lemon juice, orange juice, vinegar)* Based on the characteristics of acids listed in the text, have students brainstorm a list of other acids they are familiar with. If possible, allow them to test the substances with blue litmus paper to find out whether the substance is really an acid. **learning modality: verbal**

 ### Integrating Technology

Tell students that when the acid reacts with the zinc, zinc ions go into solution. The zinc is still present even though the metal seems to "disappear in the solution." Also, the concentration of the hydrochloric acid determines how rapidly the hydrogen gas is evolved. Ask: **Suppose you have two different hydrochloric acid solutions. How could you use zinc to tell which solution is more concentrated?** *(Pour a small amount of each solution into separate beakers, each containing a piece of zinc. The solution that causes bubbles to form more quickly is more concentrated.)* Demonstrate this for your class if possible. **learning modality: verbal**

Ongoing Assessment

Writing   Have students list the properties of acids. *(Sour taste, react with metals and carbonates, turn blue litmus paper red)*

 Students can save their lists in their portfolios.

Language Arts
CONNECTION

Ask students: **Why would the nitric acid test not be useful in testing for pure iron or zinc?** *(Iron and zinc react with acids by forming bubbles.)* Then challenge students to infer why it was important to test the purity of gold. *(Some students may know that gold was a standard of currency.)*
Extend Challenge students to find stories or newspaper or magazine articles that use the phrase "acid test." Have students identify the test referred to in the story or article.

In Your Journal Invite students to share experiences in which they proved their honesty, reliability, or courage. Encourage students to reflect on what was challenging or revealing about the experience, and how it changed their lives or their viewpoints. Ask: **What might be one way in which you could put a person's trustworthiness to the acid test?** *(Student answers will vary.)*
limited English proficiency
 Students can save their answers in their portfolios.

Integrating Earth Science

Materials *1.0 M muriatic acid (hydrochloric acid), dropper, 2 limestone rocks, 1 non-limestone rock*
Time 10 minutes

Provide students with rock samples and allow them to perform the limestone test referred to in the text. Students can apply one or two drops of acid to each rock. Ask: **What can you infer about the rocks that formed bubbles?** *(Substances in the rocks reacted with acid, so the rocks must be limestone.)* **learning modality: kinesthetic**

Language Arts
CONNECTION

Putting someone to the "acid test" has nothing to do with litmus. The phrase is a figure of speech. It refers to a situation that tests someone's character, ability, courage, or other personal qualities. It comes from an old use of nitric acid to test the purity of gold. Many metals react with acid, but gold does not. Fake gold corrodes, while the value and quality of real gold are revealed.

In Your Journal

Write about a time you or someone you know went through an "acid test." What was hard about the situation? What did you learn from it about yourself or the other person?

Reactions With Carbonates Acids also react with carbonate ions in a characteristic way. Recall that an ion is an atom or a group of atoms that has an electric charge. Carbonate ions contain carbon and oxygen atoms bonded together. They carry an overall negative charge (CO_3^{2-}). When acids react with carbonate compounds, a gas forms. In this case, the gas is carbon dioxide.

INTEGRATING EARTH SCIENCE Geologists, scientists who study Earth, use the reaction of acids with carbonates to identify limestone. Limestone is made of calcium carbonate ($CaCO_3$). If a dilute solution of hydrochloric acid (HCl) is poured on a limestone rock, bubbles of carbon dioxide appear. Look at the equation for this reaction.

$$2\ HCl + CaCO_3 \rightarrow CaCl_2 + CO_2 + H_2O$$

Many forms of limestone come from organisms that live in the ocean. Coral rock, for example, comes from coral reefs. Reefs are large structures made of the skeletons of millions of tiny sea animals that produce an outer covering of calcium carbonate. Chalk is another form of limestone. It forms from the hard parts of microscopic sea animals, deposited in thick layers. Over time, these layers are pressed together and harden into chalk.

Reactions With Indicators If you did the Discover activity, you used litmus paper to test several substances. Litmus is an example of an **indicator,** a compound that changes color when in contact with an acid or a base. Vinegar and lemon juice turn blue litmus paper red. In fact, acids always turn litmus paper red. Sometimes chemists use other indicators to test for acids, but litmus is one of the easiest to use.

☑ *Checkpoint* What is the purpose of using an indicator?

Figure 14 Hydrangea flowers are natural indicators. They may range in color from bright pink to blue, depending on the acidity of the soil in which the bush grows.

Background

Facts and Figures Litmus paper is paper that has been colored with a mixture of dyes called *litmus.* The dyes come from lichens, organisms that are actually combinations of algae and fungi or fungi and certain bacteria, living in symbiotic relationships.

To extract litmus, lichens are treated with lime, ammonia, and potassium carbonate.

Red litmus is a weak acid, but when exposed to a base, it becomes an ionized salt that appears blue. In an acid, the blue form turns red. Applying litmus to paper provides a convenient way to test for the presence of acids and bases. A solution that does not cause either form of litmus to change color is neutral, that is, neither acidic nor basic.

EXPLORING Uses of Acids

Acids play important roles in the chemistry of living things. Acids also are used to make valuable products for homes, farms, and industries.

Acids and food
Many of the vitamins in the foods you eat are acids.

Oranges and tomatoes contain ascorbic acid, or vitamin C.

Folic acid, needed for healthy cell growth, is found in green leafy vegetables.

Acids in the body
Acids are useful in the body and are also waste products of cell processes.

Acid in the stomach helps to digest protein.

During exercise, lactic acid builds up in hard-working muscles.

Acid

In solution, acids often look just like water, but they react very differently. A concentrated acid can burn a hole in metal, cloth, skin, wood, and other materials.

Acids in the home
People often use dilute solutions of acids to clean brick and other surfaces. Hardware stores sell muriatic (hydrochloric) acid, which is used to clean bricks and metals.

Acids and industry
Farmers and manufacturers depend on acids for many uses.

Sulfuric acid Is used in car batteries, to refine petroleum, and to treat iron and steel.

Nitric acid and phosphoric acid are used to make fertilizers for crops, lawns, and gardens.

Program Resources

 Science Explorer Series *Chemical Building Blocks,* Chapter 3

Answers to Self-Assessment

☑ *Checkpoint*
An indicator allows you to identify a substance as an acid or a base.

EXPLORING
Uses of Acids

As students examine each item in the visual essay, have them list the name of the acid and how it is useful to people. Ask students: **Which acids in the visual essay are found in foods?** *(Ascorbic acid, folic acid)* Tell students that gastric juices contain hydrochloric acid, which is very corrosive and can burn skin. Ask: **How can hydrochloric acid exist in your stomach without harming you?** *(There must be something in the stomach that protects it from the acid. Some students may know the stomach's internal surface is protected by a layer of mucus.)* Ask: **Why is it important to label acids in the lab or in household products?** *(Some acids look like water but can be dangerous.)*
Extend Have students take an inventory of all the acidic products they have in their homes. Students should list each product and its uses. **learning modality: verbal**

Cultural Diversity

Industries around the world use more sulfuric acid than any other chemical. This thick, corrosive liquid is used in the manufacture of fertilizers, chemicals, dyes, synthetic fabrics, photographic films, and explosives, in addition to its use in car batteries and production of petroleum products, iron, and steel. Have student teams research such topics as how and where sulfuric acid is made, where sulfur (the starting material for sulfuric acid) is found, and what products are made using sulfuric acid. Have students focus and report on which countries have industries that make or use sulfuric acid. Encourage students to compare and contrast uses in different regions of the world. **learning modality: verbal**

Ongoing Assessment

Writing Have students describe one test they could perform to determine whether an unknown substance was an acid.

 Students can save their descriptions in their portfolios.

L ◆ 93

Properties of Bases

As students examine each item in the visual, ask them to identify compounds that contain hydroxides. *(Sodium hydroxide, calcium hydroxide, magnesium hydroxide)* Explain that compounds that contain hydroxides are almost always basic. Have students rate the bases shown in order of how safe they think they are to handle. Ask: **Are all the bases shown safe to handle with your bare hands? Explain.** *(No; some of the bases shown—such as drain cleaner—are very strong and can burn your skin.)* Point out that several of the bases are described as having functions that oppose the effects of acids. Ask students to identify bases that work with or against acids. *(Samples: Calcium oxide is used to make soil less acidic, antacids are bases that counteract stomach acid.)*
Extend Have students look at recipes for baked goods and identify the bases in the recipes. *(Samples: baking soda, baking powder)* **learning modality: visual**

Addressing Naive Conceptions

Students may be surprised to learn that bases can be just as damaging to the skin as acids. Explain that the slippery feeling people associate with bases can be a sign that a base is breaking down fats in the outer layers of skin. Show students the label from a bottle of drain cleaner. Allow them to read the warning label and encourage them to identify any harm that the cleaner can cause to skin, eyes, or the linings of the nose and throat. **learning modality: verbal**

EXPLORING *Uses of Bases*

The reactions of bases make them valuable raw materials for a range of products.

Bases and food
Baking soda reacts with acids to produce carbon dioxide gas in baked goods. Without these gas bubbles, this delicious variety of breads, biscuits, cakes, and cookies would not be light and fluffy.

Bases in the home
Ammonia solutions are safe to spray with bare hands, but gloves must be worn when working with drain cleaners.

Drain cleaners contain sodium hydroxide (lye).

You can't mistake the odor of household cleaning products made with ammonia.

In solution, bases sometimes look like water, or they may be cloudy white. Strong bases can burn your skin.

Base

Bases and industry
Mortar and cement are manufactured using the bases calcium oxide and calcium hydroxide. Gardeners sometimes add calcium oxide to soil to make the soil less acidic for plants.

Bases and health
Bases such as milk of magnesia (magnesium hydroxide) and calcium carbonate help ease effects of too much stomach acid.

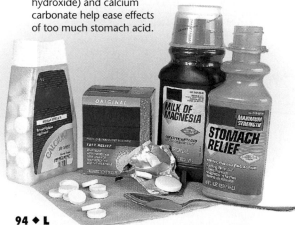

94 ◆ L

Background

Facts and Figures Baking soda has many useful purposes.
◆ Because it is a mild base, baking soda helps dirt and grease to dissolve in water so they can be removed. It is mildly abrasive and can be used as a gentle scouring powder.
◆ Many odors come from strong acids. Baking soda neutralizes acids so it can be used as a deodorant or mouthwash.

◆ Baking soda can be used as an antacid and as a paste on the skin to soothe insect bites.
◆ Heated baking soda releases CO_2 and water. When baking soda is sprinkled on a fire, the CO_2 smothers the fire and the water cools the fire.

Properties of Bases

Bases are another group of compounds that can be identified by their common properties. **A base is a substance that tastes bitter, feels slippery, and turns red litmus paper blue.** Bases often are described as the "opposites" of acids.

Bitter Taste Have you ever tasted tonic water? The slightly bitter taste is caused by the base quinine. Bases taste bitter. Soaps, some shampoos, and detergents are bases. But you wouldn't want to identify them as bases by a taste test.

Slippery Feel Picture yourself washing your hands. You reach for a bar of soap and rub it between your hands underwater. Think about how slippery your hands feel. This slippery feeling is another property of bases. But just as you avoid tasting a substance to identify it, you wouldn't want to touch it. Strong bases can irritate or burn your skin. A safer way to identify bases is by their other properties.

Reactions With Indicators As you might guess, if litmus paper can be used to test acids, it can be used to test bases too. Bases turn red litmus blue. Like acids, bases react with other indicators. But litmus paper gives a reliable, safe test. An easy way to remember which color litmus turns for acids or bases is to remember the letter *b*. **B**ases turn litmus paper **b**lue.

Reactions of Bases Unlike acids, bases don't react with metals or carbonates. At first, you may think it is useless to know that a base doesn't react with certain chemicals. But if you know what a compound *doesn't* do, you know something about it. For example, you know it's not an acid. Another important property of bases is how they react with acids. You will learn more about these reactions in Section 3.

Some Important Bases

Base	Formula
Sodium hydroxide	NaOH
Potassium hydroxide	KOH
Calcium hydroxide	$Ca(OH)_2$
Magnesium hydroxide	$Mg(OH)_2$
Aluminum hydroxide	$Al(OH)_3$
Ammonia	NH_3
Calcium oxide	CaO

Figure 15 The table lists the names and formulas of some common bases.
Predicting What color would any of these compounds turn litmus paper?

Calcium oxide, known as lime or quicklime, is used in building and farming. It is also mixed with sodium oxide to make soda-lime glass, a type of glass that was used widely throughout Europe for several hundred years. Calcium hydroxide, or slaked lime, is used to coat plaster walls so a fresco painted on the wall will adhere securely. **learning modality: verbal**

3 Assess

Section 2 Review Answers

1. Acid turns blue litmus paper red; base turns red litmus paper blue.
2. Acid: sour taste; base: bitter taste
3. Accept any two: Acids are in many foods and household cleaners. Bases can be used to unclog drains, clean windows, or cause bread and biscuits to rise.
4. Tables should include any three of these properties: acids—taste sour, produce hydrogen gas with certain metals, produce carbon dioxide gas with carbonates, turn litmus paper red; bases—taste bitter, feel slippery, do not react with metals or carbonates, turn litmus paper blue.

Check Your Progress **CHAPTER PROJECT 3**

Help students prepare procedures to extract dyes. *(Sample: chop sample, place in blender, add small amount of water; blend until smooth, then strain.)* Students should use the same amount of sample and water for each indicator and clean all equipment between samples.

Section 2 Review

1. How can you use litmus paper to distinguish an acid from a base?
2. How can you tell if a food may contain an acid or a base as one of its ingredients?
3. Name at least two ways that acids and bases are useful around your home.
4. **Thinking Critically Comparing and Contrasting** Make a table that compares at least three properties of acids and bases.

Check Your Progress **CHAPTER PROJECT 3**

Select sources for your indicators. Explore ways to crush each material and squeeze out its juice. You may have to add some water and remove any solid. (*Hint:* Refrigerate any samples you are not going to use immediately.) Write down your procedure and get your teacher's approval before preparing your indicators.

Program Resources

Science Explorer Series *Inside Earth,* Chapter 5
◆ **Teaching Resources** 3-2 Review and Reinforce, p. 79; 3-2 Enrich, p. 80

Answers to Self-Assessment

Caption Question

Figure 15 Any of these compounds would turn litmus paper blue.

Performance Assessment

Skills Check Ask students to classify as an acid or base a material that does not cause an iron bar to bubble and turns red litmus paper blue, and a material that etches a layer of zinc and turns blue litmus paper red. *(base; acid)*

Objectives

After completing the lesson, students will be able to
♦ describe the ions formed when acids and bases are dissolved in water;
♦ describe the pH scale and tell how it is used;
♦ explain what happens in a neutralization reaction.

Key Terms hydrogen ion, hydroxide ion, pH scale, acid rain, neutralization, salt

1 Engage/Explore

Activating Prior Knowledge

Ask students what is used to make lemonade. (*Sugar, water, lemons*) Ask: **Does all lemonade taste the same? Why?** (*No; it can be sweet or sour, weak or strong depending on amounts of ingredients.*) Ask: **What would you do to lemonade that was too sour?** (*Add sugar and maybe water.*)

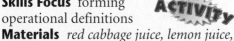
DISCOVER

Skills Focus forming operational definitions
Materials *red cabbage juice, lemon juice, ammonia cleaner, 3 plastic droppers, 3 plastic cups*
Time 15 minutes
Tips To make the cabbage juice, steep red cabbage leaves in hot water for 10 to 20 minutes until the water is a deep red. Discard the leaves. In Steps 3 and 4, lemon juice or ammonia should be added until the solution turns red or green.
Expected Outcome Cabbage juice will look red in an acid and green in a base. It may look light pink, purple, or blue in the transition between these two colors.
Think It Over Acids turn cabbage juice red. Bases turn red cabbage juice yellow, green, or blue depending on how much of them you put in.

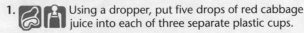
DISCOVER .... ACTIVITY

What Can Cabbage Juice Tell You?

1. Using a dropper, put five drops of red cabbage juice into each of three separate plastic cups.
2. Add 10 drops of lemon juice (an acid) to one cup. Add 10 drops of ammonia cleaner (a base) to another. Keep the third cup for comparison. Record the colors you see.
3. Now add ammonia, one drop at a time, to the cup containing lemon juice. Keep adding ammonia until the color no longer changes. Record all color changes you see.
4. Add lemon juice a drop at a time to the ammonia until the color no longer changes. Record the changes you see.

Think It Over
Forming Operational Definitions
Based on your observations, how could you expand your definitions of acids and bases?

GUIDE FOR READING

♦ What kind of ions do acids and bases form in water?
♦ What does pH tell you about a solution?
♦ What happens in a neutralization reaction?

Reading Tip As you read, write one sentence to summarize the main idea discussed under each heading.

Figure 16 You can find at least one hydrogen atom in the formula of each of these acids.

Acid Formulas	
Name	**Formula**
Hydrochloric acid	HCl
Nitric acid	HNO_3
Sulfuric acid	H_2SO_4
Acetic acid	$HC_2H_3O_2$

A chemist pours hydrochloric acid into a beaker. Then she adds sodium hydroxide to the acid. The mixture looks the same, but the beaker becomes warm. If she tested the solution with litmus paper, what color would the paper turn? Would you be surprised if it did not turn color at all? If *exactly* the right amounts and concentrations of the acid and the base were mixed, the beaker would hold nothing but salt water! How could those two corrosive chemicals produce something harmless to the touch? In this section, you will find the answer.

Acids in Solution

What do acids have in common? Notice that each formula in Figure 16 begins with hydrogen. The acids you will learn about are made of one or more hydrogen ions and a negative ion. A **hydrogen ion (H^+)** is an atom of hydrogen that has lost its electron. The negative ion may be a nonmetal or a polyatomic ion. But hydrogen ions are the key to the reactions of acids.

Acids in water solution separate into hydrogen ions (H^+) and negative ions. In the case of hydrochloric acid, hydrogen ions and chloride ions (Cl^-) form.

$$HCl \xrightarrow{\text{water}} H^+ + Cl^-$$

If another acid were substituted for HCl, the negative ions would be different. But hydrogen ions would be produced in each case.

READING STRATEGIES

Reading Tip Before students read the section, remind them that summarizing involves stating briefly and in their own words the main points and key details. Help students get started by having a volunteer read aloud the information under the first heading. Then work as a class to summarize the main points and key details. Students can use these summaries as guides.

Study and Comprehension Have students preview the section by reading the headings and subheadings, and by looking at the photographs. Encourage students to suggest questions they have about acids and bases in solution and about pH. Write the questions on the board. After students read the section, have them work as a class to answer the questions on the board.

Figure 17 Acids share certain chemical and physical properties when dissolved in water. Most acids are very soluble.

Now you can add to the definition of acids you learned in Section 2. **An acid is any substance that produces hydrogen ions (H^+) in water.** These hydrogen ions cause the properties of acids. For instance, when you add certain metals to an acid, hydrogen ions interact with the metal atoms. One product of the reaction is hydrogen gas (H_2). Hydrogen ions also react with blue litmus paper, turning it red. That's why every acid gives the same litmus test result.

Bases in Solution

The formulas of bases give you clues to what ions they have in common. Look at Figure 18. Many bases are made of metals combined with hydroxide ions. The **hydroxide ion (OH^-)** is a negative ion made of oxygen and hydrogen.

When bases dissolve in water, positive metal ions and hydroxide ions separate. Look, for example, at what happens to sodium hydroxide.

$$NaOH \xrightarrow{water} Na^+ + OH^-$$

Not every base contains hydroxide ions. For example, the gas ammonia (NH_3) does not. But in the solvent water, ammonia is a base that reacts with water to form hydroxide ions.

$$NH_3 + H_2O \rightarrow NH_4^+ + OH^-$$

Notice that in both reactions, there are negative hydroxide ions. These examples give you another way to define a base. **A base is any substance that produces hydroxide ions (OH^-) in water.** Hydroxide ions are responsible for the bitter taste and slippery feel of bases. Hydroxide ions also turn red litmus paper blue.

☑ *Checkpoint* What is a hydroxide ion made of?

Figure 18 Many, but not all, bases dissolve well in water. *Making Generalizations What do all of the base formulas in the table have in common?*

Base Formulas	
Name	**Formula**
Sodium hydroxide	NaOH
Potassium hydroxide	KOH
Calcium hydroxide	Ca(OH)$_2$
Magnesium hydroxide	Mg(OH)$_2$

2 Facilitate

Acids in Solution

Building Inquiry Skills: Applying Concepts

Based on the chemical formulas shown in Figure 16, have students write equations to show how the acid solution separates in water for nitric, sulfuric, and acetic acids. *(Students should show that they separate into positive hydrogen ions and negative ions.)* **learning modality: logical/mathematical**

Bases in Solution

Including All Students

Students who need additional help with vocabulary will benefit from examining the terms *hydroxide* and *polyatomic*. Point out that *hydro-* is a root word for hydrogen and *oxide* means oxygen. Suggest students put the two meanings together to help them remember that a hydroxide ion contains one hydrogen and one oxygen. Then have students find the meanings for *poly-* and *atomic*. Ask: **How can you use the root meanings to understand the word *polyatomic*?** (Poly- *means "more than one" and atomic means "atom," so* polyatomic *means "more than one atom."*) Finally, ask students to define a base using the terms *polyatomic* and *hydroxide*. (*A base is a substance that forms the polyatomic ion hydroxide when dissolved in water.*) **limited English proficiency**

Program Resources

◆ **Teaching Resources** 3-3 Lesson Plan, p. 81; 3-3 Section Summary, p. 82
◆ **Guided Reading and Study Workbook** Section 3-3

Media and Technology

Transparencies "Strong and Weak Acids in Solution," Transparency 14; "pH Scale," Transparency 15

Answers to Self-Assessment

Caption Question
Figure 18 The hydroxide ion
☑ *Checkpoint*
A hydroxide ion is made of oxygen and hydrogen.

Ongoing Assessment

Drawing Have students diagram molecules of hydrogen chloride dissolved in water, then indicate the types of atoms and ions present. Students can save their diagrams in their portfolios.

Strengths of Acids and Bases

Building Inquiry Skills: Making Models

Materials *plastic foam balls of different sizes, modeling clay, toothpicks*
Time 20 minutes

Challenge students to make models of the particles shown in Figure 19. Students can use plastic foam balls or modeling clay, and toothpicks. Ask students to model whole acid particles and dissolved acid particles. Have them arrange the particles first as a weak acid and then as a strong acid. *(Students' models should show that in a weak acid, not all acid molecules form ions. In a strong acid, all molecules form ions.)*
learning modality: kinesthetic

Measuring pH

Skills Focus interpreting data
Materials *variety of household substances, universal pH indicator paper, plastic droppers, plastic cups*
Time 15 minutes
Tips The ranking of substances will depend on the acidity or basicity of a substance as well as its concentration. If students want to test pure water, explain that the chemical in the pH paper is slightly acidic and will indicate that pure water is acidic rather than neutral.
Interpreting Data Sample: Ranked from lowest to highest pH: vinegar, carbonated water, orange juice, coffee/tea, milk, salt, sugar, baking soda solution, antacid. Many students will be surprised by the high acidity of some foods. Lead students to recognize that the lower the pH, the more acidic the substance; and the higher the pH, the more basic.
Extend Have students check the ingredients of various soft drinks, then predict and test whether they are basic or acidic. *(All contain an acid, such as citric or phosphoric, and are acidic.)* **learning modality: logical/mathematical**

Figure 19 In a solution of a strong acid, all the acid molecules break up into ions. In a solution of a weak acid, however, fewer molecules do so.

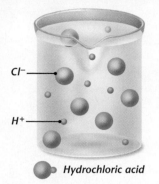
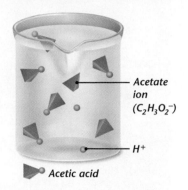

Cl^-

H^+

Hydrochloric acid

Acetate ion ($C_2H_3O_2^-$)

H^+

Acetic acid

pHone Home

Find out the pH of familiar substances in your home.

1. Put on your safety goggles and apron.
2. Select substances such as fruit juices, soda water, coffee, tea, or antacids.
3. Predict which substances are most acidic or most basic.
4. If the sample is solid, dissolve some in a cup of water. Use a liquid as is.
5. Using a plastic dropper, transfer a drop of each sample onto a fresh strip of paper for testing pH.
6. Compare the color of the strip to the pH values on the package.
7. Repeat for all your samples. Remember to rinse the dropper between tests.

Interpreting Data List the samples from lowest to highest pH. Which results, if any, surprised you?

Strengths of Acids and Bases

Acids and bases may be strong or weak. Strength refers to how well an acid or base produces ions in water. With a strong acid, most of the molecules react to form hydrogen ions in solution. With a weak acid, fewer molecules do. At the same concentration, a strong acid produces more hydrogen ions (H^+) than a weak acid does. Examples of strong acids include hydrochloric acid, sulfuric acid, and nitric acid. Most other acids, such as acetic acid, are weak acids.

Strong bases react in a water solution in a similar way to strong acids. A strong base produces more hydroxide ions (OH^-) than does an equal concentration of a weak base. Ammonia is a weak base. Lye, or sodium hydroxide, is a strong base.

Strength determines, in part, how safe acids and bases are to use. For example, all the acids that are safe to eat, such as acetic acid and citric acid, are weak. Ammonia cleaner may irritate your hands slightly if you use it. But the same concentration of drain cleaner, which contains sodium hydroxide, would burn your skin.

People often say that a solution is weak when they mean it is dilute. This could be a dangerous mistake! Even a dilute solution of hydrochloric acid can eat a hole in your clothing or sting your skin. An equal concentration of acetic acid would not.

☑ *Checkpoint* *How would a weak base differ from an equal concentration of a strong base in solution?*

Measuring pH

Knowing the concentration of hydrogen ions is the key to knowing how acidic or basic a solution is. To find out the concentration of ions, chemists use a numeric scale called pH. The **pH scale** is a range of values from 0 to 14. It expresses the concentration of hydrogen ions in a solution.

Background

Facts and Figures Common foods vary considerably in pH, as shown by the following list.

Limes	1.8	String beans	4.6
Lemons	2.2	Carrots	4.9
Grapefruit juice	3	Cottage cheese	5
Dill pickles	3.2	Ground beef	5.1
Raspberries	3.2	Watermelon	5.2
Apples	3.9	Potatoes	6.1
Bananas	4.5	Milk	6.3
		Crackers	7.0
		Eggs	7.1
		Devil's food cake	7.5

Figure 20 shows where some familiar substances fit on the pH scale. Notice that the most acidic substances are at the low end of the scale. At the same time, the most basic substances are at the high end of the scale. You need to remember two important points about pH. **A low pH tells you that the concentration of hydrogen ions is high. By comparison, a high pH tells you that the concentration of hydrogen ions is low.** If you keep these ideas in mind, you can make sense of how the scale works.

You can find the pH of a solution by using indicators. The student in Figure 20 is using indicator paper that turns a different color for each pH value. Matching the color of the paper with the colors on the test scale tells how acidic or basic the solution is. A pH lower than 7 is acidic. A pH higher than 7 is basic. If the pH is 7, the solution is neutral. That means it's neither an acid nor a base. Pure water has a pH of 7.

A concentrated solution of acetic acid can have a lower pH than a dilute solution of hydrochloric acid. In order to handle acids and bases safely, you need to know both their pH and their concentration. Hydrochloric acid is more acidic (has a lower pH) than acetic acid. But a concentrated (strong) solution of acetic acid can have a lower pH than a dilute (weak) solution of hydrochloric acid. To safely handle acids and bases, you need to know the pH of the *solutions* you are using.

Figure 20 The pH scale classifies solutions as acidic or basic. Indicator paper turns a different color for each pH value. *Interpreting Diagrams If a solution has a pH of 9, is it acidic or basic? What can you say about a solution with a pH of 3?*

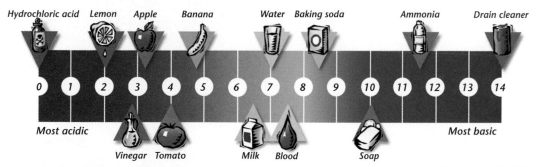

| Hydrochloric acid | Lemon | Apple | Banana | | Water | Baking soda | | Ammonia | | Drain cleaner |

0 1 2 3 4 5 6 7 8 9 10 11 12 13 14

Most acidic   Most basic

Vinegar Tomato   Milk Blood   Soap

Building Inquiry Skills: Predicting

Materials *lemon juice solution (5 drops lemon juice, 10 drops water), ammonia solution (5 drops ammonia, 10 drops water)*
Time 10 minutes

 Students can build on their Discover knowledge by measuring the pH of the lemon juice solution *(about 2)* and the ammonia solution *(around 11)*. Ask: **What do you predict would happen to the pH of each solution if you added 50 drops of water instead of 10 drops?** *(The pH of the lemon juice solution would rise; the pH of the ammonia solution would fall.)* Allow students to test their predictions. **learning modality: logical/mathematical**

Inquiry Challenge

Materials *plastic cup, vinegar, water, plastic dropper, pH indicator paper*
Time 30 minutes

Direct groups to design experiments to find out what effect a change in concentration has on the pH of a vinegar solution. Assign students individual tasks, such as monitoring concentration levels, testing pH, and drawing conclusions. Ask students: **What data should you record?** *(Students should record the number of drops of vinegar in the solution and the corresponding pH.)* Once you approve student designs, allow them to carry out their experiments. When they have finished, ask: **How many drops of vinegar did it take to lower the pH by one unit?** *(Answers will vary depending on the initial concentration of the solution. Have students compare answers with other groups.)* **cooperative learning**

Media and Technology

 Exploring Physical Science Videodisc Unit 2, Side 2, "Food From the 'Hood'"

Chapter 6

Answers to Self-Assessment

Caption Question

Figure 20 A solution with a pH of 9 is basic. A solution with a pH of 3 is acidic.

☑ *Checkpoint*

There would be fewer hydroxide ions in a solution of a weak base than in a solution of an equal concentration of a strong base.

Ongoing Assessment

Skills Check Ask students to explain which solution has more hydrogen ions, one with a pH of 4 or one with a pH of 8. *(4; a lower pH indicates a higher concentration of hydrogen ions)*

Acid Rain

Integrating Environmental Science

Materials *plastic sandwich bags, plastic spoons, soil samples, masking tape, markers, pH paper, distilled water*

ACTIVITY

Time 15 minutes

Instruct student groups to evaluate the acidity of soil samples from your area. Each student should supply a soil sample from a different part of a particular neighborhood, such as near a street or parking lot, from a vegetable garden, or from a vacant lot. Students should place about 3 spoonfuls of soil in a plastic bag and label the bag using masking tape and markers. The label should indicate where the sample came from. Have students add a small amount of distilled water to the soil to make mud, then place a dot of the mud on the pH paper to test the soil. Ask students to infer why samples taken near parking lots or streets may be more acidic than samples taken from less-developed areas. *(Pollution from cars and trucks contributes to the acidity of soil.)*
cooperative learning

Acid-Base Reactions

Building Inquiry Skills: Applying Concepts

Draw students' attention to the chemical equation for the reaction of hydrochloric acid and sodium hydroxide. Ask: **What happens to HCl when it is dissolved in water?** *(It separates into hydrogen and chloride ions.)* Then ask students: **What happens to the NaOH?** *(The sodium and hydroxide ions separate.)* Ask students which ions combine to form water. *(The hydrogen ion from HCl and the hydroxide ion from NaOH combine to form water.)*
learning modality: logical/ mathematical

Figure 21 The trees in this forest show the damaging effects of acid rain.

Acid Rain

Normal rainfall is slightly acidic, with a pH of approximately 5.5.

INTEGRATING ENVIRONMENTAL SCIENCE This acidity comes from carbon dioxide in the air. Carbon dioxide dissolves in rainwater, producing carbonic acid, a weak acid.

$$H_2O + CO_2 \rightarrow H_2CO_3$$

Acid rain is more acidic than normal rainwater. It has a pH as low as 3.5 to 3.0. The extra acidity comes from nitrogen oxides and sulfur oxides. These gases are released into the air as pollutants from industry and motor vehicles. These oxides react with water in the air to produce acids, including nitric acid and sulfuric acid. Rainwater containing these acids has more hydrogen ions. It has a lower pH and is more corrosive. Acid rain can damage statues and buildings, destroy forests, and kill fishes in lakes.

Acid-Base Reactions

The story at the start of this section describes a chemist who mixed hydrochloric acid with sodium hydroxide. She got a solution of table salt (sodium chloride) and water.

$$HCl + NaOH \rightarrow H_2O + Na^+ + Cl^-$$

If you tested the pH of the mixture, it would be close to 7, or neutral. In fact, a reaction between an acid and a base is called a **neutralization** (noo truh lih ZAY shun). As a result of neutralization, an acid-base mixture is not as acidic or basic as the individual starting solutions were.

Sometimes an acid-base reaction results in a neutral solution, with a pH of 7. But not always. The final pH depends on which acid and base react, how much of each is used, and what their concentrations are. If a small amount of a strong acid is added to a larger amount of strong base, what would be the pH of the mixture? Common sense tells you it would be higher than 7, still somewhat basic.

Figure 22 The solution on the left is acidic. The solution on the right is basic. When mixed, these solutions produced the neutral solution in the center. *Interpreting Photos What tells you if the solution is an acid, a base, or neutral?*

Acidic   Neutral   Basic

Background

Integrating Science When soil becomes too acidic, agriculturists can add a basic compound to the soil to "sweeten" it—to raise its pH. This process is called "liming" because it often involves compounds made of limestone. Ground limestone, powdered oyster shells, and pulverized chalk can all be used to counteract acidic soils.

Program Resources

Science Explorer Series *Environmental Science*, Chapter 5
◆ **Teaching Resources** 3-3 Review and Reinforce, p. 83; 3-3 Enrich, p. 84

Some Salts and Their Uses

Salt	Formula	Uses
Sodium chloride	NaCl	Food flavoring; preservative
Potassium iodide	KI	Additive in "iodized" salt that prevents iodine deficiency (goiter)
Calcium chloride	CaCl₂	De-icer for roads and walkways
Potassium chloride	KCl	Salt substitute in foods
Calcium carbonate	CaCO₃	Found in limestone and seashells
Ammonium nitrate	NH₄NO₃	Fertilizer; active ingredient in some cold packs

Figure 23 Each salt listed in this table can be formed by the reaction between an acid and a base.

Products of Acid-Base Reactions

"Salt" may be the familiar name of the stuff you sprinkle on food. But to a chemist, the word refers to a specific group of compounds. A **salt** is any ionic compound made from the neutralization of an acid with a base. A salt is made from the positive ion of a base and the negative ion of an acid. Look at the equation for the reaction of nitric acid with potassium hydroxide.

$$HNO_3 + KOH \rightarrow H_2O + K^+ + NO_3^-$$

One product of the reaction is water. The other product is potassium nitrate (KNO_3), a salt. Potassium nitrate is written in the equation as separate K^+ and NO_3^- ions because it is soluble in water. **A neutralization reaction produces water and a salt.** Some salts, such as potassium nitrate, are soluble. Others form precipitates because they are insoluble.

Figure 24 These salt flats were left behind in Death Valley, California, when the water in which the salts were dissolved evaporated.

Section 3 Review

1. What ions would you expect to find when an acid dissolves in water? What ions would you expect to find when a base dissolves in water?
2. If the pH of a solution is 6, would you expect to find more or fewer hydrogen ions (H⁺) than in a solution with a pH of 3? Explain why.
3. What does the term *salt* mean to a chemist, and how may a salt form?
4. **Thinking Critically Predicting** What salt would form from a reaction between hydrochloric acid, or HCl, and calcium hydroxide, or Ca(OH)₂? Explain your answer.

Check Your Progress

CHAPTER PROJECT 3

Use each indicator to test for acids and bases in familiar substances. For example, try vinegar, household ammonia, lemon juice, milk, and soapy water. (*Hint:* Use small amounts of indicator and test samples. Watch for a color change, especially where the sample comes in contact with the indicator. If you do not see any change, add a few more drops of the sample.) Summarize your results in a table.

Chapter 3 **L ◆ 101**

Answers to Self-Assessment

Caption Question

Figure 22 The color of the solution when an acid-base indicator is present

Products of Acid-Base Reactions

Building Inquiry Skills: Predicting

Ask students to predict the pH of a solution of table salt in pure water. *(pH 7)* Have students explain their predictions. *(pH 7 is neutral; both pure water and salt are neutral.)* If possible, allow students to test their predictions.
learning modality: logical/ mathematical

3 Assess

Section 3 Review Answers

1. Acid—hydrogen ions, negative ions; base—hydroxide ions, positive ions
2. Fewer. The more basic the solution, the lower the concentration of hydrogen ions.
3. An ionic compound; it forms from the neutralization of an acid with a base.
4. Calcium chloride (CaCl₂). Since calcium (from the base) has a charge of 2+, it reacts with two chloride ions (from the acid), with a charge of 1− each.

Check Your Progress

CHAPTER PROJECT 3

Students should test an assigned number of substances. Have them test the same substances with different indicators and compare results at the end. Students' data tables should include the indicator source, substance tested, and color of the indicator before and after it was used.

Performance Assessment

Writing Have students briefly describe the chemical reaction that takes place when an acid solution and a base solution are mixed together. (*Students should describe a reaction in which the positive ion of the base and the negative ion of the acid combine to form a salt. The result of a neutralization reaction is water and a salt.*)

L ◆ 101

Polymer Profiles

Polymers vary greatly in their appearance, properties, and uses. In this chapter, students learn to identify polymers and describe their usefulness.

Purpose In this project, students identify polymers at home, at school, and in other areas of their surroundings. They compare different polymers in order to examine how the properties of these polymers are related to their applications.

Skills Focus After completing the Chapter 4 project, students will be able to

◆ classify a variety of materials as polymers;
◆ design experiments to test different properties of polymers;
◆ compare and contrast the characteristics and functions of different polymers;
◆ communicate their findings about polymers to their classmates.

Project Time Line This project will take approximately two weeks to complete. Students should begin with a discussion of the properties of polymers and ways in which they can test these properties. Allow three or four days for students to collect polymers from different locations. At the same time, students should write procedures for testing at least three properties of each polymer. Students should clearly identify the properties they will study, such as hardness, strength, density, elasticity, or solubility. Allow three days for students to conduct several trials of each experiment. For the final two days, students should analyze their results and relate polymer characteristics to function. Before beginning the project, see Chapter 4 Project Teacher Notes on pages 94–95 in Teaching Resources for more details on carrying out the project. Also distribute to students the Chapter 4 Project Overview, Worksheets, and Scoring Rubric on pages 96–99 in Teaching Resources.

Possible Materials Provide polymer samples or encourage students to find small samples of polymers to test. There are many natural and synthetic polymers

WEB ACTIVITY www.phschool.com

Integrating Technology

SECTION 1 **Polymers and Composites**

Discover **What Did You Make?**
Sharpen Your Skills **Classifying**
Real-World Lab **Packaging With Polymers**

SECTION 2 **Metals and Alloys**

Discover **Are They Steel the Same?**

SECTION 3 **Ceramics and Glass**

Discover **Does It Get Wet?**
Try This **A Bright Idea**

that have different mechanical, chemical, and biological properties. Examples include

◆ low-density polyethylene—garbage bags, disposable diapers
◆ high-density polyethylene—milk jugs, shampoo bottles, motor oil bottles
◆ polypropylene—bags for snack foods, plastic buckets
◆ PVC (polyvinyl chloride)—plumbing pipe, swimming pool liners, shower curtains, siding, garden hose
◆ polystyrene—plastic foam packing materials, hot drink cups, plastic disposable utensils
◆ silk, wool
◆ cellulose—cotton balls, cotton cloth, paper
◆ xanthan gum—food additive
◆ collagen—gelatin, animal hides, shampoo ingredient
◆ keratin—fingernails, hair

Other commonly available polymers include those used to produce soda bottles, nylon stockings, polyester cloth, hard contact lenses, car upholstery and trim, and many other materials. Also include the materials students

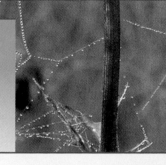

PROJECT 4

Polymer Profiles

A spider's delicate web glistens in the early morning sunshine. It was spun overnight from silken fibers produced by the spider's body. These fibers, much of the spider itself, and the flower stems that support the web are made from polymers—one of the types of materials you will study in this chapter. In your project, you will survey different polymers found around you. You will learn about the properties of these materials and see how their uses depend on their properties.

Your Goal To collect and investigate different polymers.

To complete your project you must
- collect at least eight polymer samples from at least three different locations
- identify the chemical and physical properties of the polymers by performing at least three tests
- create an informative display about these polymers
- follow the safety guidelines in Appendix A

Get Started Brainstorm with your classmates what you already know about polymers. Make a list of items you think are made of polymers. Look in Section 1 to get some hints about materials to investigate. Begin to think about how different polymers are used in everyday life, and why.

Check Your Progress You will be working on this project as you study this chapter. To keep your project on track, look for Check Your Progress boxes at the following points.
Section 1 Review, page 119: Collect samples of polymers and record data about their sources and uses.
Section 3 Review, page 132: Devise procedures to test properties of the polymers.
Section 4 Review, page 139: Carry out your tests and organize your results in your data table.

Wrap Up At the end of the chapter (page 143), you will present a showcase of polymers to the class.

SECTION 4 Radioactive Elements

Discover **How Much Goes Away?**
Sharpen Your Skills **Predicting**
Sharpen Your Skills **Calculating**
Skills Lab **That's Half-Life!**

This spider's web and the mountain thistle stems that support it are made of natural polymers.

L ◆ 111

Program Resources

- **Teaching Resources** Chapter 4 Project Teacher Notes, pp. 94–95; Chapter 4 Project Overview and Worksheets, pp. 96–99; Chapter 4 Project Scoring Rubric, p. 100

Media and Technology

 Audio CDs and **Audiotapes**
English-Spanish Section Summaries

 **WEB ACTIVITY** www.phschool.com

You will find an Internet activity, chapter self-tests for students, and links to other chapter topics at this site.

will need to test their chosen properties. For example, to study strength, students will need to apply weight to each sample. To study density, they will need to find the mass and volume of each sample.

Launching the Project Lead a class discussion about the properties of polymers. Show students several objects made from polymers in the list under Possible Materials. Ask students to describe what they know about each polymer and to explain why it is used to make that object. Ask: **What other materials could these objects be made of? What properties do these materials have that make them more suitable for making these objects?**

Allow time for students to read the description of the project in their text and the Chapter Project Overview on pages 96–97 in Teaching Resources. Then encourage discussions on types of polymers and their properties. Have groups of students brainstorm lists of natural and synthetic polymers and list the properties the polymers share. Answer any initial questions students may have. Allow time for students to review the Chapter 4 Project Worksheets on pages 98–99 in Teaching Resources.

Performance Assessment

The Chapter 4 Project Scoring Rubric on page 100 of Teaching Resources will help you evaluate how well students complete the Chapter 4 Project. Students will be assessed on
- how well they identify polymers based on their understanding of the nature of polymers;
- the thoroughness of their written procedures and experimental designs;
- the completeness of their data tables, including outcomes of their experiments, categorization of similar polymers, and applications of these polymers;
- the thoroughness and organization of their final displays.

By sharing the Chapter 4 Scoring Rubric with students at the beginning of the project, you will make it clear to them what they are expected to do.

Natural Polymers

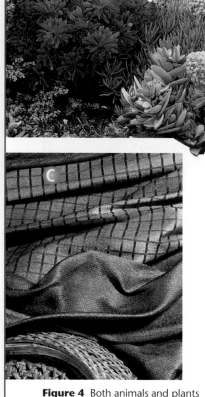

Figure 4 Both animals and plants make polymers. **A.** The leaves and stems of these desert plants are made of cellulose and other polymers. **B.** A cotton plant is a source of polymers that people make into thread and cloth. **C.** These silk fabrics were made from the threads of silkworm cocoons. *Comparing and Contrasting What do the polymers shown in these photos have in common?*

Natural Polymers

INTEGRATING LIFE SCIENCE Polymers have been around as long as life on Earth. Plants, animals, and other living things produce the polymers they need from nutrients and other materials in the environment.

Plant Polymers Look closely at a piece of coarse paper, such as a paper towel. You can see that it is made of long strings, or fibers. These fibers are bundles of cellulose. **Cellulose** (SEL yoo lohs) is a flexible but strong natural polymer that gives shape to plant cells. Cellulose is made in plants when sugar molecules (made earlier from carbon dioxide and water) are joined into long strands. The cellulose then forms cell structures.

Animal Polymers Gently touch a spider web and feel how it stretches without breaking. It is made from chemicals in the spider's body. These chemicals mix and react to form a silken polymer that is one of the strongest materials known. Spiders spin webs, egg cases, and traps for prey from these fibers. You can wear polymers made by animals. Silk is made from the fibers of silkworm cocoons. Wool is made from sheep's fur. These polymers can be woven into thread and cloth.

Your own body makes polymers. Tap your fingernail on a tabletop. Your fingernails and the muscles that just moved your finger are made of proteins. Proteins are polymers. Within your body, proteins are assembled from combinations of smaller molecules (monomers) called amino acids. The properties of a protein depend on which amino acids are used and in what order. One combination builds the protein that forms your fingernails. Another combination forms the protein that carries oxygen in your blood. Yet another forms the hair that grows on your head.

✓ Checkpoint *What are two examples of natural polymers from plants and animals?*

Synthetic Polymers

Many polymers you use every day are synthesized from simpler materials. Recall that a synthesis reaction occurs when elements or simple compounds combine to form complex compounds. The starting materials for polymers come from coal or oil. **Plastics,** which are synthetic polymers that can be molded or shaped, are the most common products. But there are many others. Carpets, clothing, glue, and even chewing gum can be made of synthetic polymers.

Figure 5 lists just a few of the hundreds of polymers people use. Although the names seem like tongue-twisters, see how many you recognize. You may be able to identify some polymers by their initials printed on the bottoms of plastic bottles.

Compare the uses of polymers listed in Figure 5 with their properties. Notice that many products require materials that are flexible, yet strong. Others must be hard or lightweight. When chemical engineers develop a new product, they have to think about how it will be used. Then they synthesize a polymer with properties to match.

Synthetic polymers are often used in place of natural materials that are too expensive or wear out too quickly. Polyester and nylon fabrics, for example, are used instead of wool, silk, and cotton to make clothes. Laminated countertops and vinyl floors replace wood in many kitchens. Other synthetic polymers have uses for which there is no suitable natural material. Compact discs, computer parts, artificial heart valves, and even bicycle tires couldn't exist without synthetic polymers.

Figure 5 You can find many synthetic polymers in your own home.

Some Synthetic Polymers You Use

Name	Properties	Uses
Low-density polyethylene (LDPE)	Flexible, soft, melts easily	Plastic bags, squeeze bottles, electric wire insulation
High-density polyethylene (HDPE)	Stronger than LDPE; higher melting temperatures	Detergent bottles, gas cans, toys, milk jugs
Polypropylene (PP)	Hard, keeps its shape	Toys, car parts, bottle caps
Polyvinyl chloride (PVC)	Tough, flexible	Garden hoses, imitation leather, piping
Polystyrene (PS)	Lightweight, can be made into foam	Foam drinking cups, insulation, furniture, "peanut" packing material
Nylon	Strong, can be drawn into flexible thread	Stockings, parachutes, fishing line, fabric
Teflon (polytetrafluoroethylene)	Nonreactive, low friction	Nonstick coating for cooking pans

---

Language Arts
CONNECTION

Many words in the English language use prefixes from Greek or Latin. In Greek, *mono-* means "one" and *poly-* means "many." These prefixes tell you that the molecules are made of either one or many parts.

In Your Journal

Make a list of words with other prefixes that tell you "how many," for example, the *tri-* in *triangle.* Tell what number the prefix indicates. Extend your list to include units of measurement, such as the millimeter. In each case, tell what information the prefix gives.

Synthetic Polymers

Real-Life Learning

Materials *empty milk jug, PVC pipe*
Time 10 minutes

Have students examine the jug and pipe. Ask: **What makes the plastic used in the milk jug different from the plastic used in the pipe?** (*The plastic in the jug is flexible and thin; the plastic in the pipe is rigid and strong.*) Have students look for markings on the milk jug that identify its composition. Encourage students to think of other applications for each plastic. Have students look for markings on other types of plastics (especially containers of food and household products), then identify and list the types of polymers used to make the items.
learning modality: kinesthetic

Portfolio Students can save their lists in their portfolios.

Language Arts
CONNECTION

Remind students that a prefix comes at the beginning of a word and modifies its meaning. Many science terms have prefixes. For example, the Precambrian era came before the Cambrian era; the prefix *pre-* means "before."

In Your Journal
Students may list such words as *polygon (many), monopoly (one), trio (three), duet (two), bifocal (two), quadrangle (four), quintet (five), septuplets (seven), decade (ten), unicycle (one),* and *century (100).* Measurement prefixes may include *centi- (hundredth), milli- (thousandth), mega- (million),* and *kilo- (thousand).* **limited English proficiency**

Media and Technology

 Transparencies "Building a Polymer," Transparency 16

 Exploring Physical Science Videodisc
Unit 2, Side 2, "Petroleum"
Chapter 7

Answers to Self-Assessment

Caption Question
Figure 4 They are made up of carbon compounds. Their molecules are made of repeating patterns of smaller molecules linked together.

✓ *Checkpoint*
Cellulose and spider webs

Ongoing Assessment

Skills Check Have students identify a characteristic that synthetic and natural polymers share. (*All polymers are made of large molecules composed of smaller molecules.*)

L ◆ 115

Synthetic Polymers, continued

After students have thoroughly examined the time line, ask: **Which materials in the time line were developed as improvements on natural substances?** *(Celluloid, synthetic rubber)* Write the headings *Strong, Flexible,* and *Lightweight* on the board. Have students identify the polymers with these properties, then list them under the headings. *(Most polymers fit more than one category.)* Help students come to the conclusion that polymers are so widely used because they have more than one useful property.

Extend Challenge students to research current uses for the polymers in the time line.

In Your Journal Remind students that good newspaper articles answer the questions: *Who? What? Why? When? Where?* and *How?* Encourage students to use these questions as a guide when they complete their paragraphs. Provide reference books with additional information for students who would like to do further research on the inventions.
learning modality: verbal

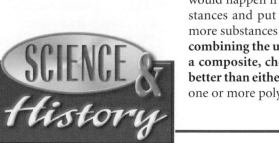

Composites

Every substance has its advantages and disadvantages. What would happen if you could take the best properties of two substances and put them together? **Composites** combine two or more substances as a new material with different properties. **By combining the useful properties of two or more substances in a composite, chemists can make a new material that works better than either one alone.** Many composite materials include one or more polymers.

The Development of Polymers

The first synthetic polymers were made by changing natural polymers in some way. Later, crude oil and coal became the starting materials. Now new polymers are designed in laboratories every year.

1869 Celluloid
Made using cellulose, celluloid became a substitute for ivory in billiard balls and combs and brushes. It was later used to make movie film. Because celluloid is very flammable, other materials have replaced it for almost all purposes, except table-tennis balls.

1825   **1875**

1839 Synthetic Rubber
Charles Goodyear invented a process that turned natural rubber into a hard, stretchable polymer. It did not get sticky and soft when heated or become brittle when cold, as natural rubber does. Bicycle tires were an early use.

116 ◆ L

1909 Bakelite
Bakelite was the first commercial polymer made from compounds in coal tar. Bakelite doesn't get soft when heated, and it doesn't conduct electricity. These properties made it useful for handles for pots and pans, telephones, and for parts in electrical outlets.

Background

History of Science In 1834, Charles Goodyear tried to discover a way to make natural rubber hard, yet flexible, at all temperatures. While in prison for debt, he experimented with raw rubber and a rolling pin. Later, he, his wife, and their small children made up several hundred pairs of rubber overshoes, but the shoes melted before he could sell them. Goodyear and his family became so destitute that they had to live in an abandoned rubber factory. Even after he discovered and patented vulcanization by heating rubber and sulfur, legal battles and pressing debt led to the loss of his patents. Goodyear died $200,000 in debt. He did not even get to name his discovery. Vulcanization was reinvented in England in 1843 before Goodyear patented it in that country. A friend of the English inventor named it after Vulcan, the Roman god of fire.

A Natural Composite The idea of putting two different materials together to get the advantages of both comes from the natural world. Many synthetic composites are designed to imitate a common natural composite—wood. Wood is made of long fibers of cellulose, held together by another plant polymer called lignin. Cellulose fibers are flexible and can't support much weight. At the same time, lignin is brittle and would crack under the weight of the tree branches. But the combination of the two polymers makes a strong tree trunk.

In Your Journal

Find out more about the invention of one of these polymers. Write a headline for a newspaper, announcing the invention. Then write the first paragraph of the news article telling how the invention will change people's lives.

1989 LEP

Light-emitting polymers (LEP) are plastics that give off light when exposed to low-voltage electricity. Research on LEPs points toward their use as flexible and more easy-to-read viewing screens in computers, digital camera monitors, watch-sized phones, and televisions.

1934 Nylon

A giant breakthrough came with a synthetic fiber that imitates silk. Nylon replaced expensive silk in women's stockings and fabric for parachutes and clothing. It can also be molded to make objects like buttons, gears, and zippers.

1925	1975	2025

1952 Fiberglass Composite

Fiberglass is mixed with polymers to form a material with the strength of glass fibers and the moldability of plastic. Fiberglass composite is useful for boat and airplane parts because it is much lighter than metal, and it doesn't rust.

1971 Kevlar

Kevlar is five times as strong as the same weight of steel. This polymer is tough enough to substitute for steel ropes and cables in offshore oil-drilling rigs, but light enough to use in spacecraft parts. Kevlar is also used in protective clothing for firefighters and police officers.

Chapter 4   **L ◆ 117**

Addressing Naive Conceptions

Students may confuse composites with compounds because both are materials with unique properties formed when two or more substances combine, and the words have similar sounds. Inform students that in composites, the individual components are still present and retain their original characteristics. Composites are formed by physical processes and the chemical compositions of the materials are not changed. Ask students: **How is this different from what happens when a compound is formed?** (*When a compound is formed, the materials react chemically to create a substance with different chemical composition and properties.*) **learning modality: verbal**

Building Inquiry Skills: Making Models

Materials *school glue, kite string, paper towels*
Time 10 minutes, plus 30 minutes drying time

ACTIVITY

Direct students to model a natural composite such as wood by designing a composite made from string and glue. Begin by having students list the properties of kite string and glue. Then ask: **What does the kite string represent in the model?** (*Cellulose fibers*) Have students assemble their composites by gluing pieces of kite string into bundles. After the bundles have dried, have students list the properties of their composites. Conclude the activity by asking: **How did the properties of the composite differ from the properties of the kite string?** (*The composite is stiff and strong. The kite string is flexible and cannot stand up on its own.*) **learning modality: kinesthetic**

Ongoing Assessment

Oral Presentation Have students choose one composite or one synthetic polymer and describe how it has made a difference in their everyday lives. (*Sample: Without synthetic rubber, it would be difficult to ride a bike.*)

Composites, continued

Physical Education Connection

Ask students to infer some specific advantages of using synthetic polymer composites in sports equipment such as bicycles, skateboards, and tennis racquets. For example, ask: **What advantage does a racer have riding a light-weight bicycle?** (*It requires less energy to move a lightweight bicycle, so racers can use their energy to pedal faster.*) **learning modality: logical/ mathematical**

Too Many Polymers?

Sharpen your *Skills*

Classifying

Materials *classroom items, clothing*

 ACTIVITY

Time 10 minutes

Tips Students may have difficulty identifying natural polymers. Point out that wool and cotton fabrics contain natural polymers. Make sure students understand how to find the percent of items not made from polymers by dividing the number of nonpolymer items by the total number of items and multiplying the answer by 100.

Extend Have students prepare circle graphs displaying their results. Students can divide their graphs into items made completely or partly of natural polymers and completely or partly of synthetic polymers.

Integrating Environmental Science

Have students brainstorm a list of ways that plastic waste can be reduced at school or in their homes. Students may be familiar with the slogan "Reduce, Reuse, Recycle." Ask: **What are some ways to take advantage of the special characteristics of plastics without contributing to problems caused by too much waste?** (*Sample: Reuse plastic items such as sealable sandwich bags and carrier bags instead of throwing them away.*) **learning modality: verbal**

Figure 6 Fiberglass makes a snowboard (left) both lightweight and strong. The composites in a fishing rod (right) make it so flexible that it will not break when pulling in a large fish.

Sharpen your Skills

Classifying **ACTIVITY**

Sit or stand where you have a clear view of the room you are in. Slowly sweep the room with your eyes, making a list of the objects you see. Do the same sweep of the clothes you are wearing. Check off those items on your list made (completely or partly) of natural or synthetic polymers. What percent of the items were *not* made with polymers?

Synthetic Composites The idea of combining the properties of two substances to make a more useful one has led to many new products. Fiberglass composites are one example. Strands of glass fiber are woven together and strengthened with a liquid plastic that sets like glue. The combination makes a strong, hard solid that may be molded around a form to give it shape. These composites are lightweight, but strong enough to be used as a boat hull or car body. Fiberglass also resists corrosion. It will not rust as metal does.

Other composites made from strong polymers combined with lightweight ones have many uses. Bicycles, automobiles, and airplanes built from such composites are much lighter than the same vehicles built from steel or aluminum. Some composites are used to make fishing rods, tennis racquets, and other sports equipment that need to be flexible but strong.

Too Many Polymers?

INTEGRATING ENVIRONMENTAL SCIENCE It is difficult to look around without seeing something made of synthetic polymers. They have replaced many natural materials for several reasons. First, polymers are inexpensive to make. Second, they are strong. Finally, they last a long time.

But synthetic polymers have caused some problems, too. Many of the disadvantages of using plastics come from the same properties that make them so useful. It is often cheaper to throw away plastic materials and make new ones than it is to reuse them. As a result, they increase the volume of trash. Most plastics don't

---

Background

Facts and Figures What products are made from recycled plastic?

Plastic	First Use	Second Use
LDPE	grocery bags	flower pots, wrapping film
HDPE	milk jugs	flower pots, pipes, toys, buckets, trash cans, sign posts
PVC	garden hoses	traffic cones, plastic pipes
PP	bottle caps, car battery casings	flower pots, car battery casings
PS	foam cups, packing material	insulation, foam packaging "peanuts," videocassette covers
PETE	soda bottles	fiber filling for pillows, jackets, sleeping bags; floor tiles; carpet backing; tool handles; auto parts

react very easily with other chemical compounds. This means they don't break down into simpler materials in the environment. In contrast, natural polymers do. Some plastics are expected to last thousands of years. How do you get rid of something that lasts that long?

Is there a way to solve these problems? One solution is to use waste plastics as raw material for making new plastic products. You know this idea as recycling. Recycling has led to industries that create new products from discarded plastics. Bottles, fabrics for clothing, and parts for new cars are just some of the many items that can come from waste plastics. A pile of empty soda bottles can even be turned into synthetic wood. Look around your neighborhood. You may see park benches or "wooden" fences made from recycled plastics. Through recycling, the disposal problem is eased and new, useful items are created.

Figure 7 These rulers are just one product made from recycled plastic bottles.
Drawing Conclusions What would have happened to these bottles if they weren't recycled?

 Section 1 Review

1. How are monomers related to polymers?
2. What advantage does a composite have over the individual materials from which it is made?
3. Why is it possible for carbon to form so many different kinds of compounds?
4. Make a list of polymers you can find in your home. Classify them as natural or synthetic.
5. **Thinking Critically Making Judgments** Think of something plastic that you have used today. Is there some other material that would be better than plastic for this use?

Check Your Progress | CHAPTER PROJECT 4
Collect a variety of different polymers. You might look in tool chests, kitchen cabinets, closets or drawers, art classrooms, hardware stores, or outdoors. Be sure to record where you found the polymer and what its function is. Record any information on labels or packaging. Try to identify each polymer as natural or synthetic. Organize this information into a list.

Chapter 4 **L ◆ 119**

Program Resources

◆ **Teaching Resources** 4-1 Review and Reinforce, p. 103; 4-1 Enrich, p. 104
◆ **Integrated Science Laboratory Manual** L-4, "Separating Plastics"

Answers to Self-Assessment

Caption Question

Figure 7 If the bottles were not recycled, they would have increased the volume of trash in a landfill.

3 *Assess*

Section 1 Review Answers

1. Monomers are the smaller molecules that are linked together to build polymers.
2. A composite combines the desirable properties of the individual materials from which it is made; this leads to a more useful material.
3. Carbon can form many compounds because carbon atoms can form four covalent bonds and connect to each other and to other kinds of atoms in chains, branches, and rings.
4. Answers will vary. Students' lists should include both natural polymers such as wool, hair, cellulose, and silk and synthetic polymers such as plastic foam, nylon, plastic food containers, and toys.
5. Sample: A cloth bag could replace a plastic grocery bag.

Check Your Progress | CHAPTER PROJECT 4
To help students collect and identify their samples, provide specific examples of polymers (such as rubber bands, plastic bags, plastic milk or juice containers, paper, and wood) and materials that are not polymers (such as rocks, metal soda cans, glass jars, sugar, and salt). Encourage students to compare the information on labels or packaging to the table in Figure 5 and to the polymers mentioned in the text.

Performance Assessment

Organizing Information Have students create compare/contrast tables to list the advantages and disadvantages of using synthetic polymers and composites.
 Students can save their tables in their portfolios.

L ◆ 119

Packaging With Polymers

Preparing for Inquiry

Key Concept Both natural and synthetic packing materials are made from polymers. These materials vary in their ability to provide the cushioning that protects breakable items during shipping.

Skills Objectives Students will be able to
- design an experiment for each property being tested;
- control variables and conduct several tests on each material;
- draw conclusions based on their observations of the results of the experiments.

Time 45 minutes

Advance Planning
- Obtain samples of at least four different polymers used in packaging. Have a small supply of each sample available for each lab group.
- To save time, assign one of the properties to be tested to each group.

Alternative Materials
- Save plastic foam and Ecofoam "peanuts." Plastic foam is polystyrene that has been "puffed up" with air. Ecofoam is water soluble because it is made from corn starch.
- Save scrap paper and polyolefin envelopes.
- Cardboard, fabric, popcorn (popped), sawdust, wood shavings, and plastic could also be tested.

Guiding Inquiry

Invitation Ask students what factors need to be taken into account when choosing a packaging material. *(Strength, resistance to tearing, and cushioning)* Invite them to imagine they are running a mail-order catalog company. Ask: **What factors would you consider in selecting packaging materials for your business?** *(Cost, cushioning, weight, resistance to pests, effect on the environment)*

Packaging With Polymers

You need to mail some breakable items to a friend. There are a variety of different polymer materials that you could use to package these items. In this lab, you will design an experiment to find out more about these materials. Then you will decide which one you would use.

Problem

Which polymer material should you choose for packaging?

Skills Focus

designing experiments, controlling variables, drawing conclusions

Materials

water	hand lens	weights (or books)
scissors	tape	thermometers
balance	clock or timer	

containers (beakers, trays, plastic cups)
iodine solution, 1% solution
hard-boiled eggs (optional)
polymers used in packaging (paper, Tyvek, plastic foam, ecofoam, cardboard, fabric, popcorn, sawdust, wood shavings, or plastic)

Procedure

1. Write a hypothesis about the ideal properties a polymer should have if it is to be used for packaging.
2. Make a list of all the ways you can think of to test the properties of polymers. Think about properties including, but not limited to, the following:
   - ability to protect a fragile object
   - reaction to water ◆ appearance
   - heat insulation ◆ strength
   - reaction to iodine ◆ mass

   (*Note:* Iodine turns a dark blue-black color when starch is present. Starch may attract insects or other pests.)

DATA TABLE

	Brief Description of Test 1	Brief Description of Test 2	Brief Description of Test 3	Brief Description of Test 4
Polymer A				
Polymer B				
Polymer C				

Sample Data Table

	Examine With Hand Lens	Expose to Water	Attempt to Tear	Test Ability to Cushion	Treat With Iodine
Paper	visible fibers	becomes very weak	tears easily	no cushioning	turns blue-black
Tyvek	visible criss-crossing of fibers	repels water	difficult to tear	no cushioning	no change
Ecofoam	answers will vary	dissolves	tears fairly easily	cushions well	turns blue-black
Plastic foam	answers will vary	no change	tears easily	cushions well	no change

3. Select a property you wish to test. Choose a method that you think would be the best way to test that property.
4. Design a step-by-step procedure for the test. Do the same for each of the other properties you decide to investigate. Be sure that you change only one variable at a time. Include any safety directions in your procedure.
5. Predict which polymers you think will perform best in each test you plan.
6. After your teacher has approved your procedure, perform the tests on a sample of each polymer.
7. Record your observations in a table similar to the one on the left.

Analyze and Conclude

1. Describe the similarities and differences that you discovered among your samples.
2. Review the different tests that you used. Which worked well? Are there any tests you would do differently if you were to do them another time?

3. Which polymer would you use to package your items for mailing? Explain your reasons for this choice.
4. Which polymer would you not want to use? Why?
5. **Apply** Tyvek costs more than paper. Ecofoam costs more than plastic foam. How would this information influence your decision on which material to use?

Design an Experiment

A vending machine must be able to drop a cookie a distance of 1.5 m without breaking it. Design an experiment to determine how you could make a package that is strong, cheap, and environmentally friendly. With your teacher's approval, perform the experiment.

 L ◆ 121

Safety

Remind students to wear safety goggles and aprons throughout the activity. They should use heat-resistant gloves when testing heat insulation properties. Caution students to take care using the iodine solution, as it is toxic and will also stain skin and clothing. Review the safety guidelines in Appendix A.

Program Resources

◆ **Teaching Resources** Real-World Lab blackline masters, pp. 117–119

Media and Technology

Lab Activity Videotape
Chemical Interactions, 7

Helping Design a Plan

Let students brainstorm ideas for tests that would determine to what extent the material has a certain property. Check students' plans for safety. Flammability should not be tested. Ask: **How could you determine whether the material is weatherproof? How could you test how strong it is? Are any of the materials better for the environment?**

Troubleshooting the Experiment

◆ Students may want to try additional tests. Evaluate procedures for safety before allowing students to proceed.
◆ Guide students in controlling variables. Emphasize that only one property and one polymer should be tested at a time.
◆ Advise students to set up the heat insulation test first. Other tests may be performed while they wait for the time to pass until a second temperature measurement is taken.

Expected Outcome

Students should use the results of their tests to rank the polymers according to the properties that make them suitable for packaging.

Analyze and Conclude

1. Students should use their test results to compare the different materials.
2. Students should analyze each test they performed and describe how well it worked. They should suggest improvements to their procedures.
3. Sample: Tyvek is water repellent and strong; it would keep the package dry. Ecofoam has good cushioning properties and is water soluble. This reduces the quantity of solid waste produced.
4. Sample: Popcorn would attract insects and other animals. Plastic foam is environmentally unfriendly.
5. Answers will vary. In business, the cost of supplies must be considered. However, students may think that the advantages of these materials are worth the extra cost.

Extending the Inquiry

Design an Experiment Check students' procedures to make sure they are safe. Make sure that tests will address the problem. Remind students that the package will have to be small and economical, as well as environmentally friendly.

Grocery Bags: Paper or Plastic?

Purpose

Whether consumers choose paper or plastic bags to carry their purchases, there are economic and environmental issues involved. Students will identify the issues and debate the merits of using each type of bag.

Debate

Time one class period for research and preparation, 30 minutes to conduct the debate

◆ Explain to students that they will be debating the pros and cons of using paper or plastic bags.

◆ Organize the class into four groups: two to support the use of paper bags, the other two to support the use of plastic bags. Have groups review and investigate the issue from their respective points of view. Remind them to examine the long-term drawbacks and advantages.

◆ Groups should support their viewpoints critically and constructively.

◆ Have small groups work together to research the topic. Review the rules of class debates.

Extend Have students contact a local landfill authority, university environmental department, or ecological organization to obtain relevant background information. Encourage them to prepare questions in advance.

You Decide

Have students complete the first two steps in their groups to prepare their arguments before the debate. Students should complete the third step after the debate. Direct students to write letters or essays in support of their opinions using points raised during the debate. Consider submitting articles to a local or school newspaper for possible publication. **Portfolio** Students can save their letters or essays in their portfolios.

Grocery Bags: Paper or Plastic?

Americans use more than 32 billion grocery bags each year. About 80 percent of the bags are plastic. The other 20 percent are paper. Plastic bags are made from crude oil, a resource that cannot be replaced. Paper bags, on the other hand, are made from trees. Trees are a renewable resource, but it takes time to grow them.

Both paper and plastic grocery bags end up in the trash. Although some bags are incinerated, or burned, most end up buried in landfills. You need a way to carry groceries home. Which bag should you choose at the grocery store—paper or plastic?

The Issues

Should People Choose Paper Bags?
Paper bags can hold more items than plastic. A typical paper bag can hold about 12 items. A plastic bag might hold half as many.

A mature tree can yield about 700 bags. But just one large supermarket can use 700 bags in less than an hour! Most trees that are used to make paper come from forests. Only about 20 percent come from tree farms.

Hazardous chemicals are used in making paper bags. Wood and certain poisonous chemical compounds are heated. The mixture is cooked into a mush of wood fibers, which is pressed into paper.

Usually, paper bags are biodegradable, which means that decay organisms break them down. But in tightly packed landfills, even paper bags don't break down easily.

Should People Choose Plastic Bags?
Plastic bags are lightweight, compact, and waterproof. They take up 80 percent less space in landfills than an equal number of paper bags. But most plastic bags are not biodegradable. They cannot be broken down by natural processes. They can last a long time in landfills.

Some plastic bags end up in the ocean. There they are a danger to seabirds and animals who may eat or get caught in them.

Plastic bags are made from a compound that's left over when crude oil is made into fuel. This waste product used to be discarded or burned.

Most plastic can be recycled. Unfortunately, only about 10 percent of all plastic products are recycled today. Most people are just not recycling.

Which Is the Right Choice? Some people want laws that would require manufacturers to make all bags—paper and plastic—out of recycled materials. Paper manufacturers say, however, that the fibers in recycled paper are too short to make bags that are strong enough.

The right choice of bags may depend on how your community handles trash. Does it collect paper or plastic or both to be recycled?

Both paper and plastic bags can be reused in many ways, such as for storage or as trash container liners. But the best choice may be neither paper nor plastic. One reusable cloth bag could replace hundreds of paper and plastic bags.

You Decide

1. Identify the Problem
In your own words, explain the problems in choosing paper or plastic bags.

2. Analyze the Options
List the pros and cons of using plastic and paper bags. In each case, who will benefit? Who might be harmed?

3. Find a Solution
Your community wants to pass a law to regulate the kind of grocery bags that stores should offer. Take a stand. Defend your position.

Background

Facts and Figures Carbon-based materials should provide a source of food and energy for bacteria and fungi. However, there are no known bacteria that consume the compounds in synthetic polymers. Some researchers are trying to make polymers from simpler carbon chains, hoping that bacteria will be able to break them down. Plastic bags made of this material would be easier to dispose of. Some plastics are being developed that are made of grains or potatoes. These plastics could be fed to animals such as cattle, not thrown away.

Another suggestion is to develop and breed bacteria capable of consuming the more complicated polymer molecules. Opponents of this line of research say that releasing new organisms into the environment may present new and unexpected hazards.

SECTION 2 Metals and Alloys

DISCOVER · ACTIVITY

Are They Steel the Same?

1. Wrap a cut nail (low-carbon steel), a wire nail (high-carbon steel), and a stainless steel bolt together in a paper towel.

2. Place the towel in a plastic bag. Add about 250 mL of salt water and seal the bag.

3. After one or two days, remove the nails and bolt. Note any changes in the metals.

Think It Over

Developing Hypotheses What happened to the three types of steel? Which one changed the most, and which changed the least? What do you think accounts for the difference?

Over 6,000 years ago, people learned to make copper knives and tools that were sharper than stone tools. Later, they discovered that they could also use tin for tools. But these metals are soft, so they bend easily and are hard to keep sharp. About 5,000 years ago, metal makers discovered a way to make better tools. Copper and tin mixed together in the right amounts make a stronger, harder metal that keeps its sharp edge after long use. This discovery was the beginning of the Bronze Age. It also was the invention of the first alloy. An **alloy** is a substance made of two or more elements that has the properties of metal. In every alloy, at least one of the elements is a metal.

Properties of Metals

You know a piece of metal when you see it. It's hard and usually shiny. At room temperature all metallic elements (except mercury) are solids. Metals share other properties, too. They can conduct electricity. They are ductile; that is, they can be drawn out into thin wire. Copper, for example, made into wire, is used to carry electric current to the outlets in your home. Metals are also malleable; that is, they can be hammered into a sheet. Aluminum, rolled flat, makes aluminum foil. You wouldn't be able to do that with a piece of glass!

GUIDE FOR READING

◆ What properties make alloys useful?

Reading Tip Before you read, rewrite the headings in the section as *how, why,* or *what* questions. As you read, look for answers to these questions.

Gold leaf dome of City Hall in Savannah, Georgia ▶

L ◆ 123

READING STRATEGIES

Reading Tip Suggest students preview the section by reading the headings, captions, and boldfaced statements and viewing *Exploring Alloys and Metals in Aircraft.* Then have students generate questions based on the section headings. Encourage students to predict answers to some or all of the questions. Then direct them to answer the questions as they read.

Program Resources

◆ **Teaching Resources** 4-2 Lesson Plan, p. 105; 4-2 Section Summary, p. 106
◆ **Guided Reading and Study Workbook** Section 4-2

INTEGRATING TECHNOLOGY

SECTION 2 Metals and Alloys

Objectives

After completing the lesson, students will be able to
◆ identify properties of alloys that make them useful;
◆ cite examples of common alloys and list uses for those alloys.

Key Term alloy

1 Engage/Explore

Activating Prior Knowledge

Tell students that 24-karat gold is pure gold and 10-karat gold is less than half gold and more than half silver. Then ask: **Why would a jeweler want to make a gold charm from 10-karat gold rather than 24-karat gold?** (*Students may say because it is less expensive, but some may know that 10-karat gold jewelry is stronger.*) Explain that, although the silver is not as valuable as pure gold, it contributes important qualities such as strength.

· · · · · · · · DISCOVER · · · · · · · ·

Skills Focus developing hypotheses
Materials *cut nail, wire nail, stainless steel bolt, paper towel, sealable plastic bag, saltwater solution*
Time 10 minutes, plus 1- or 2-day waiting period
Tips Cut nails have flat heads and are made of low-carbon steel; they are commonly used on hardwood floors. Wire nails are also called finishing nails. Buy the nails and bolts at a hardware store. If possible, leave the nails and bolt in the bag for two days so students can observe more dramatic changes.
Think It Over Both nails rusted; the bolt did not rust or rusted very little. The cut nail changed the most; the bolt changed the least. The materials in the nails determine how the nails react to salt water.

Properties of Metals

Building Inquiry Skills: Classifying

Have students identify a variety of metal objects in the classroom. As they point out each object, ask: **What other materials could be used to make this?** Have students identify the advantages and disadvantages of using the alternative materials. List students' observations and suggestions on the board. Then challenge students to infer why metals are likely the best material to use to make each object. Write students' responses next to each object or application. **cooperative learning**

Properties of Alloys

Real-Life Learning

Tell students that most United States coins are made of alloys. Ask: **What properties of alloys make them good choices for coins?** *(They are strong and do not react with water or air.)* Tell students that the specific composition of each type of coin is specifically described by law. Have students research the composition and minting of coins. Interested students may want to consult the Web site at: **www.usmint.gov learning modality: verbal**

Making Alloys

Language Arts Connection

Explain that the word *alloy* comes from the Latin word *alligare* which means "to be allied or joined together." Challenge students to use this definition to make up a memory device to remember the definition of an alloy. *(Sample: An alloy is formed by two metals that are joined together.)* **learning modality: verbal**

Figure 8 Stainless steel is the iron alloy used to make the spaghetti lifter and pot. The coins and chain of this necklace are made from alloys of gold.
Applying Concepts Why are alloys used to make these objects rather than the pure metals?

Properties of Alloys

The properties of an alloy can differ greatly from those of its individual elements. Bronze, for example, is an alloy of copper and tin. It was a much better material for early toolmaking because it was harder than either element alone.

Pure gold is soft and easily bent. Gold jewelry and coins are made of an alloy of gold with another metal, such as copper or silver. These gold alloys are much harder than pure gold but still let its beauty show. Even after thousands of years, objects made of gold alloys still look exactly the same as when they were first made.

Alloys are used much more than pure metals because they are generally stronger and less likely to react with air or water. You have seen iron objects rust when they are exposed to air and water. But forks and spoons made of stainless steel can be washed over and over again without rusting. Stainless steel is an alloy of iron, carbon, nickel, and chromium. It does not react as easily with air and water as iron does. *Exploring Alloys and Metals in Aircraft* shows how other properties of alloys may be put to use.

✓ *Checkpoint* Why is bronze more useful for tools than copper or tin?

Making Alloys

Many alloys are made by melting metals and mixing them together in carefully measured amounts. Since the beginning of the Bronze Age, this technique has been used to make copper alloys. Some modern alloys are made by mixing the elements as powders and then heating them under high pressure. This process uses less energy because the metals blend at lower temperatures. The material then can be molded into the desired shape immediately. Another recent technique, called ion implantation, involves firing a beam of ions at a metal. A thin layer of alloy then forms on the metal's surface. Titanium, for example, may be bombarded with nitrogen ions to make a strong alloy for artificial bone and joint replacements.

Background

Integrating Science Rocks contain metals. The most abundant metals include aluminum, iron, magnesium, manganese, and titanium. The other metals—including copper, gold, and lead—are considered scarce. The abundant metals are usually a part of the basic minerals in rocks, while the scarce metals are present in far smaller amounts.

Usually metals are found in hydrothermal ore deposits. In these deposits, a briny water solution dissolves and transports metals. When the dissolved metals and other substances are deposited, a vein forms. The deposits generally form as the hydrothermal solution cools. Gold, silver, tin, and nickel are frequently mined from veins.

EXPLORING Alloys and Metals in Aircraft

Much of the structure of an aircraft is made of metals. Engineers often design alloys with specific characteristics to fit the needs of the different parts of the aircraft.

Gold
A thin layer of pure gold coats the polymer (plastic) windshield. An electric current through the gold provides enough heat to keep the windshield frost-free. Gold works well for this purpose because it does not react with air and water.

Iron Alloys
The structural supports that hold the airplane together must be extremely strong. Steel made of iron with carbon and other metals is the best choice for these parts.

Aluminum Alloys
The outside of the plane has to be strong, light, and resistant to corrosion. The airplane's "skin" is aluminum, which is alloyed with magnesium, copper, and traces of other metals to increase strength.

Titanium Alloys
Landing gear must be strong enough to hold the wheels of the airplane and support its great mass. Alloys of titanium with vanadium, iron, and aluminum are strong as steel but much lighter in weight.

Nickel Alloys
The turbine blades in the jet engines have to spin around thousands of times per minute without changing shape. They also must withstand temperatures up to 1,100°C. Nickel alloyed with iron, carbon, and cobalt does the job.

Chapter 4 **L ◆ 125**

Answers to Self-Assessment

Caption Question

Figure 8 Alloys are stronger and less likely to react with water.

 Checkpoint
Bronze is harder than either copper or tin, so tools made from bronze are stronger.

Addressing Naive Conceptions

Students may have difficulty understanding why alloys are mixtures and not compounds. Explain that physical processes can be used to separate the metals in an alloy. For example, if brass is heated to a high temperature, the zinc will melt before the copper does. Explain that some alloys, such as sterling silver, require specific amounts of each metal, but other alloys can be made by mixing two metals over a range of proportion. For example, brass may be composed of up to 50 percent zinc. **learning modality: verbal**

EXPLORING

Alloys and Metals in Aircraft

As students examine the visual essay, ask them to list the different metals found on an airplane. Then ask: **Which metal is the only one named in the essay that is used in its pure form?** *(gold)* Next, have students identify the desirable property of each metal and alloy on the list. *(Gold—conducts electricity, does not react with air or water; iron—extremely strong; aluminum—strong, lightweight, resists corrosion; magnesium—very strong; copper—very strong; nickel—holds its shape, withstands high temperatures; cobalt—holds its shape, resists high temperatures; titanium—strong, lightweight)* Ask students: **Why aren't airplanes made entirely of iron, since iron is such a strong metal?** *(Iron is so heavy that an airplane made entirely out of iron could not get off the ground.)*
Extend Have students visit the NASA Web site at **www.nasa.gov** and identify how metals and metal alloys are used on the space shuttle. **learning modality: visual**

Ongoing Assessment

Oral Presentation Ask students to name three uses for metal alloys.

Using Alloys

Building Inquiry Skills: Applying Concepts

Ask students to list metallic items that they use at home. Then have them find these items, or similar ones, in Figure 9. Challenge students to infer what alloys are used to make the items on their lists. For example, if students have listed tableware, ask: **What alloys do you think were used to make the tableware?** *(Samples: Pewter, sterling silver, or stainless steel)* Ask students: **How could you determine which alloy was actually used?** *(By comparing properties such as color, density, ability to conduct electricity, tendency to tarnish or corrode)* **learning modality: logical/mathematical**

Social Studies Connection

The metals used in alloys come from around the world. Direct students to locate the following countries on a world map or globe: Australia, Canada, Sierra Leone, South Africa, Russia, Ukraine, Norway, and Malaysia. Have small groups of students choose one country and research the role mining for metals plays in that country's economy. Encourage groups to report the results of their research to the rest of the class. **learning modality: verbal**

Demonstration

Materials *soldering iron, solder, 2 wires, modeling clay, aluminum foil*

Time 15 minutes

CAUTION: *The soldering iron will become very hot. Do not allow students to touch it.* To begin, cover a table top with the foil. Press a lump of modeling clay on the foil and firmly fix one wire in the clay. Then demonstrate how melted solder can be used to join the second wire to the first. Ask: **What property of solder makes it useful to plumbers and electricians?** *(Sample: It has a low melting point.)* **limited English proficiency**

Common Alloys

Alloy	Elements	Properties	Uses
Brass	Copper, zinc	Strong, resists corrosion, polishes well	Musical instruments, faucets, decorative hardware, jewelry
Bronze	Copper, tin	Hard, resists corrosion	Marine hardware, screws, grillwork
Stainless steel	Iron, carbon, nickel, chromium	Strong, resists corrosion	Tableware, cookware, surgical instruments
Carbon steel	Iron, carbon	Inexpensive, strong	Tools, auto bodies, machinery, steel girders, rails
Plumber's solder	Lead, tin	Low melting point	Sealing joints and leaks in metal plumbing
Sterling silver	Silver, copper	Shiny, harder than pure silver	Jewelry, tableware
Dental amalgam	Mercury, silver, tin, copper, zinc	Low melting point, easily shaped	Dental fillings
Pewter	Tin, antimony, copper	Bright or satin finish, resists tarnish	Tableware*, decorative objects
Wood's metal	Bismuth, lead, tin, cadmium	Low melting point	Fire sprinklers, electric fuses

*Pewter containing lead cannot be used with food.

Figure 9 Alloys have a wide variety of uses.
Making Generalizations How do the properties of each alloy make it well suited for its uses?

Using Alloys

When you want to describe something very hard or tough, you may use the expression "hard as steel." Steel is an alloy of iron with other elements. It is used for its strength, hardness, and resistance to corrosion. Without steel, suspension bridges, skyscrapers, and surgical knives would not exist. Neither would artificial joints that replace damaged knees and hips.

Steels Not all steel is alike. Its properties depend on which elements are added to iron. High-carbon steel, for example, consists of about 0.5 percent manganese and up to 0.8 percent carbon. Carbon steel is stronger and harder than wrought iron, which is almost pure iron. Tools, knives, machinery, and appliances are just some of the uses for carbon steel. Steels with less than 0.8 percent carbon are more ductile and malleable. They may be used for nails, cables, and chains.

There are hundreds of different types of steel. Usually carbon is added to the iron plus one or more of the following metals: chromium, manganese, molybdenum, nickel, tungsten, and vanadium. Steel made with these metals is generally stronger and harder than carbon steel, and usually more corrosion-resistant. Depending on their properties, these steels may become bicycle frames, train rails, steel tubing, or construction equipment.

Background

History of Science The manufacture of alloyed metals made soaring skyscrapers a reality. The first metal to be used as a primary structural material was cast iron, an alloy of iron and carbon. In the late eighteenth century, cast iron was used to support bridges. By the nineteenth century, cast iron, which tends to break when formed into long sections, was replaced with steel. Compared to cast iron, steel is relatively light in weight and high in strength. These characteristics made the construction of skyscrapers possible. The first steel-girder building, the ten-story Home Insurance Company Building in Chicago, was completed in 1855. Two years later, a department store in New York City installed the first safe passenger elevator; this made skyscrapers practical to use.

Figure 10 A plumber (left) takes advantage of the low melting point of the alloy solder to seal a leaking pipe. The brass in this doorknocker (below) is an alloy of copper and zinc.

Other Alloys Bronze, brass, and solder (SAHD ur) are just a few examples of other kinds of alloys. These materials are used to make items ranging from plumbing materials and sprinkler systems to tableware and doorknobs. Even your dentist uses alloys. Have you ever had a cavity in a tooth? A mixture of mercury with silver or gold (called an amalgam) makes a pasty solid. It rapidly hardens, filling a hole in the tooth. Look at Figure 9 and see how many of the examples listed in the table are alloys you have seen or used.

Section 2 Review

1. Name two properties of alloys that make them more useful than pure metals.
2. Describe one way in which alloys are made.
3. What advantage does stainless steel cookware have over cookware made of iron?
4. **Thinking Critically Applying Concepts** What properties would you look for to find out if an object was made of metal?
5. **Thinking Critically Problem Solving** The purity of gold is expressed in units called karats. A piece of 24-karat gold is pure gold metal. A piece of 12-karat gold is one half gold and one half another metal, often silver or copper. What fraction of the metal in a piece of 18-karat gold jewelry is actually gold?

Science at Home

Find items in your home that are made from metals or alloys. Look for cooking utensils, tools, toys, sports equipment, appliances, and other household items that are made with these materials. Discuss with members of your family how properties of the metals or alloys relate to the uses of the objects.

Chapter 4 **L ◆ 127**

Answers to Self-Assessment

Caption Question

Figure 9 Each alloy has unique properties. For example, dental amalgam is easily shaped, so it is ideal for fillings that must be made in the shape of a natural tooth.

SECTION 3 Ceramics and Glass

Objectives

After completing the lesson, students will be able to

◆ identify properties of ceramics and tell how ceramics are used;

◆ describe the composition of glass and tell how glass can be changed to serve many different purposes.

Key Terms ceramics, glass, optical fiber

1 Engage/Explore

Activating Prior Knowledge

Show students a clear drinking glass and ask them to describe its properties. *(Sample: clear, holds water, can break if dropped, conducts heat)* Then ask students to list other uses for glass, other than as a container to hold liquids. *(Samples: windows, eyeglasses)*

••••••• DISCOVER •••••••

Skills Focus inferring  **Materials** *1 glazed and 1 unglazed flowerpot of the same size, sink or basin, water, balance, paper towels*

Time 10 minutes

Tips You may wish to lead students in a review of how to find the percent of change:

$$\frac{(\text{new mass} - \text{initial mass})}{\text{initial mass}} \times 100$$

If the pots have approximately the same initial mass, students can compare the raw data instead of the percent of change of mass. Larger pots and pots soaked longer than 10 minutes will show a more dramatic change.

Think It Over The unglazed pot gained the most mass. The glazing keeps water from soaking into the pot.

DISCOVER •• ACTIVITY

Does It Get Wet?

1. Find the masses of a glazed pottery flowerpot and an unglazed one of similar size. Record both values.

2. Place both pots in a basin of water for ten minutes.

3. Remove the pots from the water and blot dry gently with paper towels.

4. Find and record the masses of both flowerpots again.

5. Calculate the percent of change in mass for each pot.

Think It Over

Inferring Which pot gained the most mass? What can you infer about the effect that glazing has on the pot?

GUIDE FOR READING

◆ What properties of ceramics make them useful?

◆ How can glass be changed to make it useful?

Reading Tip Before you read, make a list of ceramic or glass items you use. As you read, look for reasons why these materials are well suited for their uses.

Picture yourself on a warm day, walking through a slow-flowing stream. The mud at the bottom is soft. It squishes up between your toes. When you pick it up and shape it with your hands, it holds its form. If you let it dry in the sun, it becomes hard. This material is clay. You could also shape the clay into blocks, add some straw to make a composite material, and let the blocks dry. If you live where there is not much rain, you could use the blocks to build a house. In fact, people have used this type of brick to build sturdy homes. The Pueblo homes of the Southwest, for example, were built this way over a thousand years ago. Some of them are still standing today.

Making Ceramics

A discovery made thousands of years ago increased the usefulness of dried clay objects. Heating clay to about 1,000°C makes it harder and stronger. **Ceramics** are hard, crystalline solids made by heating clay and other mineral materials to high temperatures. Clay is made of very small mineral particles containing silicon, aluminum, and oxygen. Other elements, such as magnesium and iron, may be present in clay, too. Clay forms when the minerals in

◀ Pueblo homes in Taos, New Mexico

128 ◆ L

READING STRATEGIES

Reading Tip Explain to students that some ceramic and glass objects, such as coffee mugs and drinking glasses, serve practical purposes, whereas others, such as figurines and ornamental plates, serve decorative purposes. Suggest students list both practical and decorative items made of ceramics and glass. Have students speculate as to why some artists prefer working with ceramics and some prefer glass.

Study and Comprehension After students read the section, organize them into four groups. Assign each group one of the major headings in the section: *Making Ceramics, Properties and Uses of Ceramics, Making Glass,* and *Communication Through Glass.* Instruct each group to review the information under the heading and create a presentation in which they summarize the information and present visual aids such as diagrams, flowcharts, or concept maps.

rock are broken down. Unheated clay also contains water. When a clay object is heated, much of the water present on its surface evaporates, and the particles of clay stick together.

This process forms the hard ceramic pottery used for bricks and flowerpots. Once cooled, these materials have tiny spaces in their structure that absorb and hold water. If you grow a plant in this kind of pot, you can feel the moisture in the outer surface of the clay after you water the plant. When pottery is brushed with a layer of silicon dioxide and heated again, a glassy coating, called a glaze, forms. This glaze is shiny and waterproof. You might see glazed pottery used to serve or store food. Potters often use colorful glazes to create artistic designs on their work.

☑️ *Checkpoint* *How does a glaze change the properties of a ceramic?*

Figure 11 Wet clay takes shape in the hands of a potter. *Predicting What will happen to the water in the clay when the potter heats it in a kiln, or hot oven?*

Properties and Uses of Ceramics

Have you ever heard the phrase "a bull in a china shop"? Imagine the damage. A bull in a bronze shop just wouldn't be as dramatic! The phrase comes from the fact that ceramics are brittle and can shatter when struck. Despite their tendency to break, ceramics have several properties that make them useful. **Ceramics resist moisture, do not conduct electricity, and can withstand temperatures higher than molten metals.**

Ceramic pottery has been used for thousands of years to store food, protecting it from moisture and animals. Roofing tiles, bricks, and sewer pipes all are long-standing uses of ceramics. Ceramics also are used as insulators in electric equipment and light fixtures.

Figure 12 Some ceramics, such as these roof tiles (left), have practical uses. Other ceramics (right) are valued for their delicate beauty.

Chapter 4 **L** ◆ **129**

Answers to Self-Assessment

Caption Question

Figure 11 The water in the clay will evaporate.

☑️ *Checkpoint*

A glaze makes a ceramic shiny and waterproof.

2 *Facilitate*

Making Ceramics

Using the Visuals: Figure 12

Direct students to examine the roof tiles in the photograph. Ask them to infer what properties of ceramics make them useful to use for roof tiles. *(Ceramics resist moisture, withstand heat, and can easily be formed into shapes.)* **learning modality: visual**

Properties and Uses of Ceramics

Cultural Diversity

When people talk about china, they are often referring to a type of pottery first made in China during the T'ang dynasty, A.D. 618–907. Porcelain is made from a fine white clay called kaolin, which is mixed with a powdered rock called petuntse. The mixture is shaped, and then fired. In Western countries, porcelain usually refers to pottery that is translucent so that it appears to glow when held up to the light. In China, porcelain is pottery that resonates and produces a musical tone when struck. Europeans spent centuries attempting to reproduce Chinese porcelain, and it was not until 1707 that the first porcelain was made in Europe. Another ceramic also referred to as china is *bone china*, which was developed around 1800 in England. Bone china contains bone ash. Encourage students to research the history of Chinese porcelain, or the European efforts to reproduce it, and report back to the class. **learning modality: verbal**

Ongoing Assessment

Skills Check Have students make flowcharts that describe how a waterproof piece of pottery is made from clay.

 Students can save their flowcharts in their portfolios.

Properties and Uses of Ceramics, continued

Language Arts Connection

Have students use a dictionary to find the origin of the word *ceramic*. *(It comes from the Greek word* keramos, *which means "potter's clay.")* Ask: **What are some synonyms for** *ceramic*? *(pottery, earthenware, china)* **learning modality: verbal**

Making Glass

Real-Life Learning

Tell students that some people claim that glass is a liquid, not a solid. The evidence usually given for this is that in very old windows, such as stained glass windows in medieval churches, the glass pieces are thicker at the bottom, as if the glass had flowed downward over the centuries. Explain to students that the old glass was made by spinning a circle of glass. This resulted in a disc of glass that was thicker at the rim. When the glass was cut into sections, one edge was thicker than the others. Ask students: **Why would the window-makers put the thick edge at the bottom of the window?** *(To make it more stable)* **learning modality: verbal**

Including All Students

Materials *several kinds of glass including colored bottles, eyeglasses, baking dish, window glass, beaker*

ACTIVITY

Time 10 minutes

Allow students who need additional help understanding the concepts to carefully handle the glass samples. Ask: **Is all this glass the same? Explain.** *(No; the glass has different properties such as color, density, ability to bend light, ability to withstand heat.)* Ask students to infer what gives the glass different properties. *(The materials that were mixed with the melting sand)* **learning modality: kinesthetic**

Figure 13 Before the space shuttle *Columbia* can be launched again, tiles damaged during its last reentry must be replaced. *Predicting What would happen to the spacecraft if many of the tiles were missing?*

New uses for ceramics continue to be developed. The walls of ovens for making steel and other metal products are made of a type of brick that does not melt at the temperature of red-hot iron. And ceramic tiles are the only materials that can withstand the temperatures of over 1,600°C that build up on the bottom of the space shuttle during its reentry into the atmosphere. These tiles insulate the shuttle and protect the astronauts.

✓ *Checkpoint* What are some uses of ceramics?

Making Glass

Have you ever looked closely at a handful of sand, or watched the varied grains as they slipped through your fingers? Thousands of years ago people learned that sand mixed with limestone can be melted into a thick, hot liquid. Most sand consists of tiny, hard pieces of quartz, a mineral made of silicon dioxide. When sand is heated to about 1,600°C, it flows like thick molasses. If this liquid cools quickly, it forms a clear, solid material with no crystal structure, called **glass.**

The first glass objects were formed in clay molds that were chipped away after the glass hardened. Then about 2,000 years ago, glassmakers in ancient Persia invented glassblowing. The

Figure 14 Glass objects made in ancient Rome are on display at the Corning Museum in Corning, New York.

130 ◆ L

Background

Integrating Science Obsidian, a type of rock, forms from extremely hot lava that cools very quickly. It is usually black and shiny. Since it forms from lava, obsidian is found near volcanoes. It has a high percentage of silica, one of the primary components of sand. The properties of obsidian vary when different chemicals are present in the liquid lava. For example, traces of iron compounds can produce reddish or brownish obsidian.

The lava that forms obsidian is extremely viscous. When the lava cools, it forms a glassy, solid material. Obsidian shares properties with glass. It forms sharp edges that can be used as cutting tools, and its shiny surface can be used as a mirror. Many ancient cultures used obsidian to make tools, arrowheads and other weapons, and decorations.

Figure 15 The lenses in this microscope are made from lead oxide glass. *Applying Concepts* How do the microscope lenses help this girl view a small object?

glassmaker put a blob of melted glass on the end of an iron pipe. By blowing air through the pipe, the glassmaker could produce a hollow glass vessel. If the glass was blown inside a wooden mold, jars and vases in beautiful patterns and shapes could be created.

Different materials may be added to glass to make it useful for particular purposes. Early glassmakers added calcium (as limestone) and sodium (as sodium carbonate) to the melting sand. This mixture melts at a lower temperature than sand alone, so it is easier to work with. Window glass and the bottles and jars you use every day are still made with this type of glass.

Substituting lead oxide for the limestone makes a glass that bends light in useful ways. This kind of glass is used to make lenses for eyeglasses, telescopes, and microscopes. Adding boron oxide creates a glass that resists heat better than ordinary glass. It is used for cooking surfaces and laboratory glassware that must be heated. Colored glass is made by adding minerals containing various metals to the molten glass. Selenium and gold produce red glass. Cobalt makes beautiful, deep blue glass.

Communication Through Glass

INTEGRATING PHYSICS There's a good chance that the next time you make a phone call, your message will travel through glass. An **optical fiber** is a threadlike piece of glass (or plastic) that can be used for transmitting light. Light shining into one end of the fiber travels through the glass to the other end. The effect is similar to electrons that carry a signal in copper wire. When you speak into a telephone, the signal created by your voice is converted to light signals that travel through the glass fiber. At the other end, the light may be converted into electronic signals that can then be converted to sound.

A Bright Idea

Can you communicate using an optical fiber?

1. Construct a barrier between you and a partner so that you cannot see each other.
2. Run a plastic optical fiber past the barrier.
3. Bring the bulb of a penlight flashlight close to your end of the fiber.
4. Using a single flash for "yes" and two flashes for "no," send your partner a message by responding to a series of yes and no questions he or she asks.
5. Change roles so that your partner has a chance to send signals in response to your questions.

Observing What happened when you and your partner sent signals to each other?

Communication Through Glass

Integrating Physics

Materials *laser pointer, 1-L clear plastic soda bottle with 3-mm hole in the side about 2 cm from the bottom, paper, masking tape*
Time 10 minutes

CAUTION: *Do not allow students to use the pointer. Do not shine the laser in anyone's eyes.* This demonstration is similar to an experiment conducted by John Tyndall in England in 1854. Use the tape to seal the hole in the bottle. Fill the bottle with water and have a volunteer hold it over the sink. Carefully aim the laser through one side of the bottle so the light beam shines through the bottle and hits the hole on the other side. Remove the tape. The light from the laser will appear to move along the stream of water leaving the bottle. Explain that this principle is used in fountains with colored lights, as well as in fiber optic technology.
limited English proficiency

Skills Focus *observing*
Materials *barrier material, such as a notebook or cardboard; penlight flashlight; optical fibers*
Time 15 minutes
Tips For safety reasons, use only the plastic optical fibers available from scientific supply houses. Suggest students ask questions about the identity of a small object hidden behind the barrier.
Observing Light traveled through the fiber from one end to the other, carrying the flashes of light through the fiber.
Extend Have students experiment to find out how efficient the optical fibers are over longer distances. **learning modality: visual**

Program Resources

 Science Explorer Series *Sound and Light,* Chapter 4

Answers to Self-Assessment

Caption Questions

Figure 13 The spacecraft might burn up if many of its insulating tiles were missing.
Figure 15 The lenses bend light, and produce a magnified image.

✓ *Checkpoint*

Samples: roof tiles, pottery, bricks, sewer pipes, insulators, walls of ovens that make steel, tiles to protect spacecraft

Ongoing Assessment

Writing Ask students to list several objects and processes that are made of or make use of glass and identify the properties of glass that allow it to be used for each.

 Students can save their lists in their portfolios.

3 Assess

Section 3 Review Answers

1. Ceramics are heat-resistant and do not conduct electricity.

2. By adding other materials to the sand when the glass is made, the glass can become colored, heat-resistant, or able to bend light in useful ways.

3. Light travels through the fiber from one end to the other without being lost through the walls of the fiber.

4. The earlier materials could rot from exposure to sun and water. They could be chewed by animals. Ceramics are resistant to the sun, and they are resistant to water if glazed.

Check Your Progress

CHAPTER PROJECT 4

Check students' written procedures for safety and thoroughness. Make sure students explain how they will control variables and clearly identify the variable they are testing. For example, if a student wanted to test the strength of the polymers, he or she could attach paper cups to equal-sized pieces of the polymers and add pennies to the cups until the polymers break. Check the organization of students' data tables. Before students begin their tests, make sure they have collected samples that they are permitted to test, or that they have devised tests that will not damage the samples.

Figure 16 Even if optical fibers are twisted into a loop, the light moves within the fibers. *Making Generalizations* *How can this property of optical fibers be useful?*

You know that light can pass through glass from one side to the other. That's one reason you can see through a window. But when light moves through an optical fiber, it is reflected within the fiber. It doesn't pass through the outside surface. For this reason, there is little loss of light from one end to the other—an important condition for transmitting messages!

A pair of optical fibers, each the thickness of a human hair, can carry 625,000 phone calls at one time. One quarter pound of glass fiber can replace over two tons of copper wire. This difference is a big advantage when installing long lines like those that carry messages under the ocean. Because optical fibers are so efficient, they are being used to replace most copper telephone and cable television lines. Another benefit of glass fiber is its stability. Since the glass does not corrode as metals do, the lines are easier to maintain.

Section 3 Review

1. What property of ceramics makes them useful as the walls for ovens or as insulating materials?

2. In what ways can the properties of glass be changed?

3. How is a message transmitted through a glass fiber?

4. **Thinking Critically Applying Concepts** Before ceramics were invented, people stored food in containers such as baskets, leather bags, and wooden bowls. What properties of ceramics made them better containers for food?

Check Your Progress

CHAPTER PROJECT 4

Devise a plan to test some chemical and physical properties of the polymers you have collected. Tests might include hardness, fiber strength, flexibility, color, density, solubility in water, or reaction to corrosive chemicals. Construct a data table on which you can record results of your tests.

Program Resources

◆ **Teaching Resources** 4-3 Review and Reinforce, p. 111; 4-3 Enrich, p. 112

Answers to Self-Assessment

Caption Question

Figure 16 The light that enters the fiber will still carry a signal even if the fiber is bent.

SECTION
4 Radioactive Elements

DISCOVER ● ACTIVITY

How Much Goes Away?

1. Make a circle about 8–10 centimeters in diameter on a piece of paper. You can do this by tracing the rim of a round container.

2. Use a straightedge to draw a line dividing the circle in half. Then divide one half into quarters, then into eighths, and so on, as shown in the diagram.

3. ✂ With scissors, cut out your circle. Now cut away the undivided half circle. Next, cut away the undivided quarter circle. Continue until you are left with one segment.

4. Place the segments on your desktop in the order you cut them.

Think It Over
Making Models How is the piece of paper changing each time? Suppose the original circle was a model for a sample of radioactive material, and the paper you cut away is material that became nonradioactive. What would eventually happen?

More than a thousand years ago, some people came up with what they thought was a great idea. Take some dull, cheap lead metal and turn it into valuable gold! They heated the lead, cooled it, added acid to it. They ground it into a powder and mixed it with everything they could think of. Of course, nothing worked. There is no chemical reaction that converts one element into another.

Even so, elements do sometimes change into other elements. A uranium atom can become a thorium atom. Atoms of carbon can become atoms of nitrogen. (But lead never changes into gold, unfortunately!) How is it possible for these changes to happen?

GUIDE FOR READING

◆ What happens during radioactive decay?

◆ How is half-life a useful property of radioactive isotopes?

◆ In what ways are radioactive isotopes useful?

Reading Tip As you read, use the headings to make an outline about the properties and uses of radioactive isotopes.

Figure 17 This painting from 1570 shows people trying to change lead into gold. No such chemical reaction was ever accomplished.

READING STRATEGIES

Reading Tip As a class, outline the information under the first section heading.
I. Nuclear Reactions
   A. Element can change to another element through nuclear reaction
   B. Nuclear reaction involves particles in an atom's nucleus

Program Resources

◆ **Teaching Resources** 4-4 Lesson Plan, p. 113; 4-4 Section Summary, p. 114
◆ **Guided Reading and Study Workbook** Section 4-4

SECTION
4 Radioactive Elements

Objectives
After completing the lesson, students will be able to
◆ describe radioactive decay and the emissions produced during decay;
◆ explain why half-life is a useful property of radioactive isotopes;
◆ identify uses and dangers of radioactive isotopes;
◆ explain isotopes in terms of mass numbers.

Key Terms nuclear reaction, isotope, mass number, radioactive decay, nuclear radiation, alpha particle, beta particle, gamma radiation, half-life, radioactive dating, tracer, radiation therapy

1 Engage/Explore

Activating Prior Knowledge

Ask students to tell you what they know about radioactivity. (*Samples: It is bad for you, it comes from uranium, it makes your hair fall out.*) Tell them that in this section, they learn how atoms change when they are radioactive. They also learn how radioactivity can be useful in science, medicine, and industry.

● ● ● ● ● ● ● ● DISCOVER ● ● ● ● ● ● ● ●

Skills Focus making models
Materials *round or cylindrical object, such as a coffee can; ruler; scissors*
Time 10 minutes
Tips Draw a sample circle on the board to show students how to make the correct divisions on their paper circles. Caution students to be careful when using scissors.
Expected Outcome Students will cut away half their paper each time.
Think It Over The piece of paper decreases by half each time. The radioactive material would continue to decrease by half until it became so small that it could not break down further.

L ◆ 133

2 Facilitate

Nuclear Reactions

Building Inquiry Skills: Comparing and Contrasting

Ask: **What happens to an atom of an element in a chemical change?** (*It gains, loses, or shares electrons, but its nucleus does not change. The element does not become another element.*) Then ask: **What happens to an atom of an element in a nuclear reaction?** (*The number or arrangement of the protons and neutrons in its nucleus change, and the element becomes another element.*) Suggest students summarize this comparison in a compare/contrast table. **learning modality: visual**

Isotopes

Language Arts Connection

Explain to students that the prefix *iso-* comes from a Greek word that means "equal" or "the same." Then tell students that the Greek word *topos* means "place." Have students define *isotope* based on the meanings of the root words. (*Sample: All isotopes of the same atom occupy the same place on the periodic table.*) Make sure students understand that all isotopes of an element have the same number of protons but each has a different number of neutrons. **learning modality: verbal**

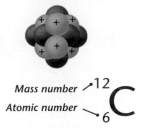

Carbon-12

Mass number ⟋12
Atomic number ⟍ 6 C

Carbon-14

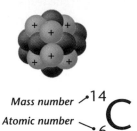

Mass number ⟋14
Atomic number ⟍ 6 C

Figure 18 All carbon atoms have 6 protons in each nucleus, but the isotope carbon-12 has 6 neutrons and the isotope carbon-14 has 8 neutrons.

Figure 19 Radioactive elements give off mass and energy during radioactive decay.
Interpreting Diagrams Which type of decay does not result in a different element?

Nuclear Reactions

You have already learned that an atom consists of a nucleus of protons and neutrons, surrounded by a cloud of electrons. A chemical change always involves the electrons but doesn't affect the nucleus. Since the number of protons determines the identity of the atom, one element can't be made into another element by a chemical reaction. Such a change happens only during **nuclear reactions** (NOO klee ur)—reactions involving the particles in the nucleus of an atom.

Isotopes

Remember that all the atoms of an element have the same number of protons (same atomic number), but the number of neutrons can vary. Atoms with the same number of protons and different numbers of neutrons are called **isotopes** (EYE suh tohps).

To show the difference between isotopes of the same element, you write both the name of the element and the mass number of the isotope. **Mass number** is the sum of the protons and neutrons in the nucleus of an atom. Consider, for example, isotopes of carbon. Most carbon atoms are carbon-12, having six protons and six neutrons (and six electrons). About one out of every trillion carbon atoms, however, has eight neutrons. That isotope is carbon-14. Figure 18 shows you how to write the symbols for the two isotopes. Note that the atomic number is included, too.

✓ *Checkpoint* Why do mass numbers for isotopes differ?

Radioactive Decay

Some isotopes are unstable. The nucleus of an unstable atom does not hold together well. Unstable isotopes undergo nuclear reactions, often forming atoms with different atomic numbers or atomic masses. In a process called **radioactive decay,** the atomic nuclei of unstable isotopes release fast-moving particles and energy. There are three types of radioactive decay, each determined by the type of radiation released by the unstable

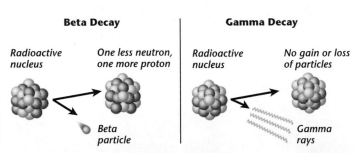

Alpha Decay

Radioactive nucleus → *2 protons and 2 neutrons lost* — *Alpha particle*

Beta Decay

Radioactive nucleus → *One less neutron, one more proton* — *Beta particle*

Gamma Decay

Radioactive nucleus → *No gain or loss of particles* — *Gamma rays*

Background

History of Science About 100 years ago, physicist Ernest Rutherford performed a series of experiments that led to the development of the nuclear theory of atomic structure and opened an entire new branch of physics. Rutherford discovered that some elements released charged rays or particles, which he called alpha and beta rays. Rutherford found that atoms of a radioactive element would give off alpha and beta particles, causing the atoms to become a different element. Rutherford's findings were challenged by some skeptical physicists who did not believe that atoms of one element could change to become atoms of a different element. In 1908, Rutherford collected alpha particles and demonstrated that they were helium nuclei. That year he won the Nobel Prize for chemistry for his work on radioactivity.

nucleus. **Radioactive decay can produce alpha particles, beta particles, and gamma rays.** (Alpha, beta, and gamma are the first three letters of the Greek alphabet.) The particles and energy produced during radioactive decay are forms of **nuclear radiation.**

Alpha Decay An **alpha particle** consists of two protons and two neutrons. It is the same as a helium nucleus. Release of an alpha particle by an atom decreases the atomic number by 2 and the mass number by 4. Although alpha particles move very fast, they are stopped by collisions with atoms. Alpha radiation can cause an injury much like a bad burn. But a sheet of paper or thin piece of metal foil will act as a shield.

Beta Decay When a neutron inside the nucleus of an unstable atom breaks apart, it forms a beta particle and a proton. A **beta particle** is an electron given off by a nucleus during radioactive decay. The new proton remains inside the nucleus. That means that the nucleus now has one less neutron and one more proton. Its mass number remains the same, but its atomic number increases by 1.

Beta particles travel much faster than alpha particles. They can pass through an aluminum sheet 3 millimeters thick. They can also travel into the human body and damage its cells.

Gamma Decay Alpha and beta decay are almost always accompanied by gamma radiation. **Gamma radiation** is high-energy waves, similar to X-rays. Gamma radiation (also called gamma rays) does not cause a change in either the atomic mass or the atomic number of the atom formed. But the energy released is the most penetrating type of radiation. You would need a piece of lead several centimeters thick or a concrete wall about a meter thick to stop gamma rays. They can pass right through a human body, causing severe damage to cells.

Sharpen your Skills

Predicting ACTIVITY

Look at the table of radioactive isotopes below.

Isotope	Type of Decay
$^{238}_{92}$U	Alpha
$^{63}_{28}$Ni	Beta
$^{131}_{53}$I	Beta
$^{226}_{88}$Ra	Alpha

1. With the help of a periodic table (see Appendix D), predict the element that forms in each case.
2. Label the symbol for each new element. Include the atomic number and mass number.

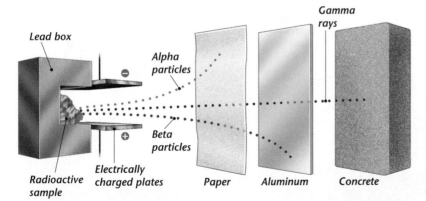

Figure 20 The three types of nuclear radiation can be separated according to charge and penetrating power. *Inferring Which type of radiation is the most penetrating?*

Lead box
Alpha particles
Gamma rays
Beta particles
Radioactive sample
Electrically charged plates
Paper
Aluminum
Concrete

Media and Technology

 Transparencies "Types of Radioactive Decay," Transparency 17

 Transparencies "Penetration of Alpha, Beta, and Gamma Radiation," Transparency 18

Answers to Self-Assessment

Caption Questions
Figure 19 Gamma decay
Figure 20 Gamma radiation

☑ *Checkpoint*
Mass numbers for isotopes differ because different isotopes have different numbers of neutrons.

Radioactive Decay

Using the Visuals: Figure 19
Have students count the protons (green) and neutrons (purple) for each atom shown in the figure. *(Alpha decay—first atom: 9 of each; second atom: 7 of each; beta decay—first atom: 8 protons, 10 neutrons; second atom: 9 of each; gamma decay—first atom: 10 protons, 9 neutrons; second atom: no change)* Ask: **Would you look to the left or right of the original element on the periodic table to find the element resulting from alpha decay?** *(To the left)* **From beta decay?** *(To the right)* **learning modality: logical/mathematical**

Including All Students
Students who have difficulty making connections between concepts may need extra help to understand why scientists say that alpha particles are the same as helium nuclei. Some students may think this means that radioactive elements are composed of helium. Explain that the atoms of radioactive elements contain neutrons and protons in a specific arrangement. During alpha decay, protons and neutrons are lost and these particles take on the same arrangement as a helium nucleus. **learning modality: verbal**

Sharpen your Skills

Predicting

Materials periodic table ACTIVITY
Time 15 minutes
Tips Students can refer to Figure 18 to find how to write the symbols for the new elements. Suggest students present their findings in a table.

Answers $^{238}_{92}$U → $^{234}_{90}$Th; $^{63}_{28}$Ni → $^{63}_{29}$Cu;

$^{131}_{53}$I → $^{131}_{54}$Xe; $^{226}_{88}$Ra → $^{222}_{86}$Rn

Extend Ask: **Which element produces protactinium when it undergoes beta decay?** *(thorium)*

Ongoing Assessment

Skills Check Ask students to compare and contrast alpha, beta, and gamma decay.

Half-Life

Building Inquiry Skills: Making Models

Materials *items from the* 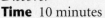 **ACTIVITY** *Discover*

Time 10 minutes

Have students choose one of the radioactive elements from Figure 21 and repeat the Discover activity to model the decay of the chosen element. Ask: **What does each cut represent?** *(The amount of the sample that decays in one half-life)* Have students write the half-life on each segment they cut off. Students can find the sum of all the cut-off pieces to calculate the amount of time needed to reduce the radioactive element to $\frac{1}{32}$ of its original mass. Ask students to explain why finding places to store radioactive waste is such an important issue. *(Sample: The half-life of some radioactive elements is billions of years, so radioactive waste will be around for a long time.)* **learning modality: kinesthetic**

Integrating Earth Science

Ask students to infer what kinds of objects can be studied using radioactive dating with carbon-14. *(Students should realize that carbon-14 dating can only be used to find the age of objects that originally contained carbon, such as plants, animals, living things, and objects made from living things.)* Lead a class discussion about the specific objects an archaeologist might find. Write students' suggestions on the board. Then ask: **Can carbon-14 be used to find the ages of these objects?** *(Samples: Carbon-14 dating cannot be used on objects that do not contain carbon or, because of its relatively short half-life, on objects that are more than 60,000 years old.)* **learning modality: verbal**

Half-Lives of Some Radioactive Elements	
Element	**Half-Life**
Carbon-14	5,730 years
Chlorine-36	400,000 years
Cobalt-60	5.26 years
Iodine-131	8.07 days
Phosphorus-32	14.3 days
Polonium-216	0.16 second
Radium-226	1,600 years
Sodium-24	15 hours
Uranium-235	710 million years
Uranium-238	4.5 billion years

Figure 21 The half-lives of radioactive elements vary greatly. *Interpreting Data Which isotope in this table decays most rapidly?*

Half-Life

Not all the atoms of a sample of a radioactive isotope decay at once. They decay randomly, one at a time. If you watched a sample of iodine-131, for example, you couldn't predict when any particular nucleus would decay. But the time it takes for half the atoms to change can be measured. The **half-life** of an isotope is the length of time needed for half of the atoms of a sample to decay. Half-life is different for each isotope. As you can see in Figure 21, half-lives can range from less than a second to billions of years!

INTEGRATING EARTH SCIENCE Fossils are the traces or remains of living things that have been preserved. **The half-lives of certain radioactive isotopes are useful in determining the ages of rocks and fossils.** For example, as plants grow they use carbon dioxide (CO_2) from the air. Some carbon dioxide contains carbon-14. This becomes part of the plant's structures the same way carbon-12 does. After the plant dies, it stops taking in carbon dioxide. If the plant's remains are preserved as a fossil, the amount of carbon-14 present can be measured. From the data, scientists can calculate how many half-lives have passed since the plant was alive. Thus they can estimate the age of the plant and its surrounding rock. This process is called **radioactive dating.**

The half-life of carbon-14 is short compared to some other radioactive isotopes. It cannot be used to find the ages of objects older than about 60,000 years. Other isotopes, such as potassium-40 and uranium-238, are used to study older fossils, rocks, and objects used by early humans.

☑ *Checkpoint* How does the mass of a radioactive sample change after one half-life?

Figure 22 Using the known half-lives of certain radioactive elements, such as carbon-14 and uranium-238, scientists can determine the age of ancient objects. This saber-toothed cat lived about 25 million years ago.

Background

Facts and Figures Here are some further uses for radioactive isotopes.

◆ Americium-241—used in smoke detectors
◆ Californium-252—used to inspect airline luggage for hidden explosives
◆ Cobalt-60—used to sterilize surgical instruments and to preserve meat, poultry, fruits, and spices
◆ Promethium-147—used in thermostats in electric blankets

Program Resources

Science Explorer Series *Earth's Changing Surface*, Chapter 4; *From Bacteria to Plants*, Chapter 1

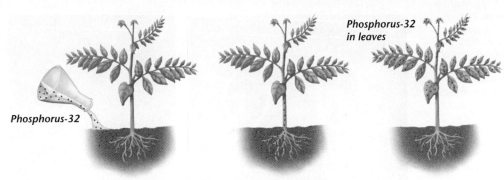

Phosphorus-32

Phosphorus-32 in leaves

Figure 23 Phosphorus-32 added to soil is absorbed through the plant's roots. The tracer can be detected in any plant structures in which the phosphorus is used.

Using Radioactive Isotopes

In addition to studying objects from the past, people use radioactive isotopes for work in the present. **Radioactive isotopes are useful both as sources of radiation and as tracers.** The radiation released by radioactive isotopes is itself useful. Nuclear power plants and some medical treatments, for example, depend on nuclear reactions as sources of radiation.

Another important use depends on the fact that the radiation given off by isotopes can be detected. Like a lighthouse flashing in the night, a radioactive isotope "signals" where it is. **Tracers** are radioactive isotopes that can be followed through the steps of a chemical reaction or industrial process. In chemical reactions, tracers behave the same way as nonradioactive forms of an element.

Tracers in Chemical Reactions Scientists can make use of tracers in chemical reactions. Equipment that detects radiation can track the tracer wherever it goes. This technique is helpful for studying reactions in living organisms. For example, phosphorus is used by plants in small amounts for healthy growth. A plant will absorb radioactive phosphorus-32 added to the soil just as it does the nonradioactive form. Radiation will be present in any part of the plant that contains the isotope. In this way, biologists can learn where and how plants use phosphorus.

Uses in Industry Radioactive isotopes are valuable in industry as tracers and for the radiation they produce. For example, tracers are used in finding weak spots in metal pipes, especially oil pipelines. When added to a liquid, tracers can easily be detected if they leak out of the lines.

Engineers use gamma radiation from radioactive isotopes to look for flaws in metal. Gamma rays can pass through metal and be detected on a photographic film. This is similar to using X-rays to take a picture inside your body. By looking at the

Sharpen your **Skills**

Calculating ACTIVITY
Carbon-14 has a half-life of 5,730 years. Data from several newly discovered fossils shows that carbon-14 has undergone decay in the fossils for five half-lives. Calculate the age of the fossils.

Chapter 4 **L ◆ 137**

Answers to Self-Assessment

Caption Question
Figure 21 Polonium-216

☑ *Checkpoint*
After one half-life, one-half of the atoms of a radioactive sample have decayed.

Using Radioactive Isotopes

Building Inquiry Skills: Designing Experiments
Direct student groups to design experiments in which radioactive tracers are used to determine whether the seeds of a plant contain phosphorus absorbed from the soil. Assign each student a task such as formulating a hypothesis, identifying variables, developing a procedure, and organizing a data table for the information they would collect. (*Sample experiment: Add a radioactive phosphorus isotope to the soil, then look for the radioactive isotope in the seeds the plant forms.*) **cooperative learning**

 Students can save their designs in their portfolios.

Sharpen your **Skills**

Calculating
Materials *calculator* ACTIVITY
Time 10 minutes
Tips Students may have difficulty determining what operation to perform. Help them assign units to each number. Students can use the units to guide them through the calculation.
Answer 5 half-lives × 5,730 years / half-life = 28,650 years. The fossils are 28,650 years old.
Extend Ask students how much older the fossil could have been before its age would have had to be found using a different isotope. (*60,000 years − 28,650 years = 31,350 years. If it had been 31,350 years older, carbon-14 could not be used to find its age.*)

Ongoing Assessment

Writing Ask students to describe two uses for radioactive isotopes and explain the properties of radioactive isotopes that make these uses possible.

L ◆ 137

Using Radioactive Isotopes, continued

Integrating Health

Students may wonder how gamma rays can be targeted at cancer cells without affecting healthy body cells. Explain that healthy cells are affected during radiation therapy but that doctors shield the surrounding areas from radiation and use equipment that can deliver strong doses of radiation to a concentrated area. Because cancer cells divide rapidly, they are more affected by radiation than other cells. However, side effects of radiation therapy, such as hair loss and skin disorders, often occur when the radiation affects healthy cells that usually divide rapidly. **learning modality: verbal**

Safe Use of Radioactive Materials

Social Studies CONNECTION

Have students brainstorm considerations that must be made when storing or disposing of radioactive wastes. Ask students to consider issues such as whether it is better to store small amounts of waste in many places, or large amounts in one or two places. Encourage students to discuss problems with transporting the waste as well as of dealing with the long half-lives of some radioactive isotopes.

In Your Journal Students' speeches should address issues raised when brainstorming. Students may work in small groups. You may want to have the class role-play a public meeting in which different viewpoints are expressed. **learning modality: verbal**

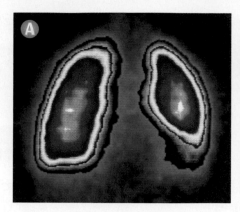
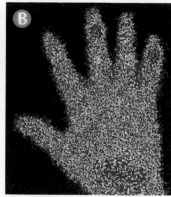

Figure 24 The radioactive isotope technetium-99 is used in medical studies of the heart, lungs, liver, and bones. **A.** In these healthy lungs, the red areas show greater absorption of the isotope than the yellow or green areas. **B.** In the hand, the bones are colored orange.

Social Studies CONNECTION

Using radioactive materials can provide benefits such as electricity or advanced medical care. But what happens to the unavoidable radioactive waste? People aren't so comfortable having that around!

NIMBY is short for the phrase "not in my backyard." It stands for the idea that people don't want unpleasant or possible hazardous conditions near where they live. They would prefer to see radioactive wastes go elsewhere.

In Your Journal

Your local government has invited citizens to a meeting to discuss possible options for storing radioactive wastes from nearby medical or industrial uses. Write a one- or two-paragraph speech to the public meeting, expressing your opinion.

gamma-ray images, structural engineers can detect small cracks in the metal of bridges and building frames. Without these images, a problem might not be discovered until a disaster occurs.

Uses in Medicine Doctors use radioactive isotopes to detect **INTEGRATING HEALTH** medical problems and to treat some diseases. Tracers injected into the body travel to organs and other structures where that chemical is normally used. Using equipment that detects radiation, technicians make images of the bone, blood vessel, or organ affected. For example, tracers made with technetium-99 are frequently used to diagnose problems in the bones, liver, kidneys, and digestive system. Other isotopes, such as thallium-201 in the heart and xenon-133 in the lungs, help doctors diagnose disease in these organs.

In a process called **radiation therapy,** radioactive elements are used to destroy unhealthy cells. Iodine-131, for example, is given to patients with tumors of the thyroid gland, a gland in the neck that controls the rate at which nutrients are used. Because the thyroid gland uses iodine, the radioactive iodine-131 collects in the gland. Radiation from this isotope destroys unwanted cells in the gland without serious effects on other parts of the body.

Cancer tumors of different kinds often are treated from outside the body with high-energy gamma rays. Many hospitals use cobalt-60 for this purpose. When gamma radiation is focused on a cancer tumor, it causes changes that kill the cancer cells.

Nuclear Power Nuclear reactions release enormous quantities of energy compared to chemical reactions. For this reason, some power plants use radioactive isotopes as fuel. Carefully controlled reactions, most often using uranium-235, provide electric power in many parts of the world.

✓ *Checkpoint* *What is a tracer?*

Background

Facts and Figures A nuclear power plant captures the energy from a nuclear reactor and converts it into electricity. Inside a nuclear reactor, uranium atoms split into two, releasing energy and neutrons. The neutrons strike other uranium atoms and cause those atoms to split. This occurs over and over again in a chain reaction. All these reactions release a tremendous amount of energy.

Program Resources

- **Science Explorer Series** *Human Biology and Health,* Chapter 6
- ◆ **Teaching Resources** 4-4 Review and Reinforce, p. 115; 4-4 Enrich, p. 116

Figure 25 Waste Isolation Pilot Plant (WIPP) is a site in New Mexico where the United States government is developing safe storage for radioactive wastes. Large underground rooms (left), will house the wastes in secure barrels (right).

Safe Use of Radioactive Materials

Despite the positive uses for radioactive materials, they also are dangerous. Radiation penetrates living tissue, knocking electrons from atoms. This process produces ions that then can interfere with chemical reactions in living cells. Illness, disease, and even death may result from overexposure to radiation.

The dangers of radioactive materials mean that their use must be carefully managed. People who work with these materials must wear protective clothing and use insulating shields. Radioactive wastes can't just be thrown away. After radiation therapy, for example, contaminated equipment and clothing can still be hazardous. These items must be disposed of properly. Materials with low levels of radiation may be buried in landfills. Such landfills are carefully monitored to prevent contamination of the environment. Isotopes with long half-lives, however, will remain hazardous for hundreds or even thousand of years. Plans are under way to dispose of these kinds of materials in specially designed containers that will be buried in very dry underground tunnels. In that way the radioactive wastes can be isolated for many generations.

Section 4 Review

1. Describe the three types of radiation given off during radioactive decay.
2. How are radioactive isotopes helpful for studying rocks and fossils?
3. Give two examples of how tracers are used. Tell why radioactive isotopes work as tracers.
4. **Thinking Critically Making Judgments** If there were a proposal in your state to ban the use of radioactive materials because of the hazards of radioactive waste, would you support the idea? Why or why not?

Check Your Progress

CHAPTER PROJECT 4

After your teacher approves your plan, perform your tests. Record all results in your data table. If there is time, perform your tests more than once to obtain multiple sets of data. Try to organize your samples into groups based on the results of your tests. Identify similarities and differences among the groups.

Media and Technology

Exploring Physical Science Videodisc
Unit 2, Side 2,
"Hot Pocket Change"
Chapter 9

Answers to Self-Assessment

☑ *Checkpoint*

A tracer is a radioactive isotope that can be followed through the steps of a chemical reaction or industrial process.

---

3 Assess

Section 4 Review Answers

1. Alpha particles—two protons and two neutrons; beta particles—one electron; gamma radiation—high-energy waves
2. Scientists can determine how old a rock or fossil is by measuring the amount of radioactive isotope left in the object and determining how many half-lives have passed since the object was formed or died.
3. Sample: A plant absorbs a radioactive isotope from the soil, so scientists can detect where it goes and find out what structures use the chemical. A patient is given a radioactive isotope that becomes concentrated in the organ to be studied. Radioactive isotopes work as tracers because they react chemically just like nonradioactive isotopes, but give off radiation that can be detected.
4. Students should back up their judgments with logical statements. They may support the proposal because of the hazards of the waste, or argue against the idea because of the benefits of using radioactive materials.

Check Your Progress

CHAPTER PROJECT 4

Make sure students' plans observe safety guidelines. Students should compare the results of their tests to determine the properties of different polymers. Help students group their samples by relating polymer properties to polymer function. For example, noncorrosive, insoluble PVC (polyvinyl chloride) is well suited for use as a water pipe and is commonly used in plumbing.

Performance Assessment

Writing Ask small groups of students to prepare pamphlets to inform the school or community of the benefits and hazards of nuclear power. Pamphlets should include scientific descriptions of radioactive decay. Students can save their pamphlets in their portfolios.

That's Half-Life!

Preparing for Inquiry

Key Concept The half-life of a substance is the amount of time it takes for one half of the sample to decay.

Skills Objectives Students will be able to
◆ model radioactive decay by a random scattering of coins;
◆ interpret data collected from their models.

Time 25 minutes

Advance Planning
◆ Because each group of students needs at least 100 pennies, you may want to ask them to bring in pennies. Record how many pennies each student has brought in and return the same number after the lab.
◆ Provide graph paper. Encourage students to make their two graphs in different colors to help distinguish between data.

Guiding Inquiry

Invitation

Show students a loaf of bread with 16 slices. Ask: **How many slices will remain if half the slices are removed?** *(eight)* **How many will remain if half the remaining slices are removed?** *(four)* Continue in this manner until you get down to a single slice of bread. Ask: **How many steps of halving did it take to get to a single slice?** *(four)*

Introducing the Procedure

Tell students the decay of an individual nucleus in a sample is a random event that can be modeled by a coin toss. Explain that about half of all coin tosses land on heads, even though an individual coin toss is random. Because students will be removing about one half of the pennies after each trial, they are modeling the half-life of a radioactive substance.

Skills Lab

Making Models

THAT'S HALF-LIFE!

In this lab, you will use pennies to model how half-life is related to the decay of radioactive isotopes.

Problem

How does a sample of radioactive waste decay to a nonhazardous level?

Materials

100 pennies   graph paper
container such as a jar or a box
colored pencils (optional)

Procedure

1. Copy the data table into your notebook. Then place 100 pennies in a container.
2. Shake the pennies out onto the desktop. Separate the ones showing heads from those showing tails.
3. Count the number of pennies showing tails and calculate the number of pennies showing heads. Record both these values.
4. Put back only the pennies showing tails.
5. Repeat the process until there are two or fewer pennies left in the container.
6. Keep a tally of the total number of pennies removed from the container. Record this number after each trial.

DATA TABLE

Trial	Tails Remaining	Heads Removed (each trial)	Total Pennies Removed
1			
2			
3			

Analyze and Conclude

1. Make a graph of your data. Label the horizontal axis with the trial number. Label the vertical axis with the number of pennies left in the container after each trial. Connect the data points with a smooth, curved line.
2. What does the graph tell you?
3. On the same set of axes, plot the total number of pennies removed from the container after each trial. Use a dotted line or different colored pencil to make this graph.
4. What does your second graph tell you?
5. Suppose the pennies represent nuclei of a radioactive element. What do you think the heads and tails represent?
6. What do you think is represented by each trial or shake of the pennies?
7. How many half-lives does it take for the substance modeled in this lab to decay to two or fewer "nuclei"?
8. **Think About It** Suppose 1,600 grams of low-level radioactive waste is buried at a waste disposal site. Assuming that 10 grams of radioactive material is an acceptable level of radiation exposure, about how many half-lives must pass before there is no longer a health risk at the site?

More to Explore

How could you use this model to show the decay of a sample that was twice as massive as the sample used in this lab? What would you do differently? Predict how you think the results would differ.

Program Resources

◆ **Teaching Resources** Skills Lab blackline masters, pp. 120–121

Media and Technology

Lab Activity Videotape
Chemical Interactions, 8

Sample Data Table

Trial	Tails Remaining	Heads Removed (each trial)	Total Pennies Removed
1	48	52	52
2	24	24	76
3	11	13	89

SECTION 1 Polymers and Composites

Key Ideas
- Polymers are large compounds made of many small molecules called monomers.
- Polymers occur naturally as products of living cells. Polymers also are synthesized in factories and laboratories for a variety of uses.
- Composite materials combine the useful properties of two different substances.

Key Terms
polymer   cellulose   composite
monomer   plastic

SECTION 2 Metals and Alloys
INTEGRATING TECHNOLOGY

Key Ideas
- An alloy is a mixture of two or more elements, one of which is a metal. Alloys have the properties of metals, but also have other properties that make them more useful than the metals alone.
- Steel is one of the most frequently used alloys. Its strength and resistance to corrosion make it useful in such things as building materials, tools, and machinery.

Key Term
alloy

SECTION 3 Ceramics and Glass

Key Ideas
- Ceramics are made by heating clay mixed with other materials to temperatures that produce a brittle, crystalline solid. Food storage, building materials, and heat insulators are some uses of ceramics.
- Glass results when sand is melted to make a thick liquid that can be shaped when hot. Adding other materials gives glass properties such as heat resistance and color.

Key Terms
ceramics   glass   optical fiber

SECTION 4 Radioactive Elements

Key Ideas
- Radioactive decay is a change in the nucleus of an atom that releases particles and energy. The products of radioactive decay are alpha and beta particles and gamma rays.
- Half-life is the amount of time it takes for half of the radioactive atoms of an isotope to decay.
- Radioactive isotopes are used as sources of radiation in industry, medicine, and research.

Key Terms
nuclear reaction   beta particle
isotope   gamma radiation
mass number   half-life
radioactive decay   radioactive dating
nuclear radiation   tracer
alpha particle   radiation therapy

Organizing Information

Compare/Contrast Table Copy the table about polymers, alloys, ceramics, and glass onto a separate sheet of paper. Then complete it and add a title. (For more on compare/contrast tables, see the Skills Handbook.)

Material	Made From	How Made	How Used
Polymers	Monomers (carbon compounds)	a. __?__	b. __?__
Alloys	c. __?__	Metals heated and mixed	d. __?__
Ceramics	Clay; other minerals	e. __?__	f. __?__
Glass	g. __?__	Melted, then cooled in desired shapes	h. __?__

Program Resources
- **Teaching Resources** Chapter 4 Project Scoring Rubric, p. 100; Chapter 4 Performance Assessment Teacher Notes, p. 155; Chapter 4 Performance Assessment Student Worksheet, p. 157; Chapter 4 Test, pp. 158–161; Book Test, pp. 162–165

Media and Technology
 Interactive Student Tutorial CD-ROM L-4

 Computer Test Bank *Chemical Interactions*, Chapter 4 Test

Troubleshooting the Experiment
Make sure students read the procedure through before they begin the experiment. Students who need additional help understanding the procedure may benefit from doing a practice run so they can demonstrate each step without feeling pressured.

Analyze and Conclude
1. Students' graphs should show a curve decreasing from upper left to lower right.
2. The graph shows that the number of pennies remaining in the container is reduced by approximately half for each trial.
3. Students' graphs should show a curve increasing from lower right to upper left.
4. The graph shows that the total number of pennies removed increases.
5. The heads represent decayed nuclei, the tails represent undecayed nuclei.
6. Each trial represents a half-life.
7. Answers will vary, but most students should say that it takes about 5 or 6 half-lives.
8. 1) $1,600 \div 2 = 800$; 2) $800 \div 2 = 400$; 3) $400 \div 2 = 200$; 4) $200 \div 2 = 100$; 5) $100 \div 2 = 50$; 6) $50 \div 2 = 25$; 7) $25 \div 2 = 12.5$; 8) $12.5 \div 2 = 6.25$ It would take 8 half-lives to reach a level of less than 10 grams.

Extending the Inquiry

More to Explore Each penny represents a nucleus. A sample of the same element that is twice as massive has twice as many nuclei. So to show the decay of a sample with twice as much mass, use twice as many pennies. Students should predict that it will take one more half-life for a sample with twice the mass to decay to two or fewer nuclei.

Organizing Information

Compare/Contrast Table Sample title: Properties of Polymers, Alloys, Ceramics, and Glass; **a.** Chemical bonds link monomers in a repeating pattern **b.** Fabrics, packaging materials, household items, containers, toys, insulation **c.** Metals and other elements **d.** Construction materials, jewelry, tools, machinery, hardware **e.** Heated until crystalline solid forms **f.** Containers, insulating materials, building materials **g.** Sand **h.** Windows, lenses, glassware, cookware, optical fibers

L ◆ 141

Reviewing Content
Multiple Choice
1. b **2.** d **3.** c **4.** b **5.** c

True or False
6. Carbon **7.** natural **8.** bronze **9.** true
10. nuclear reactions

Checking Concepts
11. Wool from sheep, cotton from cotton plants, cellulose from plants, silk from silkworms, proteins from all living things

12. Synthetic polymers do not react easily with other chemicals. This keeps them from breaking down into simpler materials but contributes to the volume of trash. Synthetic polymers are inexpensive to make, and this can make them cheaper to throw away than to reuse.

13. Metals conduct electricity, and can be drawn into a thin wire and hammered into sheets. Sample uses: Copper is used to make thin wires to conduct electricity. Gold is hammered into sheets used to cover parts of buildings.

14. Pure gold is too soft for jewelry. Alloys of gold with other metals are harder and stronger.

15. It provides a nonporous (water-resistant) coating.

16. Each element is defined by the number of protons contained within the nucleus. A chemical reaction involves electrons but does not change the number of protons.

17. The isotopes give off radiation, which makes them useful for killing unhealthy cells such as those in tumors. As tracers, they can be used in medical diagnosis and in monitoring chemical reactions.

18. Accept answers that include descriptions of the properties of the product and why it is useful. Answers should also give logical arguments for why the polymer would be advantageous over the natural material.

Thinking Critically
19. Accept all answers based on logical reasoning. Students should consider environmental aspects, and the availability, convenience, and cost of their alternative material.

Reviewing Content

 For more review of key concepts, see the Interactive Student Tutorial CD-ROM.

Multiple Choice
Choose the letter of the best answer.

1. A large molecule made of many monomers is called a
  a. plastic.
  b. polymer.
  c. protein.
  d. chain.

2. Fiberglass is a type of
  a. polymer.
  b. alloy.
  c. ceramic.
  d. composite.

3. The properties of alloys most resemble
  a. ceramics.
  b. glass.
  c. metals.
  d. polymers.

4. Clean sand is heated to its melting point to make
  a. ceramics.
  b. glass.
  c. alloys.
  d. composites.

5. Atoms that have the same atomic number but different mass numbers are
  a. radioactive.
  b. alloys.
  c. isotopes.
  d. alpha particles.

True or False
If the statement is true, write true. If it is false, change the underlined word or words to make the statement true.

6. <u>Oxygen</u> is the element that forms the backbone of most polymers.

7. Cellulose molecules are examples of <u>synthetic</u> polymers.

8. A useful alloy of copper and tin is <u>steel</u>.

9. The furnaces used to melt metals are insulated with <u>ceramic</u> materials.

10. Alpha, beta, and gamma radiation form as the result of <u>chemical reactions</u>.

20. Because they were not fired at a high temperature, the bricks still contain some water and are not as strong as fired bricks. Rain or moisture would soften them.

21. Cup for hot chocolate—polystyrene because it is a good insulator; hammer—steel because it is hard, heavy, and unbreakable; aquarium wall—glass because it is transparent, strong, and does not corrode; egg carton—polystyrene because it is soft, flexible, and protective

Checking Concepts
11. Name some polymers that are products of nature. Tell where they come from.

12. Explain why some advantages of using polymers can become disadvantages.

13. List three properties of metals. Then for each property, give an example of how a specific metal is put to use.

14. Why is gold always mixed with other metals to make jewelry?

15. What is the purpose of the glaze on the surface of a pottery vase?

16. Explain why a chemical reaction cannot change one element into another element.

17. What properties of radioactive isotopes make them useful?

18. Writing to Learn You are a chemist. You invent a polymer that can be a substitute for a natural material such as wood, cotton, or leather. Write a short speech to make at a science conference, explaining why you think your polymer is a good replacement for the natural material.

Thinking Critically
19. Making Judgments The plastic rings that hold beverage cans together are sometimes hazardous to living things in the ocean. Do you think companies that make soft drinks should be allowed to continue using plastic rings? Consider what could replace them and the effects of the change.

20. Applying Concepts The earliest building bricks were dried by being left out in the sun. Why can this kind of brick be used only in areas with a dry climate?

21. Comparing and Contrasting Explain which material—steel, glass or polystyrene foam—would be the best choice for each of the following uses: cup for hot chocolate; hammer; wall of a salt-water aquarium; egg carton.

22. Calculating A wooden tool found in a cave has one fourth as much carbon-14 as a living tree. How old is the tool? (*Hint:* The half-life of carbon-14 is 5,730 years.)

22. Two half-lives have passed, so the tool is 11,460 years old.

Applying Skills
23. Four elements (uranium, thorium, protactinium, radium); two isotopes of uranium (U-238, U-234), two isotopes of thorium (Th-234, Th-230), and one isotope each of protactinium and radium (Pa-234, Ra-226)

Applying Skills

The diagram below shows the first few steps of the radioactive decay of uranium-238. Use the diagram to answer Questions 23–25.

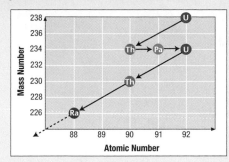

23. Interpreting Data How many elements are in the diagram? How many different isotopes of each element are there?

24. Classifying What type of radioactive decay resulted in uranium-238 becoming thorium-234? How do you know?

25. Inferring How do you know from the diagram that thorium-230 is radioactive?

Project Wrap Up Prepare a chart or poster to display the polymers you examined. Provide a sample of each polymer and include information such as its name, where it was found, what monomers it is made of (if known), and significant physical and chemical properties as shown by your tests. Be prepared to compare the polymers with other types of materials such as glass, ceramics, and metals.

Reflect and Record In your journal, explain how you might improve your collection and testing process. Describe one of the more interesting polymers that you found. Why do you think it is interesting?

Test Preparation

Use these questions to prepare for standardized tests.

Use the diagram to answer Questions 26–29.

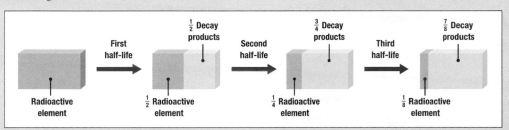

26. What is shown in this diagram?
   a. the fraction of a radioactive element remaining after each half-life
   b. the decay series for uranium
   c. a three-step chemical reaction
   d. the difference between long and short half-lives

27. How much of a radioactive-element sample will be left after the fourth half-life?
   a. 1/8   **b.** 7/8
   c. 1/16   **d.** 7/16

28. The half-life of sodium-24 is 15 hours. How much of a 100-gram sample will be left after 45 hours?
   a. 50 grams   **b.** 25 grams
   c. 15 grams   **d.** 12.5 grams

29. What is the decay product?
   a. the element undergoing decay
   b. the element that causes radioactive decay
   c. the energy released during decay
   d. one or more elements that form when the radioactive element changes

---

24. Alpha decay; the atomic number decreased by 2 and the mass number decreased by 4, which is what happens when an atom loses an alpha particle.
25. Thorium-230 must be radioactive because it decays into radium-226.

Present Your Project During class presentations, students should explain how they were able to identify as polymers the items they collected. They should be able to discuss various properties of these polymers and explain how these properties relate to the polymers' functions.

Reflect and Record Students should include any problems they had identifying or testing polymers and suggest improvements they would like to make. Students' descriptions should be detailed and include specific examples.

Test Preparation

26. a **27.** c **28.** d **29.** d

Program Resources

◆ **Inquiry Skills Activity Book** Provides teaching and review of all inquiry skills
◆ **Standardized Test Preparation Book** Provides standardized test practice
◆ **Reading in the Content Area** Provides strategies for improving science reading skills
◆ **Teacher's ELL Handbook** Provides multiple strategies for English language learners

Bread on the Rise

This interdisciplinary feature presents the central theme of bread by connecting four different disciplines: science, social studies, mathematics, and language arts. The four explorations are designed to capture students' interest and help them see how the content they are studying in science relates to other school subjects and to real-world events. The unit is particularly suitable for team teaching.

1 Engage/Explore

Activating Prior Knowledge

Help students recall what they learned in Chapter 1, Section 3, Controlling Chemical Reactions, by asking questions such as: **How does temperature affect a reaction?** (*Heat increases the rate of a reaction.*) and **How does surface area affect a reaction?** (*More material is exposed if the surface area is increased so the reaction happens faster.*) Later you can apply these questions to lead students to recognize why bread flour must be mixed thoroughly (to increase surface area) and left to rise in a warm place (increase temperature).

Introducing the Unit

Point out that much of cooking depends on chemistry. In fact, understanding chemistry helps a person be a better cook. Ask: **What is bread made of?** (*grain flour, water, yeast or other leaven, salt, sugar*) Ask: **How does chemistry play a role in baking bread?** (*Chemistry is responsible for turning the mixture of ingredients into the loaf.*) Ask: **Do you know what yeast is or what it does in bread?** (*Students may not know that yeast is an organism and that it makes the bread rise.*)

Point out that bread is eaten in some form in almost every country in the world. Ask: **Why do you think bread is so popular?** (*Accept all reasonable answers. Sample: Bread is tasty, nutritious, and simple to make.*)

BREAD
ON THE RISE

HAVE YOU EVER . . .
- ◆ **WATCHED BREAD RISING IN A PAN?**
- ◆ **TASTED A FRESHLY BAKED SLICE?**
- ◆ **NOTICED DIFFERENT-SIZED HOLES IN BREAD?**
- ◆ **WONDERED WHY THE HOLES ARE THERE?**

A San Ildefonso Pueblo woman and child test their bread made in an outside oven.

144 ◆ L

Bread is one of the first foods known. It's eaten all over the world. Because it is a main source of nutrition for many people, bread is sometimes called the "staff of life." Flour, water, and salt are the basic ingredients of most breads. Usually bread also contains a leavening agent—an ingredient that makes the bread "rise."

To vary the taste, this simple bread mix is often changed in a variety of ways. Different kinds of flour and liquids as well as other ingredients, such as eggs, fruits, nuts, and spices, all change the flavor.

There are three types of bread. Flat breads, such as pita, don't have any leavening agent—thus the name "flat." Quick breads, such as biscuits, rise because they're made with the chemicals baking soda or baking powder. Yeast breads, such as whole wheat and rye bread, are make with a living organism—yeast—which causes the bread to rise. How many of these breads do you eat?

Explain that after students complete this unit, they will understand more about how bread is made than most cooks! Consequently, students will be able to experiment with different bread recipes and be better able to predict how varying recipes will affect the chemistry of the bread.

Program Resources

- ◆ **Teaching Resources** Interdisciplinary Explorations, Social Studies, pp. 122-124; Science, pp. 125-127; Mathematics, pp. 128-130; Language Arts, pp. 131-133

Flat Breads Around the World

Have you ever eaten pita bread? A tortilla? Matzo? These breads share a history that is older than any other kind of bread. They are all flat breads that originated among specific peoples in different parts of the world.

People made flat bread long before the leavening properties of yeast were discovered and even longer before chemical leavening agents were found. Nearly 12,000 years ago, people learned how to crush grains, add water, and bake dough on hot stones. In the ruins of an ancient village in Switzerland, scientists found a piece of flat bread more than 4,000 years old.

The ingredients in flat breads—and other breads as well—usually depend on the kinds of grains people grow. Grains such as wheat, corn, barley, buckwheat, and millet are all common ingredients. Today, flat breads made of these grains are the basic foods in many people's diets. Here are some traditional flat breads.

- People in Greece and Middle Eastern countries, such as Syria, Lebanon, and Jordan, eat pita bread, a round bread with a large pocket inside.
- Scandinavians sometimes eat a traditional flat bread called lefse. It can be made with flour or potatoes.
- In Mexico and Central America, the traditional flat bread is the tortilla, made of cornmeal.

Papadum, an Indian flat bread

Matzo is a flat bread made from flour, which Jews eat most often during the religious holiday of Passover.

- During the holiday of Passover, Jews around the world eat matzo, a cracker-like flat bread.
- People in Brazil eat flat cakes made from the root of the cassava plant.
- Millet cakes and a flat bread called chapati are widely eaten in India.

Social Studies Activity

On a world map, locate some of the countries and regions where flat breads are eaten: Middle Eastern countries, Greece, Mexico, Central America, Brazil, India, and South Africa. With a partner, learn more about one of the flat breads mentioned here. Or choose another kind of bread. Find out how the bread is made and eaten.

- What are the primary ingredients of the bread? What grain is used?
- What do people eat on or with the bread?
- Is the bread usually eaten every day, during a certain season, or on holidays?
- In what countries are the breads most frequently eaten?

2 Facilitate

- Ask: **How do flat breads differ from loaves of bread?** (*Flat breads do not rise.*) **What is missing from the ingredients of flat breads that they do not rise?** (*They have no leaven.*)
- Ask students to name other flat breads they know. If any students are familiar with how to prepare flat breads, invite them to share or demonstrate their knowledge to the class.
- Invite interested students to learn how to make a flat bread they are familiar with, such as pita or tortillas.
- To extend this exploration, invite a cooking expert who is familiar with the different kinds of flat breads to address the class. Ask the cooking expert to compare and contrast the different kinds of flat breads. Ask what variety of ingredients are used in flat breads.

Social Studies Activity

Although students may find general information in encyclopedias, they may have to consult cookbooks specializing in international cuisine to find the answers. Alternatively, some travel books describe the principal foods eaten in regions and the ceremonies, if any, that go along with those foods. For some flat breads, students may be able to find a student from the country in which it is eaten who knows or has relatives who know about the foods.

Teaching Resources The following worksheets correlate with this page: Bread Around the World, page 122; and Where Is Bread Loaf, Vermont?, pages 123–124.

3 Assess

Activity Assessment

Ask students how they researched their answers. Make sure students answer all the parts of the activity.

Background

Integrating Science and Technology

Bakeries that produce crackers, pretzels, tortillas, pita, and other flat breads have an advantage because they do not use yeast. Yeast-leavened breads produce chemical emissions as the breads rise.

For commercial bakeries, these emissions are large enough that the Environmental Protection Agency has enacted legislation to ensure that bakeries control their emissions. Most of the approximately 600 commercial bakeries in the United States are located near well-populated areas.

The EPA reports that baking with yeast produces carbon dioxide, ethanol, glycerol, organic acids, and minor amounts of some other compounds. All these substances are released into the air.

Science

2 Facilitate

◆ Ask students: **Why are quick breads so named?** *(They can be prepared relatively quickly.)* Clarify that baking soda and baking powder produce carbon dioxide faster than yeast does. Ask: **If faster leavening agents are available, why do people in so many countries still use yeast?** *(Answers may vary. Samples: Yeast contributes to the flavor, yeast is easier to acquire.)*

Science Activity

Urge students to read through all the instructions before they begin. Stress that students must keep the conditions identical for the different test tubes. Students must work quickly. Before conducting the experiment, students in each group should decide who will be responsible for what tasks.

Students should measure the balloons before they begin. They can lay them flat and find the width at the widest part of the balloon. Two times the width is the circumference of the flat balloon.

To measure the inflated balloons, students can gently wind a piece of string around the balloon at the widest part and then measure the length of string.

Stress to students that the temperature in all four of the test tubes should start out the same.

Teaching Resources The following worksheets correlate with this page: Grow Bread Mold, page 125; Understanding Gluten, page 126; and Comparing Bread Nutrition, page 127.

3 Assess

Activity Assessment

Students' results may easily differ from those of other groups if students did not follow the instructions precisely and work quickly to reattach the balloon. Students may need to repeat the experiment in order to get results more similar to those of other groups.

146 ◆ L

Science

Quick Breads

Bran, blueberry, and raisin muffins are forms of quick breads.

Most of the bread you eat needs to rise before it is baked. Why is rising necessary? How does it happen?

Flour and water mixed together are the basis of bread. But this dough is dense. A leavening agent is needed to make the dough rise so it's less dense. The leavening agent works by producing carbon dioxide gas (CO_2), which then expands as it is heated. Hundreds of tiny bubbles enlarge and lift the dough. The spaces made by the bubbles are baked into the bread.

Most quick breads use either baking soda or baking powder as leavening agents. Baking soda and baking powder are very similar. Which one you use depends on the other ingredients in the recipe.

Baking soda is a chemical compound, also called sodium bicarbonate ($NaHCO_3$). As baking soda is heated, it decomposes into carbon dioxide gas and sodium hydroxide:

$$NaHCO_3 \rightarrow CO_2 + NaOH$$

Sodium hydroxide is a base. It can give an unpleasant, soapy taste to the bread. Therefore, the recipe needs to include an acidic ingredient. Orange juice, lemon juice, sour cream, and buttermilk contain weak acids. The acid in any one of these ingredients neutralizes the sodium hydroxide. Some breads taste better with acidic ingredients. However, there are many quick breads that are made without acids. These breads often use baking powder.

Baking powder has baking soda as its main ingredient. It also includes one or more acidic compounds, such as cream of tartar. The cream of tartar neutralizes the base that forms. Another ingredient in baking powder—cornstarch— keeps the compounds from clumping. Baking powder can be used in recipes that don't have an acidic ingredient.

Science Activity

Set up an experiment to measure the amount of carbon dioxide released by 3 leavening agents—yeast, baking soda, and baking powder.

◆ Fill 4 test tubes with equal amounts of warm water, between 38°C and 46°C. The water in each test tube should be the same temperature. Add $\frac{1}{2}$ spoonful of granulated sugar to each test tube. Shake to dissolve.

◆ Add 1 spoonful of one leavening agent per test tube (except for the control): active dry yeast, baking soda, and baking powder.

◆ Quickly attach a large balloon to each test tube. All balloons should be the same size. Gently shake each test tube to mix solid and water.

◆ Measure the circumference of each balloon after 5 minutes and then again after 15 minutes. Record your results.

Which ingredient caused the balloon to expand the fastest? Which ingredient caused a slow change in the balloon size? Therefore, which ingredient gave off the most CO_2?

146 ◆ L

Background

History Louis Pasteur was a French chemist and biologist who contributed an enormous amount to knowledge of microbiology. He lived from 1822 to 1895.

Pasteur was not the first to suspect that yeast played some role in the fermentation of alcoholic beverages, but he proved to himself that yeast caused fermentation and that certain bacteria caused wine to turn sour. He solved the problem of wine turning sour by heating the sugary water to kill the bacteria before fermentation started. This discovery helped to save France's wine and beer industry. The process is now known as pasteurization.

Pasteur also thought that certain microbes could be the cause of disease in people. At that time, few medical professionals believed that microorganisms caused disease. Pasteur proved his theories and died a hero.

How Yeast Works

Yeast is different from other leavening agents because it is actually a one-celled living organism whose activities produce carbon dioxide. Yeast breads include white and whole wheat breads as well as French and Italian bread. Rye bread and black breads are yeast breads that originated in Germany, Russia, and Scandinavia.

In yeast bread recipes, water and flour are mixed by stirring or kneading. As a result, proteins in the flour interconnect. The mixture develops long, strong, elastic strands of a new substance called gluten. Flour contains an enzyme, which breaks starch molecules in the flour into simple sugars. The yeast cells feed on simple sugars in the flour and begin to reproduce. One of the products of this process is carbon dioxide. The carbon dioxide gas forms air bubbles in the dough, causing it to expand. The gluten stretches but does not allow the bubbles to escape. So, the bread rises.

Bread dough is shaped into loaves before it is baked.

The effect of spice on yeast activity
(yeast activity for 2 grams of sugar, 1 gram of yeast, 30 mL of water)

Cardamom
Cinnamon
Ginger
Dry Mustard
Thyme

-150 -100 -50 0 50 100 150 200

Amount of Yeast Activity
(mL CO$_2$, increase or decrease)

For flavor, other ingredients, including spices, are often added. But spices in yeast breads can do more than just add flavor. Certain amounts of some spices can actually help yeast grow and release more carbon dioxide gas. Some spices—such as dry mustard—reduce yeast growth. The bar graph on this page shows how yeast activity will increase or decrease when different spices are added to a mixture of 2 grams sugar, 1 gram yeast, and 30 milliliters water.

Math Activity

Read the bar graph to answer the questions below. The effects of five spices are shown: cardamom, cinnamon, ginger, dry mustard, and thyme. For each spice, the amount added is 0.5 gram. The vertical line in the middle of the graph shows the amount of yeast activity before any spices are added.

◆ Which spice increased yeast activity the most?
◆ Which spice decreased yeast activity?
◆ About how much greater was the change in yeast activity for ginger than for cardamom?
◆ How much did yeast activity increase when thyme was added? About how much greater was the change in activity for thyme compared to cinnamon?
◆ What do you think would happen if 1 gram of cinnamon were added instead of 0.5 gram?

L ◆ 147

2 Facilitate

◆ Clarify that baking powder and baking soda are manufactured chemicals; they are not living organisms like yeast.
◆ The science interdisciplinary exploration worksheet on page 126 demonstrates glutens forming in a flour-water mixture.
◆ Ask: **Do you think the yeast is alive or dead after the bread has been baked? Explain.** *(The yeast was probably killed by the heat.)* **How would you know if the yeast were still alive?** *(The yeast would continue to make carbon dioxide and the bread would keep rising.)*
◆ Explain that people knead bread rather than beat it because kneading is gentle and helps the gluten to form long chains. Beating the bread dough would break up the chains.
◆ To extend this exploration, encourage students to modify the science activity to test the effect different spices have on yeast activity. Students can write directions for the activity and may wish to perform the activity if there is time.

Math Activity

Suggest that students use a transparent straight-edge laid vertically to read the values of the bar graph.

Teaching Resources The following worksheets correlate with this page: Do Bread Types Vary in Price?, page 128; Finding the Cost of Bread, page 129; and Sandwiches from Giant Bread, page 130.

3 Assess

Activity Assessment

Answers:
Ginger
Dry Mustard
about 20 mL greater
160 mL; about 115 mL
The amount of yeast activity would double to about 80 mL.

Background

Facts and Figures There are many microorganisms that are called yeasts. They live in the soil and on plants. Yeasts are classified by their biological names so that scientists can clarify whether they are talking about, for example, baker's yeast or brewer's yeast.

After Louis Pasteur proved the role of yeast in fermentation, yeasts began to be cultivated and used in large quantities.

Today, yeasts play a role in a variety of fermentation processes, such as baking and brewing alcoholic beverages. They are also used to make medicines, antibiotics, hormones, animal feed, and food.

2 Facilitate

- Ask students: **What is a tradition?** *(Something you do a particular way for many years)* **Besides passing on family recipes, what other kinds of traditions do families have?** *(Answers may vary. Samples: getting together every year on a particular holiday, vacationing at a special place)*

- Ask: **Does your family have traditional recipes that are passed down? What kinds of foods are they for?** *(Accept all answers.)*

- Ask: **Is there anybody here who collects and keeps little things as Grandma in the story does? Do your friends think this is odd?** *(Accept all answers.)*

- As students are discussing the story, look for ways to help students be sensitive to those who are less fortunate than themselves. Some students may live in families that struggle financially, and they may be hurt by remarks of others who do not know what it is like to go without.

- Ask: **How does the author's attitude toward bread sacks change?** *(At the beginning, the author hates the bread sacks. Later, she is proud to use them.)*

Language Arts Activity

To prompt student thinking, ask them to think of things a parent does that students imagine they would like to do if they had children. Some students may not have strong family ties. Some students may prefer to write about a tradition that they imagine a family would enjoy having.

Teaching Resources The following worksheets correlate with this page: "Starter" Breads, page 131; Write a Haiku, page 132; and Make a Bread Web, page 133.

A Family Tradition

In some families, traditions are handed down from one generation to another for years. Even the way something is made can be passed on, such as when an older person shows a younger one the secrets of a special recipe.

In this article, Janet Knickerbocker describes how her grandmother passed on the family bread recipe to the author. (*Note:* A bread sack may have been made from a cloth flour sack.)

GRANDMA ALWAYS MADE THE BREAD

Grandma always made the bread.

For every occasion, we could always count on those crusty loaves, sliced and slathered thick with butter.

Grandma always made the bread.

Now, Grandma had some peculiar ways. She was always saving this or that, slightly used pieces of tinfoil, bits of string, and bread sacks. Bread sacks. How I hated those. Carrying lunch to school in a bread sack. All the other children had shiny lunch pails where nothing got squashed together. But every time Grandma came for a visit, she packed our lunches and off we went, bread sack in hand.

Grandma always made the bread.

Grandma decided another family member should learn to make "the bread." As she gathered the ingredients and placed them in the bowl she explained each step.

"Heat the milk, just so. Add the butter and eggs now." Then came the flour, scoop after scoop. She deftly worked it into a smooth ball. Then she scraped the bowl with her hand, to gather each tiny bit of the dough. "We will need this," she said.

Suddenly, I realized why Grandma was a saver of oddities, why she went around snapping lights off and scolding us gently for being wasteful. Grandma had never had "enough" of anything in her life. Those tiny scraps of dough could help feed another hungry mouth, for whom bread had not been a treat, but a necessity. I felt very small.

Background

Facts and Figures Sourdough bread is made from a mixture of flour, water, and a beneficial bacteria that is left to ferment for several days. Different bacteria in the air cause the mixture to ferment differently in different regions. San Francisco sourdough bread is slightly different from sourdough bread made elsewhere in the country because of the airborne bacteria and yeasts that are more prevalent in that region.

Sourdough starter can be made by mixing one cup each of flour and water with a pinch of commercial starter. This mixture is left in a covered glass bowl unrefrigerated to ferment. The bacteria form bubbles in the mixture and give it a unique odor. Metal bowls cannot be used because they react with the mixture.

Language Arts Activity

Think about a tradition passed down in your family. It might be something that began long ago, with your grandparents or even earlier. Or it might be a newer tradition, such as one started by your parents. Write a description of this tradition. Express what it means to you by using concrete sensory details in your description.

The years have passed. Everything has changed, except Grandma. She always makes the bread, still saves bits of this and that in her starched apron pocket. I grew up and now I have a son.

The other day, I was making the bread. I instructed my small child how to heat the milk, just so. "Add the butter and eggs now." Then we added scoop after scoop of flour. We worked until we had a smooth ball of dough. Then we scraped the bowl with our hands, to gather each tiny bit. "We will need this," I stated matter-of-factly.

The smell of baking bread filled our little house as the bread sacks dried on the clothesline.

—*from "Grandma Always Made the Bread," in* Countryside & Small Stock Journal, *by Janet Knickerbocker*

Make Your Own Bread

One of the best ways to learn about bread is to make it yourself. Work as a class to make the Irish whole-wheat soda bread recipe on this page. Or work in groups to find other bread recipes to make.

◆ Take turns kneading the dough.
◆ Try to determine when leavening agents are working in your bread.
◆ After the bread has cooled, examine a slice of it closely. How big are the bubbles of carbon dioxide gas in your slice of bread?

Irish Soda Bread

3 cups whole-wheat flour

1 cup all-purpose flour

1 tablespoon salt

1 teaspoon baking soda

$\frac{3}{4}$ teaspoon double-acting baking powder

1 $\frac{2}{3}$ cups buttermilk

Combine the dry ingredients and mix thoroughly.
Add buttermilk to make a soft dough.
Knead on a lightly floured board for 2 or 3 minutes.
Form into a round loaf and place in a well-buttered 8-inch cake pan.
Bake in a preheated oven at 375°F for 35 to 40 minutes.
Let the loaf cool before cutting very thin slices.

3 Assess

Activity Assessment

Students may describe a real or imagined family tradition. Look for details and clear sentences. Students may range in their ability to express how the tradition feels to them.

Tie It Together

Time 2 days (1 day to arrange for the ingredients and kitchen facilities; two hours on the second day to make the bread, wait for it to cool, and eat it)

Tips Group students in threes. If ingredients are not available at school, have each student bring two ingredients. Stress that students must be careful to bring the correct ingredient (for example, all-purpose flour instead of bread flour).

◆ Remind students that they must measure ingredients precisely. Suggest that one student read the list of ingredients and amounts while the other two students measure and mix.
◆ Students should thoroughly wash, rinse, and dry their hands before working with ingredients or kneading.
◆ You may have to demonstrate kneading to students or ask a volunteer to demonstrate.
◆ If the dough is too sticky, students can lightly dust the dough and their hands with flour.
◆ Slice the bread for the students. Do not allow them to handle knives themselves.

Extend Challenge students to find other bread recipes and try them at home with adult supervision. Ask students to note how the ingredients varied and what effect that had on the final product.

Developing scientific thinking in students is important for a solid science education. To learn how to think scientifically, students need frequent opportunities to practice science process skills, critical thinking skills, as well as other skills that support scientific inquiry. The *Science Explorer* Skills Handbook introduces the following key science skills:

♦ Science Process Skills
♦ SI Measuring Skills
♦ Skills for Conducting a Scientific Investigation
♦ Critical Thinking Skills
♦ Information Organizing Skills
♦ Data Table and Graphing Skills

The Skills Handbook is designed as a reference for students to use whenever they need to review a science skill. You can use the activities provided in the Skills Handbook to teach or reinforce the skills.

Think Like a Scientist

Observing   ACTIVITY

Before students look at the photograph, remind them that an observation is what they can see, hear, smell, taste, or feel. Ask: **Which senses will you use to make observations from this photograph?** *(Sight is the only sense that can be used to make observations from the photograph.)* **What are some observations you can make from the photograph?** *(Answers may vary. Sample answers: The boy is wearing sneakers, sports socks, shorts, and a T-shirt; the boy is sitting in the grass holding something blue against his knee; the boy is looking at his knee; there is a soccer ball laying beside the boy.)* List the observations on the board. If students make any inferences or predictions about the boy at this point, ask: **Can you be sure your statement is accurate from just observing the photograph?** Help students understand how observations differ from inferences and predictions.

Inferring   ACTIVITY

Review students' observations from the photograph. Then ask: **What inferences can you make from your observations?** *(Students*

Think Like a Scientist

Although you may not know it, you think like a scientist every day. Whenever you ask a question and explore possible answers, you use many of the same skills that scientists do. Some of these skills are described on this page.

Observing

When you use one or more of your five senses to gather information about the world, you are **observing.** Hearing a dog bark, counting twelve green seeds, and smelling smoke are all observations. To increase the power of their senses, scientists sometimes use microscopes, telescopes, or other instruments that help them make more detailed observations.

An observation must be an accurate report of what your senses detect. It is important to keep careful records of your observations in science class by writing or drawing in a notebook. The information collected through observations is called evidence, or data.

Inferring

When you interpret an observation, you are **inferring,** or making an inference. For example, if you hear your dog barking, you may infer that someone is at your front door. To make this inference, you combine the evidence—the barking dog—and your experience or knowledge—you know that your dog barks when strangers approach—to reach a logical conclusion.

Notice that an inference is not a fact; it is only one of many possible interpretations for an observation. For example, your dog may be barking because it wants to go for a walk. An inference may turn out to be incorrect even if it is based on accurate observations and logical reasoning. The only way to find out if an inference is correct is to investigate further.

Predicting

When you listen to the weather forecast, you hear many predictions about the next day's weather—what the temperature will be, whether it will rain, and how windy it will be. Weather forecasters use observations and knowledge of weather patterns to predict the weather. The skill of **predicting** involves making an inference about a future event based on current evidence or past experience.

Because a prediction is an inference, it may prove to be false. In science class, you can test some of your predictions by doing experiments. For example, suppose you predict that larger paper airplanes can fly farther than smaller airplanes. How could you test your prediction?

ACTIVITY   Use the photograph to answer the questions below.

Observing Look closely at the photograph. List at least three observations.

Inferring Use your observations to make an inference about what has happened. What experience or knowledge did you use to make the inference?

Predicting Predict what will happen next. On what evidence or experience do you base your prediction?

may say that the boy hurt his knee playing soccer and is holding a coldpack against his injured knee.)* **What experience or knowledge helped you make this inference?** *(Students may have experienced knee injuries from playing soccer, and they may be familiar with coldpacks like the one the boy is using.)* **Can anyone suggest another possible interpretation for these observations?** *(Answers may vary. Sample answer: The boy hurt his knee jogging, and he just happened to sit beside a soccer ball his sister left in the yard.)* **How can you find out whether an inference is correct?** *(by further investigation)*

Predicting   ACTIVITY

After students come to some consensus about the inference that the boy hurt his knee, encourage them to make predictions about what will happen next. *(Students' predictions may vary. Sample answers: The boy will go to the doctor. A friend will help the boy home. The boy will get up and continue playing soccer.)*

Classifying

Could you imagine searching for a book in the library if the books were shelved in no particular order? Your trip to the library would be an all-day event! Luckily, librarians group together books on similar topics or by the same author. Grouping together items that are alike in some way is called **classifying.** You can classify items in many ways: by size, by shape, by use, and by other important characteristics.

Like librarians, scientists use the skill of classifying to organize information and objects. When things are sorted into groups, the relationships among them become easier to understand.

> **ACTIVITY**
> Classify the objects in the photograph into two groups based on any characteristic you choose. Then use another characteristic to classify the objects into three groups.

Making Models

Have you ever drawn a picture to help someone understand what you were saying? Such a drawing is one type of model. A model is a picture, diagram, computer image, or other representation of a complex object or process. **Making models** helps people understand things that they cannot observe directly.

Scientists often use models to represent things that are either very large or very small, such as the planets in the solar system, or the parts of a cell. Such models are physical models—drawings or three-dimensional structures that look like the real thing. Other models are mental models—mathematical equations or words that describe how something works.

> **ACTIVITY**
> This student is using a model to demonstrate what causes day and night on Earth. What do the flashlight and the tennis ball in the model represent?

Communicating

Whenever you talk on the phone, write a letter, or listen to your teacher at school, you are communicating. **Communicating** is the process of sharing ideas and information with other people. Communicating effectively requires many skills, including writing, reading, speaking, listening, and making models.

Scientists communicate to share results, information, and opinions. Scientists often communicate about their work in journals, over the telephone, in letters, and on the Internet. They also attend scientific meetings where they share their ideas with one another in person.

> **ACTIVITY**
> On a sheet of paper, write out clear, detailed directions for tying your shoe. Then exchange directions with a partner. Follow your partner's directions exactly. How successful were you at tying your shoe? How could your partner have communicated more clearly?

L ◆ 151

On what did you base your prediction? *(Scientific predictions are based on knowledge and experience.)* Point out that in science, predictions can often be tested with experiments.

Classifying   ACTIVITY

Encourage students to think of other common things that are classified. Then ask: **What things at home are classified?** *(Clothing might be classified in order to place it in the appropriate dresser drawer; glasses, plates, and silverware are grouped in different parts of the kitchen; screws, nuts, bolts, washers, and nails might be separated into small containers.)* **What are some things that scientists classify?** *(Scientists classify many things they study, including organisms, geological features and processes, and kinds of machines.)* After students have classified the different fruits in the photograph, have them share their criteria for classifying them. *(Some characteristics students might use include shape, color, size, and where they are grown.)*

Making Models   ACTIVITY

Ask students: **What are some models you have used to study science?** *(Students may have used human anatomical models, solar system models, maps, stream tables.)* **How did these models help you?** *(Models can help you learn about things that are difficult to study, because they are either too big, too small, or complex.)* Be sure students understand that a model does not have to be three dimensional. For example, a map in a textbook is a model. Ask: **What do the flashlight and tennis ball represent?** *(The flashlight represents the sun, and the ball represents Earth.)* **What quality of each item makes this a good model?** *(The flashlight gives off light, and the ball is round and can be rotated by the student.)*

Communicating   ACTIVITY

Challenge students to identify the methods of communication they've used today. Then ask: **How is the way you communicate with a friend similar to and different from the way scientists communicate about their work to other scientists?** *(Both may communicate using various methods, but scientists must be very detailed and precise, whereas communication between friends may be less detailed and precise.)* Encourage students to communicate like a scientist as they carry out the activity. *(Students' directions should be detailed and precise enough for another person to successfully follow.)*

Making Measurements

Measuring in SI

Review SI units in class with students. Begin by providing metric rulers, graduated cylinders, balances, and Celsius thermometers. Use these tools to reinforce that the meter is the unit of length, the liter is the unit of volume, the gram is the unit of mass, and the degree Celsius is the unit for temperature. Ask: **If you want to measure the length and width of your classroom, which SI unit would you use?** *(meter)* **Which unit would you use to measure the amount of matter in your textbook?** *(gram)* **Which would you use to measure how much water a drinking glass holds?** *(liter)* **When would you use the Celsius scale?** *(To measure the temperature of something)* Then use the measuring equipment to review SI prefixes. For example, ask: **What are the smallest units on the metric ruler?** *(millimeters)* **How many millimeters are there in 1 cm?** *(10 mm)* **How many in 10 cm?** *(100 mm)* **How many centimeters are there in 1 m?** *(100 cm)* **What does 1,000 m equal?** *(1 km)*

Length

ACTIVITY

(Students should state that the shell is 4.6 centimeters, or 46 millimeters, long.) If students need more practice measuring length, have them use meter sticks and metric rulers to measure various objects in the classroom.

Liquid Volume

ACTIVITY

(Students should state that the volume of water in the graduated cylinder is 62 milliliters.) If students need more practice measuring liquid volume, have them use a graduated cylinder to measure different volumes of water.

Making Measurements

When scientists make observations, it is not sufficient to say that something is "big" or "heavy." Instead, scientists use instruments to measure just how big or heavy an object is. By measuring, scientists can express their observations more precisely and communicate more information about what they observe.

Measuring in SI

The standard system of measurement used by scientists around the world is known as the International System of Units, which is abbreviated as SI (in French, *Système International d'Unités*). SI units are easy to use because they are based on multiples of 10. Each unit is ten times larger than the next smallest unit and one tenth the size of the next largest unit. The table lists the prefixes used to name the most common SI units.

Common SI Prefixes

Prefix	Symbol	Meaning
kilo-	k	1,000
hecto-	h	100
deka-	da	10
deci-	d	0.1 (one tenth)
centi-	c	0.01 (one hundredth)
milli-	m	0.001 (one thousandth)

Length To measure length, or the distance between two points, the unit of measure is the **meter (m).** The distance from the floor to a doorknob is approximately one meter. Long distances, such as the distance between two cities, are measured in kilometers (km). Small lengths are measured in centimeters (cm) or millimeters (mm). Scientists use metric rulers and meter sticks to measure length.

Common Conversions

1 km = 1,000 m
1 m = 100 cm
1 m = 1,000 mm
1 cm = 10 mm

The larger lines on the metric ruler in the picture show centimeter divisions, while the smaller, unnumbered lines show millimeter divisions. How many centimeters long is the shell? How many millimeters long is it? **ACTIVITY**

Liquid Volume To measure the volume of a liquid, or the amount of space it takes up, you will use a unit of measure known as the **liter (L).** One liter is the approximate volume of a medium-size carton of milk. Smaller volumes are measured in milliliters (mL). Scientists use graduated cylinders to measure liquid volume.

Common Conversion

1 L = 1,000 mL

The graduated cylinder in the picture is marked in milliliter divisions. Notice that the water in the cylinder has a curved surface. This curved surface is called the *meniscus*. To measure the volume, you must read the level at the lowest point of the meniscus. What is the volume of water in this graduated cylinder? **ACTIVITY**

Mass To measure mass, or the amount of matter in an object, you will use a unit of measure known as the **gram (g)**. One gram is approximately the mass of a paper clip. Larger masses are measured in kilograms (kg). Scientists use a balance to find the mass of an object.

Common Conversion

1 kg = 1,000 g

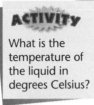

The mass of the apple in the picture is measured in kilograms. What is the mass of the apple? Suppose a recipe for applesauce called for one kilogram of apples. About how many apples would you need? **ACTIVITY**

Temperature
To measure the temperature of a substance, you will use the **Celsius scale**. Temperature is measured in degrees Celsius (°C) using a Celsius thermometer. Water freezes at 0°C and boils at 100°C.

ACTIVITY
What is the temperature of the liquid in degrees Celsius?

Converting SI Units

To use the SI system, you must know how to convert between units. Converting from one unit to another involves the skill of **calculating**, or using mathematical operations. Converting between SI units is similar to converting between dollars and dimes because both systems are based on multiples of ten.

Suppose you want to convert a length of 80 centimeters to meters. Follow these steps to convert between units.

1. Begin by writing down the measurement you want to convert—in this example, 80 centimeters.
2. Write a conversion factor that represents the relationship between the two units you are converting. In this example, the relationship is *1 meter = 100 centimeters*. Write this conversion factor as a fraction, making sure to place the units you are converting from (centimeters, in this example) in the denominator.

3. Multiply the measurement you want to convert by the fraction. When you do this, the units in the first measurement will cancel out with the units in the denominator. Your answer will be in the units you are converting to (meters, in this example).

Example

80 centimeters = ___?___ meters

$$80 \text{ centimeters} \times \frac{1 \text{ meter}}{100 \text{ centimeters}} = \frac{80 \text{ meters}}{100}$$

$$= 0.8 \text{ meters}$$

Convert between the following units. **ACTIVITY**
1. 600 millimeters = _?_ meters
2. 0.35 liters = _?_ milliliters
3. 1,050 grams = _?_ kilograms

Mass *(Students should state that the mass of the apple is 0.1 kilograms. They would need 10 apples to make 1 kilogram.)* If students need practice determining mass, have them use a balance to determine the mass of various common objects, such as coins, paper clips, and books. **ACTIVITY**

Temperature *(Students should state that the temperature of the liquid is 35°C.)* If students need practice measuring temperature, have them use a Celsius thermometer to measure the temperature of various water samples. **ACTIVITY**

Converting SI Units **ACTIVITY**

Review the steps for converting SI units and work through the example with students. Then ask: **How many millimeters are in 80 centimeters?** *(Students should follow the steps to calculate that 80 centimeters is equal to 800 millimeters.)*

Have students do the conversion problems in the activity. *(1. 600 millimeters = 0.6 meters; 2. 0.35 liters = 350 milliliters; 3. 1,050 grams = 1.05 kilograms)* If students need more practice converting SI units, have them make up conversion problems and trade with a partner.

Conducting a Scientific Investigation

Posing Questions

Before students do the activity on the next page, walk them through the steps of a typical scientific investigation. Begin by asking: **Why is a scientific question important to a scientific investigation?** (*It is the reason for conducting a scientific investigation.*) **What is the scientific question in the activity at the bottom of the next page?** (*Is a ball's bounce affected by the height from which it is dropped?*)

Developing a Hypothesis

Emphasize that a hypothesis is a possible explanation for a set of observations or answer to a scientific question, but it is *not* a guess. Ask: **On what information do scientists base their hypotheses?** (*Their observations and previous knowledge or experience*) Point out that a hypothesis does not always turn out to be correct. Ask: **In that case, do you think the scientist wasted his or her time? Explain your answer.** (*No, because the scientist probably learned from the investigation and may be able to develop another hypothesis that could be supported.*)

Designing an Experiment

Have a volunteer read the Experimental Procedure in the box. Then call on students to identify the manipulated variable (*amount of salt added to water*), the variables that are kept constant (*amount and starting temperature of water, placing containers in freezer*), the responding variable (*time it takes water to freeze*), and the control (*Container 3*).

Ask: **How might the experiment be affected if Container 1 had only 100 mL of water?** (*It wouldn't be a fair comparison with the containers that have more water.*) **What if Container 3 was not included in the experiment?** (*You wouldn't have anything to compare the other two containers with to know if their freezing times were faster or slower than normal.*) Help students understand the importance of keeping all variables constant except the manipulated variable. Also, be sure

Conducting a Scientific Investigation

In some ways, scientists are like detectives, piecing together clues to learn about a process or event. One way that scientists gather clues is by carrying out experiments. An experiment tests an idea in a careful, orderly manner. Although experiments do not all follow the same steps in the same order, many follow a pattern similar to the one described here.

Posing Questions

Experiments begin by asking a scientific question. A scientific question is one that can be answered by gathering evidence. For example, the question "Which freezes faster—fresh water or salt water?" is a scientific question because you can carry out an investigation and gather information to answer the question.

Developing a Hypothesis

The next step is to form a hypothesis. A **hypothesis** is a possible explanation for a set of observations or answer to a scientific question. In science, a hypothesis must be something that can be tested. A hypothesis can be worded as an *If…then…* statement. For example, a hypothesis might be *"If I add salt to fresh water, then the water will take longer to freeze."* A hypothesis worded this way serves as a rough outline of the experiment you should perform.

they understand the role of the control. Then ask: **What operational definition is used in this experiment?** (*"Frozen" means the time at which a wooden stick can no longer move in a container.*)

Designing an Experiment

Next you need to plan a way to test your hypothesis. Your plan should be written out as a step-by-step procedure and should describe the observations or measurements you will make.

Two important steps involved in designing an experiment are controlling variables and forming operational definitions.

Controlling Variables In a well-designed experiment, you need to keep all variables the same except for one. A **variable** is any factor that can change in an experiment. The factor that you change is called the **manipulated variable.** In this experiment, the manipulated variable is the amount of salt added to the water. Other factors, such as the amount of water or the starting temperature, are kept constant.

The factor that changes as a result of the manipulated variable is called the responding variable. The **responding variable** is what you measure or observe to obtain your results. In this experiment, the responding variable is how long the water takes to freeze.

An experiment in which all factors except one are kept constant is a **controlled experiment.** Most controlled experiments include a test called the control. In this experiment, Container 3 is the control. Because no salt is added to Container 3, you can compare the results from the other containers to it. Any difference in results must be due to the addition of salt alone.

Forming Operational Definitions

Another important aspect of a well-designed experiment is having clear operational definitions. An **operational definition** is a statement that describes how a particular variable is to be measured or how a term is to be defined. For example, in this experiment, how will you determine if the water has frozen? You might decide to insert a stick in each container at the start of the experiment. Your operational definition of "frozen" would be the time at which the stick can no longer move.

EXPERIMENTAL PROCEDURE

1. Fill 3 containers with 300 milliliters of cold tap water.

2. Add 10 grams of salt to Container 1; stir. Add 20 grams of salt to Container 2; stir. Add no salt to Container 3.

3. Place the 3 containers in a freezer.

4. Check the containers every 15 minutes. Record your observations.

Interpreting Data

The observations and measurements you make in an experiment are called data. At the end of an experiment, you need to analyze the data to look for any patterns or trends. Patterns often become clear if you organize your data in a data table or graph. Then think through what the data reveal. Do they support your hypothesis? Do they point out a flaw in your experiment? Do you need to collect more data?

Drawing Conclusions

A conclusion is a statement that sums up what you have learned from an experiment. When you draw a conclusion, you need to decide whether the data you collected support your hypothesis or not. You may need to repeat an experiment several times before you can draw any conclusions from it. Conclusions often lead you to pose new questions and plan new experiments to answer them.

Is a ball's bounce affected by the height from which it is dropped? Using the steps just described, plan a controlled experiment to investigate this problem. **ACTIVITY**

L ◆ 155

Interpreting Data

Emphasize the importance of collecting accurate and detailed data in a scientific investigation. Ask: **What if you forgot to record some data during your investigation?** *(They wouldn't be able to completely analyze their data to draw valid conclusions.)* Then ask: **Why are data tables and graphs a good way to organize data?** *(They often make it easier to compare and analyze data.)* You may wish to have students review the Skills Handbook pages on Creating Data Tables and Graphs at this point.

Drawing Conclusions

Help students understand that a conclusion is not necessarily the end of a scientific investigation. A conclusion about one experiment may lead right into another experiment. Point out that in scientific investigations, a conclusion is a summary and explanation of the results of an experiment.

Tell students to suppose that for the Experimental Procedure described on this page, they obtained the following results: Container 1 froze in 45 minutes, Container 2 in 80 minutes, and Container 3 in 25 minutes. Ask: **What conclusions can you draw about this experiment?** *(Students might conclude that the more salt that is added to fresh water, the longer it takes the water to freeze. The hypothesis is supported, and the question of which freezes faster is answered—fresh water.)*

You might wish to have students work in pairs to plan the controlled experiment. **ACTIVITY** *(Students should develop a hypothesis, such as "If I increase the height from which a ball is dropped, then the height of its bounce will increase." They can test the hypothesis by dropping balls from varying heights (the manipulated variable). All trials should be done with the same kind of ball and on the same surface (constant variables). For each trial, they should measure the height of the bounce (responding variable).)* After students have designed the experiment, provide rubber balls and invite them to carry out the experiment so they can collect and interpret data and draw conclusions.

Thinking Critically

Comparing and Contrasting

Emphasize that the skill of comparing and contrasting often relies on good observation skills, as in this activity. *(Students' answers may vary. Sample answer: Similarities—both are dogs and have four legs, two eyes, two ears, brown and white fur, black noses, pink tongues; Differences—smooth coat vs. rough coat, more white fur vs. more brown fur, shorter vs. taller, long ears vs. short ears.)*

Applying Concepts

Point out to students that they apply concepts that they learn in school in their daily lives. For example, they learn to add, subtract, multiply, and divide in school. If they get a paper route or some other part-time job, they can apply those concepts. Challenge students to practice applying concepts by doing the activity. *(Antifreeze lowers the temperature at which the solution will freeze, and thus keeps the water in the radiator from freezing.)*

Interpreting Illustrations

Again, point out the need for good observation skills. Ask: **What is the difference between "interpreting illustrations" and "looking at the pictures"?** *("Interpreting illustrations" requires thorough examination of the illustrations, captions, and labels, while "looking at the pictures" implies less thorough examination.)* Encourage students to thoroughly examine the diagram as they do the activity. *(Students' paragraphs will vary, but should describe the internal anatomy of an earthworm, including some of the organs in the earthworm.)*

Thinking Critically

Has a friend ever asked for your advice about a problem? If so, you may have helped your friend think through the problem in a logical way. Without knowing it, you used critical-thinking skills to help your friend. Critical thinking involves the use of reasoning and logic to solve problems or make decisions. Some critical-thinking skills are described below.

Comparing and Contrasting

When you examine two objects for similarities and differences, you are using the skill of **comparing and contrasting.** Comparing involves identifying similarities, or common characteristics. Contrasting involves identifying differences. Analyzing objects in this way can help you discover details that you might otherwise overlook.

Compare and contrast the two animals in the photo. First list all the similarities that you see. Then list all the differences. **ACTIVITY**

Applying Concepts

When you use your knowledge about one situation to make sense of a similar situation, you are using the skill of **applying concepts.** Being able to transfer your knowledge from one situation to another shows that you truly understand a concept. You may use this skill in answering test questions that present different problems from the ones you've reviewed in class.

You have just learned that water takes longer to freeze when other substances are mixed into it. Use this knowledge to explain why people need a substance called antifreeze in their car's radiator in the winter.

Interpreting Illustrations

Diagrams, photographs, and maps are included in textbooks to help clarify what you read. These illustrations show processes, places, and ideas in a visual manner. The skill called **interpreting illustrations** can help you learn from these visual elements. To understand an illustration, take the time to study the illustration along with all the written information that accompanies it. Captions identify the key concepts shown in the illustration. Labels point out the important parts of a diagram or map, while keys identify the symbols used in a map.

▲ Internal anatomy of an earthworm

Study the diagram above. Then write a short paragraph explaining what you have learned. **ACTIVITY**

Relating Cause and Effect

If one event causes another event to occur, the two events are said to have a cause-and-effect relationship. When you determine that such a relationship exists between two events, you use a skill called **relating cause and effect.** For example, if you notice an itchy, red bump on your skin, you might infer that a mosquito bit you. The mosquito bite is the cause, and the bump is the effect.

It is important to note that two events do not necessarily have a cause-and-effect relationship just because they occur together. Scientists carry out experiments or use past experience to determine whether a cause-and-effect relationship exists.

You are on a camping trip and your flashlight has stopped working. **ACTIVITY** List some possible causes for the flashlight malfunction. How could you determine which cause-and-effect relationship has left you in the dark?

Making Generalizations

When you draw a conclusion about an entire group based on information about only some of the group's members, you are using a skill called **making generalizations.** For a generalization to be valid, the sample you choose must be large enough and representative of the entire group. You might, for example, put this skill to work at a farm stand if you see a sign that says, "Sample some grapes before you buy." If you sample a few sweet grapes, you may conclude that all the grapes are sweet—and purchase a large bunch.

A team of scientists needs to determine whether the water in a large reservoir is safe to drink. **ACTIVITY** How could they use the skill of making generalizations to help them? What should they do?

Making Judgments

When you evaluate something to decide whether it is good or bad, or right or wrong, you are using a skill called **making judgments.** For example, you make judgments when you decide to eat healthful foods or to pick up litter in a park. Before you make a judgment, you need to think through the pros and cons of a situation, and identify the values or standards that you hold.

Should children and teens be required to wear helmets when bicycling? **ACTIVITY** Explain why you feel the way you do.

Problem Solving

When you use critical-thinking skills to resolve an issue or decide on a course of action, you are using a skill called **problem solving.** Some problems, such as how to convert a fraction into a decimal, are straightforward. Other problems, such as figuring out why your computer has stopped working, are complex. Some complex problems can be solved using the trial and error method—try out one solution first, and if that doesn't work, try another. Other useful problem-solving strategies include making models and brainstorming possible solutions with a partner.

L ◆ 157

Relating Cause and Effect

Emphasize that not all events that occur together have a cause-and-effect relationship. For example, tell students that you went to the grocery and your car stalled. Ask: **Is there a cause-and-effect relationship in this situation? Explain your answer.** (*No, because going to the grocery could not cause a car to stall. There must be another cause to make the car stall.*) Have students do the activity to practice relating cause and effect. (*Students should identify that the flashlight not working is the effect. Some possible causes include dead batteries, a burned-out light bulb, or a loose part.*)

Making Generalizations

Point out the importance of having a large, representative sample before making a generalization. Ask: **If you went fishing at a lake and caught three catfish, could you make the generalization that all fish in the lake are catfish? Why or why not?** (*No, because there might be other kinds of fish you didn't catch because they didn't like the bait or they may be in other parts of the lake.*) **How could you make a generalization about the kinds of fish in the lake?** (*By having a larger sample*) Have students do the activity in the Student Edition to practice making generalizations. (*The scientists should collect and test water samples from a number of different parts of the reservoir.*)

Making Judgments

Remind students that they make a judgment almost every time they make a decision. Ask: **What steps should you follow to make a judgment?** (*Gather information, list pros and cons, analyze values, make judgment*) Invite students to do the activity, and then to share and discuss the judgments they made. (*Students' judgments will vary, but should be supported by valid reasoning. Sample answer: Children and teens should be required to wear helmets when bicycling because helmets have been proven to save lives and reduce head injuries.*)

Problem Solving **ACTIVITY**

Challenge student pairs to solve a problem about a soapbox derby. Explain that their younger brother is building a car to enter in the race. The brother wants to know how to make his soapbox car go faster. After student pairs have considered the problem, have them share their ideas about solutions with the class. (*Most will probably suggest using trial and error by making small changes to the car and testing the car after each change. Some students may suggest making and manipulating a model.*)

L ◆ 157

Organizing Information

Concept Maps

Challenge students to make a concept map with at least three levels of concepts to organize information about types of transportation. All students should start with the phrase *types of transportation* at the top of the concept map. After that point, their concept maps may vary. *(For example, some students might place* private transportation *and* public transportation *at the next level, while other students might have* human-powered *and* gas-powered. *Make sure students connect the concepts with linking words. Challenge students to include cross-linkages as well.)*

Compare/ Contrast Tables **ACTIVITY**

Have students make their own compare/contrast tables using two or more different sports or other activities, such as playing musical instruments. Emphasize that students should select characteristics that highlight the similarities and differences between the activities. *(Students' compare/contrast tables should include several appropriate characteristics and list information about each activity for every characteristic.)*

Organizing Information

As you read this textbook, how can you make sense of all the information it contains? Some useful tools to help you organize information are shown on this page. These tools are called **graphic organizers** because they give you a visual picture of a topic, showing at a glance how key concepts are related.

Concept Maps

Concept maps are useful tools for organizing information on broad topics. A concept map begins with a general concept and shows how it can be broken down into more specific concepts. In that way, relationships between concepts become easier to understand.

A concept map is constructed by placing concept words (usually nouns) in ovals and connecting them with linking words. Often, the most general concept word is placed at the top, and the words become more specific as you move downward. Often the linking words, which are written on a line extending between two ovals, describe the relationship between the two concepts they connect. If you follow any string of concepts and linking words down the map, it should read like a sentence.

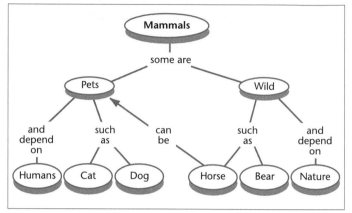

Some concept maps include linking words that connect a concept on one branch of the map to a concept on another branch. These linking words, called cross-linkages, show more complex interrelationships among concepts.

Compare/Contrast Tables

Compare/contrast tables are useful tools for sorting out the similarities and differences between two or more items. A table provides an organized framework in which to compare items based on specific characteristics that you identify.

To create a compare/contrast table, list the items to be compared across the top of a table. Then list the characteristics that will form the basis of your comparison in the left-hand

Characteristic	Baseball	Basketball
Number of Players	9	5
Playing Field	Baseball diamond	Basketball court
Equipment	Bat, baseball, mitts	Basket, basketball

column. Complete the table by filling in information about each characteristic, first for one item and then for the other.

Venn Diagrams

Another way to show similarities and differences between items is with a Venn diagram. A Venn diagram consists of two or more circles that partially overlap. Each circle represents a particular concept or idea. Common characteristics, or similarities, are written within the area of overlap between the two circles. Unique characteristics, or differences, are written in the parts of the circles outside the area of overlap.

To create a Venn diagram, draw two overlapping circles. Label the circles with the names of the items being compared. Write the

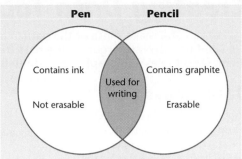

unique characteristics in each circle outside the area of overlap. Then write the shared characteristics within the area of overlap.

Flowcharts

A flowchart can help you understand the order in which certain events have occurred or should occur. Flowcharts are useful for outlining the stages in a process or the steps in a procedure.

To make a flowchart, write a brief description of each event in a box. Place the first event at the top of the page, followed by the second event, the third event, and so on. Then draw an arrow to connect each event to the one that occurs next.

Preparing Pasta

Boil water → Cook pasta → Drain water → Add sauce

Cycle Diagrams

A cycle diagram can be used to show a sequence of events that is continuous, or cyclical. A continuous sequence does not have an end because, when the final event is over, the first event begins again. Like a flowchart, a cycle diagram can help you understand the order of events.

To create a cycle diagram, write a brief description of each event in a box. Place one event at the top of the page in the center. Then, moving in a clockwise direction around an imaginary circle, write each event in its proper sequence. Draw arrows that connect each event to the one that occurs next, forming a continuous circle.

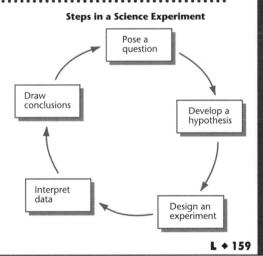

Steps in a Science Experiment

L ◆ 159

Venn Diagrams **ACTIVITY**

Students can use the same information from their compare/contrast tables to create a Venn diagram. Make sure students understand that the overlapping area of the circles is used to list similarities and the parts of the circles outside the overlap area are used to show differences. If students want to list similarities and differences among three activities, show them how to add a third circle that overlaps each of the other two circles and has an area of overlap for all three circles. (*Students' Venn diagrams will vary. Make sure they have accurately listed similarities in the overlap area and differences in the parts of the circles that do not overlap.*)

Flowcharts **ACTIVITY**

Encourage students to create a flowchart to show the things they did this morning as they got ready for school. Remind students that a flowchart should show the correct order in which events occurred or should occur. (*Students' flowcharts will vary somewhat. A typical flowchart might include: got up → ate breakfast → took a shower → brushed teeth → got dressed → gathered books and homework → put on jacket.*)

Cycle Diagrams **ACTIVITY**

Review that a cycle diagram shows a sequence of events that is continuous. Then challenge students to create a cycle diagram that shows how the weather changes with the seasons where they live. (*Students' cycle diagrams may vary, though most will include four steps, one for each season.*)

Creating Data Tables and Graphs

Data Tables

Have students create a data table to show how much time they spend on different activities during one week. Suggest that students first list the main activities they do every week. Then they should determine the amount of time they spend on each activity each day. Remind students to give this data table a title. *(Students' data tables will vary. A sample data table is shown below.)*

Bar Graphs

Students can use the data from the data table they created to make a bar graph showing how much time they spend on different activities during a week. The vertical axis should be divided into units of time, such as hours. Remind students to label both axes and give their graph a title. *(Students' bar graphs will vary. A sample bar graph is shown below.)*

Creating Data Tables and Graphs

How can you make sense of the data in a science experiment? The first step is to organize the data to help you understand them. Data tables and graphs are helpful tools for organizing data.

Data Tables

You have gathered your materials and set up your experiment. But before you start, you need to plan a way to record what happens during the experiment. By creating a data table, you can record your observations and measurements in an orderly way.

Suppose, for example, that a scientist conducted an experiment to find out how many Calories people of different body masses burn while doing various activities. The data table shows the results.

Notice in this data table that the manipulated variable (body mass) is the heading of one column. The responding variable (for Experiment 1, the number of Calories burned while bicycling) is the heading of the next column. Additional columns were added for related experiments.

CALORIES BURNED IN 30 MINUTES OF ACTIVITY			
Body Mass	Experiment 1 Bicycling	Experiment 2 Playing Basketball	Experiment 3 Watching Television
30 kg	60 Calories	120 Calories	21 Calories
40 kg	77 Calories	164 Calories	27 Calories
50 kg	95 Calories	206 Calories	33 Calories
60 kg	114 Calories	248 Calories	38 Calories

Bar Graphs

To compare how many Calories a person burns doing various activities, you could create a bar graph. A bar graph is used to display data in a number of separate, or distinct, categories. In this example, bicycling, playing basketball, and watching television are three separate categories.

To create a bar graph, follow these steps.

1. On graph paper, draw a horizontal, or *x*-, axis and a vertical, or *y*-, axis.
2. Write the names of the categories to be graphed along the horizontal axis. Include an overall label for the axis as well.
3. Label the vertical axis with the name of the responding variable. Include units of measurement. Then create a scale along the axis by marking off equally spaced numbers that cover the range of the data collected.
4. For each category, draw a solid bar using the scale on the vertical axis to determine the

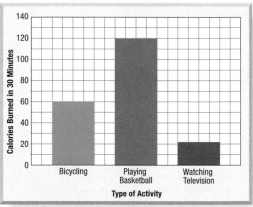

Calories Burned by a 30-kilogram Person in Various Activities

appropriate height. For example, for bicycling, draw the bar as high as the 60 mark on the vertical axis. Make all the bars the same width and leave equal spaces between them.
5. Add a title that describes the graph.

Time Spent on Different Activities in a Week				
	Going to Classes	Eating Meals	Playing Soccer	Watching Television
Monday	6	2	2	0.5
Tuesday	6	1.5	1.5	1.5
Wednesday	6	2	1	2
Thursday	6	2	2	1.5
Friday	6	2	2	0.5
Saturday	0	2.5	2.5	1
Sunday	0	3	1	2

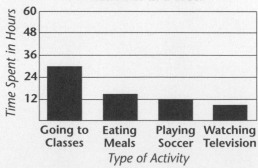

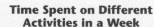

Time Spent on Different Activities in a Week

Line Graphs

To see whether a relationship exists between body mass and the number of Calories burned while bicycling, you could create a line graph. A line graph is used to display data that show how one variable (the responding variable) changes in response to another variable (the manipulated variable). You can use a line graph when your manipulated variable is *continuous*, that is, when there are other points between the ones that you tested. In this example, body mass is a continuous variable because there are other body masses between 30 and 40 kilograms (for example, 31 kilograms). Time is another example of a continuous variable.

Line graphs are powerful tools because they allow you to estimate values for conditions that you did not test in the experiment. For example, you can use the line graph to estimate that a 35-kilogram person would burn 68 Calories while bicycling.

To create a line graph, follow these steps.

1. On graph paper, draw a horizontal, or *x*-, axis and a vertical, or *y*-, axis.
2. Label the horizontal axis with the name of the manipulated variable. Label the vertical axis with the name of the responding variable. Include units of measurement.
3. Create a scale on each axis by marking off equally spaced numbers that cover the range of the data collected.
4. Plot a point on the graph for each piece of data. In the line graph above, the dotted lines show how to plot the first data point (30 kilograms and 60 Calories). Draw an imaginary vertical line extending up from the horizontal axis at the 30-kilogram mark. Then draw an imaginary horizontal line extending across from the vertical axis at the 60-Calorie mark. Plot the point where the two lines intersect.

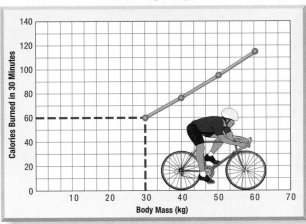

Effect of Body Mass on Calories Burned While Bicycling

5. Connect the plotted points with a solid line. (In some cases, it may be more appropriate to draw a line that shows the general trend of the plotted points. In those cases, some of the points may fall above or below the line. Also, not all graphs are linear. It may be more appropriate to draw a curve to connect the points.)
6. Add a title that identifies the variables or relationship in the graph.

> **ACTIVITY**
> Create line graphs to display the data from Experiment 2 and Experiment 3 in the data table.

> **ACTIVITY**
> You read in the newspaper that a total of 4 centimeters of rain fell in your area in June, 2.5 centimeters fell in July, and 1.5 centimeters fell in August. What type of graph would you use to display these data? Use graph paper to create the graph.

L ◆ 161

Line Graphs

Walk students through the steps involved in creating a line graph using the example illustrated on the page. For example, ask: **What is the label on the horizontal axis? On the vertical axis?** *(Body Mass (kg); Calories Burned in 30 Minutes)* **What scales are used on each axis?** *(3 squares per 10 kg on the x-axis and 2 squares per 20 calories on the y-axis)* **What does the second data point represent?** *(77 Calories burned for a body mass of 40 kg)* **What trend or pattern does the graph show?** *(The number of Calories burned in 30 minutes of cycling increases with body mass.)*

Have students follow the steps to carry out the first activity. *(Students should make a different graph for each experiment with different y-axis scales to practice making scales appropriate for data. See sample graphs below.)*

Have students carry out the second activity. *(Students should conclude that a bar graph would be best for displaying the data. A sample bar graph for these data is shown below.)*

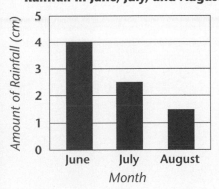

Rainfall in June, July, and August

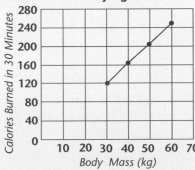

Effect of Body Mass on Calories Burned While Playing Basketball

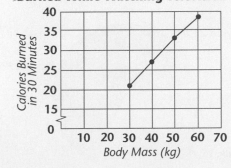

Effect of Body Mass on Calories Burned While Watching Television

Circle Graphs

Emphasize that a circle graph has to include 100 percent of the categories for the topic being graphed. For example, ask: **Could the data in the bar graph titled "Calories Burned by a 30-kilogram Person in Various Activities" (on the previous page) be shown in a circle graph? Why or why not?** *(No, because it does not include all the possible ways a 30-kilogram person can burn Calories.)* Then walk students through the steps for making a circle graph. Help students to use a compass and a protractor. Use the protractor to illustrate that a circle has 360 degrees. Make sure students understand the mathematical calculations involved in making a circle graph.

You might wish to have students work in pairs to **ACTIVITY** complete the activity. *(Students' circle graphs should look like the graph below.)*

Circle Graphs

Like bar graphs, circle graphs can be used to display data in a number of separate categories. Unlike bar graphs, however, circle graphs can only be used when you have data for *all* the categories that make up a given topic. A circle graph is sometimes called a pie chart because it resembles a pie cut into slices. The pie represents the entire topic, while the slices represent the individual categories. The size of a slice indicates what percentage of the whole a particular category makes up.

The data table below shows the results of a survey in which 24 teenagers were asked to identify their favorite sport. The data were then used to create the circle graph at the right.

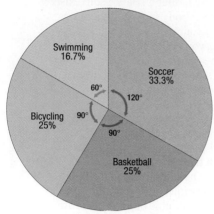

Sports That Teens Prefer

Swimming 16.7%
Soccer 33.3%
Bicycling 25%
Basketball 25%

FAVORITE SPORTS	
Sport	Number of Students
Soccer	8
Basketball	6
Bicycling	6
Swimming	4

To create a circle graph, follow these steps.
1. Use a compass to draw a circle. Mark the center of the circle with a point. Then draw a line from the center point to the top of the circle.
2. Determine the size of each "slice" by setting up a proportion where x equals the number of degrees in a slice. (NOTE: A circle contains 360 degrees.) For example, to find the number of degrees in the "soccer" slice, set up the following proportion:

$$\frac{\text{students who prefer soccer}}{\text{total number of students}} = \frac{x}{\text{total number of degrees in a circle}}$$

$$\frac{8}{24} = \frac{x}{360}$$

Cross-multiply and solve for x.
$$24x = 8 \times 360$$
$$x = 120$$
The "soccer" slice should contain 120 degrees.

3. Use a protractor to measure the angle of the first slice, using the line you drew to the top of the circle as the 0° line. Draw a line from the center of the circle to the edge for the angle you measured.
4. Continue around the circle by measuring the size of each slice with the protractor. Start measuring from the edge of the previous slice so the wedges do not overlap. When you are done, the entire circle should be filled in.
5. Determine the percentage of the whole circle that each slice represents. To do this, divide the number of degrees in a slice by the total number of degrees in a circle (360), and multiply by 100%. For the "soccer" slice, you can find the percentage as follows:

$$\frac{120}{360} \times 100\% = 33.3\%$$

6. Use a different color to shade in each slice. Label each slice with the name of the category and with the percentage of the whole it represents.
7. Add a title to the circle graph.

In a class of 28 students, 12 students **ACTIVITY** take the bus to school, 10 students walk, and 6 students ride their bicycles. Create a circle graph to display these data.

Ways Students Get to School

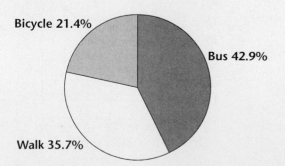

Bicycle 21.4%
Bus 42.9%
Walk 35.7%

Safety Symbols

These symbols alert you to possible dangers in the laboratory and remind you to work carefully.

Safety Goggles Always wear safety goggles to protect your eyes in any activity involving chemicals, flames or heating, or the possibility of broken glassware.

Lab Apron Wear a laboratory apron to protect your skin and clothing from damage.

Breakage You are working with materials that may be breakable, such as glass containers, glass tubing, thermometers, or funnels. Handle breakable materials with care. Do not touch broken glassware.

Heat-resistant Gloves Use an oven mitt or other hand protection when handling hot materials. Hot plates, hot glassware, or hot water can cause burns. Do not touch hot objects with your bare hands.

Heating Use a clamp or tongs to pick up hot glassware. Do not touch hot objects with your bare hands.

Sharp Object Pointed-tip scissors, scalpels, knives, needles, pins, or tacks are sharp. They can cut or puncture your skin. Always direct a sharp edge or point away from yourself and others. Use sharp instruments only as instructed.

Electric Shock Avoid the possibility of electric shock. Never use electrical equipment around water, or when the equipment is wet or your hands are wet. Be sure cords are untangled and cannot trip anyone. Disconnect the equipment when it is not in use.

Corrosive Chemical You are working with an acid or another corrosive chemical. Avoid getting it on your skin or clothing, or in your eyes. Do not inhale the vapors. Wash your hands when you are finished with the activity.

Poison Do not let any poisonous chemical come in contact with your skin, and do not inhale its vapors. Wash your hands when you are finished with the activity.

Physical Safety When an experiment involves physical activity, take precautions to avoid injuring yourself or others. Follow instructions from your teacher. Alert your teacher if there is any reason you should not participate in the activity.

Animal Safety Treat live animals with care to avoid harming the animals or yourself. Working with animal parts or preserved animals also may require caution. Wash your hands when you are finished with the activity.

Plant Safety Handle plants in the laboratory or during field work only as directed by your teacher. If you are allergic to certain plants, tell your teacher before doing an activity in which those plants are used. Avoid touching harmful plants such as poison ivy, poison oak, or poison sumac, or plants with thorns. Wash your hands when you are finished with the activity.

Flames You may be working with flames from a lab burner, candle, or matches. Tie back loose hair and clothing. Follow instructions from your teacher about lighting and extinguishing flames.

No Flames Flammable materials may be present. Make sure there are no flames, sparks, or other exposed heat sources present.

Fumes When poisonous or unpleasant vapors may be involved, work in a ventilated area. Avoid inhaling vapors directly. Only test an odor when directed to do so by your teacher, and use a wafting motion to direct the vapor toward your nose.

Disposal Chemicals and other laboratory materials used in the activity must be disposed of safely. Follow the instructions from your teacher.

Hand Washing Wash your hands thoroughly when finished with the activity. Use antibacterial soap and warm water. Lather both sides of your hands and between your fingers. Rinse well.

General Safety Awareness You may see this symbol when none of the symbols described earlier appears. In this case, follow the specific instructions provided. You may also see this symbol when you are asked to develop your own procedure in a lab. Have your teacher approve your plan before you go further.

L ◆ 163

Laboratory Safety

Laboratory safety is an essential element of a successful science class. It is important for you to emphasize laboratory safety to students. Students need to understand exactly what is safe and unsafe behavior, and what the rationale is behind each safety rule.

Review with students the Safety Symbols and Science Safety Rules listed on this and the next two pages. Then follow the safety guidelines below to ensure that your classroom will be a safe place for students to learn science.

◆ Post safety rules in the classroom and review them regularly with students.
◆ Familiarize yourself with the safety procedures for each activity before introducing it to your students.
◆ Review specific safety precautions with students before beginning every science activity.
◆ Always act as an exemplary role model by displaying safe behavior.
◆ Know how to use safety equipment, such as fire extinguishers and fire blankets, and always have it accessible.
◆ Have students practice leaving the classroom quickly and orderly to prepare them for emergencies.
◆ Explain to students how to use the intercom or other available means of communication to get help during an emergency.
◆ Never leave students unattended while they are engaged in science activities.
◆ Provide enough space for students to safely carry out science activities.
◆ Keep your classroom and all science materials in proper condition. Replace worn or broken items.
◆ Instruct students to report all accidents and injuries to you immediately.

Laboratory Safety

Additional tips are listed below for the Science Safety Rules discussed on these two pages. Please keep these tips in mind when you carry out science activities in your classroom.

General Precautions

◆ For open-ended activities such as Chapter Projects, go over general safety guidelines with students. Have students submit their procedures or design plans in writing and check them for safety considerations.

◆ In an activity where students are directed to taste something, be sure to store the material in clean, *nonscience* containers. Distribute the material to students in *new* plastic or paper dispensables, which should be discarded after the tasting. Tasting or eating should never be done in a lab classroom.

◆ During physical activity, make sure students do not overexert themselves.

◆ Remind students to handle microscopes and telescopes with care to avoid breakage.

Heating and Fire Safety

◆ No flammable substances should be in use around hot plates, light bulbs, or open flames.

◆ Test tubes should be heated only in water baths.

◆ Students should be permitted to strike matches to light candles or burners *only* with strict supervision. When possible, you should light the flames, especially when working with younger students.

◆ Be sure to have proper ventilation when fumes are produced during a procedure.

◆ All electrical equipment used in the lab should have GFI switches.

Using Chemicals Safely

◆ When students use both chemicals and microscopes in one activity, microscopes should be in a separate part of the room from the chemicals so that when students remove their goggles to use the microscopes, their eyes are not at risk.

Science Safety Rules

To prepare yourself to work safely in the laboratory, read over the following safety rules. Then read them a second time. Make sure you understand and follow each rule. Ask your teacher to explain any rules you do not understand.

Dress Code

1. To protect yourself from injuring your eyes, wear safety goggles whenever you work with chemicals, burners, glassware, or any substance that might get into your eyes. If you wear contact lenses, notify your teacher.
2. Wear a lab apron or coat whenever you work with corrosive chemicals or substances that can stain.
3. Tie back long hair to keep it away from any chemicals, flames, or equipment.
4. Remove or tie back any article of clothing or jewelry that can hang down and touch chemicals, flames, or equipment. Roll up or secure long sleeves.
5. Never wear open shoes or sandals.

General Precautions

6. Read all directions for an experiment several times before beginning the activity. Carefully follow all written and oral instructions. If you are in doubt about any part of the experiment, ask your teacher for assistance.
7. Never perform activities that are not assigned or authorized by your teacher. Obtain permission before "experimenting" on your own. Never handle any equipment unless you have specific permission.
8. Never perform lab activities without direct supervision.
9. Never eat or drink in the laboratory.
10. Keep work areas clean and tidy at all times. Bring only notebooks and lab manuals or written lab procedures to the work area. All other items, such as purses and backpacks, should be left in a designated area.
11. Do not engage in horseplay.

First Aid

12. Always report all accidents or injuries to your teacher, no matter how minor. Notify your teacher immediately about any fires.
13. Learn what to do in case of specific accidents, such as getting acid in your eyes or on your skin. (Rinse acids from your body with lots of water.)
14. Be aware of the location of the first-aid kit, but do not use it unless instructed by your teacher. In case of injury, your teacher should administer first aid. Your teacher may also send you to the school nurse or call a physician.
15. Know the location of emergency equipment, such as the fire extinguisher and fire blanket, and know how to use it.
16. Know the location of the nearest telephone and whom to contact in an emergency.

Heating and Fire Safety

17. Never use a heat source, such as a candle, burner, or hot plate, without wearing safety goggles.
18. Never heat anything unless instructed to do so. A chemical that is harmless when cool may be dangerous when heated.
19. Keep all combustible materials away from flames. Never use a flame or spark near a combustible chemical.
20. Never reach across a flame.
21. Before using a laboratory burner, make sure you know proper procedures for lighting and adjusting the burner, as demonstrated by your teacher. Do not touch the burner. It may be hot. And never leave a lighted burner unattended!
22. Chemicals can splash or boil out of a heated test tube. When heating a substance in a test tube, make sure that the mouth of the tube is not pointed at you or anyone else.
23. Never heat a liquid in a closed container. The expanding gases produced may blow the container apart.
24. Before picking up a container that has been heated, hold the back of your hand near it. If you can feel heat on the back of your hand, the container is too hot to handle. Use an oven mitt to pick up a container that has been heated.

Using Glassware Safely

◆ Use plastic containers, graduated cylinders, and beakers whenever possible. If using glass, students should wear safety goggles.

◆ Use only nonmercury thermometers with anti-roll protectors.

◆ Check all glassware periodically for chips and scratches, which can cause cuts and breakage.

Using Chemicals Safely

25. Never mix chemicals "for the fun of it." You might produce a dangerous, possibly explosive substance.

26. Never put your face near the mouth of a container that holds chemicals. Many chemicals are poisonous. Never touch, taste, or smell a chemical unless you are instructed by your teacher to do so.

27. Use only those chemicals needed in the activity. Read and double-check labels on supply bottles before removing any chemicals. Take only as much as you need. Keep all containers closed when chemicals are not being used.

28. Dispose of all chemicals as instructed by your teacher. To avoid contamination, never return chemicals to their original containers. Never simply pour chemicals or other substances into the sink or trash containers.

29. Be extra careful when working with acids or bases. Pour all chemicals over the sink or a container, not over your work surface.

30. If you are instructed to test for odors, use a wafting motion to direct the odors to your nose. Do not inhale the fumes directly from the container.

31. When mixing an acid and water, always pour the water into the container first and then add the acid to the water. Never pour water into an acid.

32. Take extreme care not to spill any material in the laboratory. Wash chemical spills and splashes immediately with plenty of water. Immediately begin rinsing with water any acids that get on your skin or clothing, and notify your teacher of any acid spill at the same time.

Using Glassware Safely

33. Never force glass tubing or thermometers into a rubber stopper or rubber tubing. Have your teacher insert the glass tubing or thermometer if required for an activity.

34. If you are using a laboratory burner, use a wire screen to protect glassware from any flame. Never heat glassware that is not thoroughly dry on the outside.

35. Keep in mind that hot glassware looks cool. Never pick up glassware without first checking to see if it is hot. Use an oven mitt. See rule 24.

36. Never use broken or chipped glassware. If glassware breaks, notify your teacher and dispose of the glassware in the proper broken-glassware container. Never handle broken glass with your bare hands.

37. Never eat or drink from lab glassware.

38. Thoroughly clean glassware before putting it away.

Using Sharp Instruments

39. Handle scalpels or other sharp instruments with extreme care. Never cut material toward you; cut away from you.

40. Immediately notify your teacher if you cut your skin when working in the laboratory.

Animal and Plant Safety

41. Never perform experiments that cause pain, discomfort, or harm to animals. This rule applies at home as well as in the classroom.

42. Animals should be handled only if absolutely necessary. Your teacher will instruct you as to how to handle each animal species brought into the classroom.

43. If you know that you are allergic to certain plants, molds, or animals, tell your teacher before doing an activity in which these are used.

44. During field work, protect your skin by wearing long pants, long sleeves, socks, and closed shoes. Know how to recognize the poisonous plants and fungi in your area, as well as plants with thorns, and avoid contact with them. Never eat any part of a plant or fungus.

45. Wash your hands thoroughly after handling animals or a cage containing animals. Wash your hands when you are finished with any activity involving animal parts, plants, or soil.

End-of-Experiment Rules

46. After an experiment has been completed, turn off all burners or hot plates. If you used a gas burner, check that the gas-line valve to the burner is off. Unplug hot plates.

47. Turn off and unplug any other electrical equipment that you used.

48. Clean up your work area and return all equipment to its proper place.

49. Dispose of waste materials as instructed by your teacher.

50. Wash your hands after every experiment.

Using Sharp Instruments

◆ Always use blunt-tip safety scissors, except when pointed-tip scissors are required.

Animal and Plant Safety

◆ When working with live animals or plants, check ahead of time for students who may have allergies to the specimens.

◆ When growing bacteria cultures, use only disposable petri dishes. After streaking, the dishes should be sealed and not opened again by students. After the lab, students should return the unopened dishes to you. Students should wash their hands with antibacterial soap.

◆ Two methods are recommended for the safe disposal of bacteria cultures. *First method:* Autoclave the petri dishes and discard without opening. *Second method*: If no autoclave is available, carefully open the dishes (never have a student do this) and pour full-strength bleach into the dishes and let stand for a day. Then pour the bleach from the petri dishes down a drain and flush the drain with lots of water. Tape the petri dishes back together and place in a sealed plastic bag. Wrap the plastic bag with a brown paper bag or newspaper and tape securely. Throw the sealed package in the trash. Thoroughly disinfect the work area with bleach.

◆ To grow mold, use a new, sealable plastic bag that is two to three times larger than the material to be placed inside. Seal the bag and tape it shut. After the bag is sealed, students should not open it. To dispose of the bag and mold culture, make a small cut near an edge of the bag and cook in a microwave oven on high setting for at least 1 minute. Discard the bag according to local ordinance, usually in the trash.

◆ Students should wear disposable nitrile, latex, or food-handling gloves when handling live animals or nonliving specimens.

End-of-Experiment Rules

◆ Always have students use antibacterial soap for washing their hands.

Using a Laboratory Balance

The laboratory balance is an important tool in scientific investigations. You can use a balance to determine the masses of materials that you study or experiment with in the laboratory.

Different kinds of balances are used in the laboratory. One kind of balance is the triple-beam balance. The balance that you may use in your science class is probably similar to the balance illustrated in this Appendix. To use the balance properly, you should learn the name, location, and function of each part of the balance you are using. What kind of balance do you have in your science class?

The Triple-Beam Balance

The triple-beam balance is a single-pan balance with three beams calibrated in grams. The back, or 100-gram, beam is divided into ten units of 10 grams each. The middle, or 500-gram, beam is divided into five units of 100 grams each. The front, or 10-gram, beam is divided into ten major units of 1 gram each. Each of these units is further divided into units of 0.1 gram. What is the largest mass you could find with a triple-beam balance?

The following procedure can be used to find the mass of an object with a triple-beam balance:

1. Place the object on the pan.
2. Move the rider on the middle beam notch by notch until the horizontal pointer drops below zero. Move the rider back one notch.
3. Move the rider on the back beam notch by notch until the pointer again drops below zero. Move the rider back one notch.
4. Slowly slide the rider along the front beam until the pointer stops at the zero point.
5. The mass of the object is equal to the sum of the readings on the three beams.

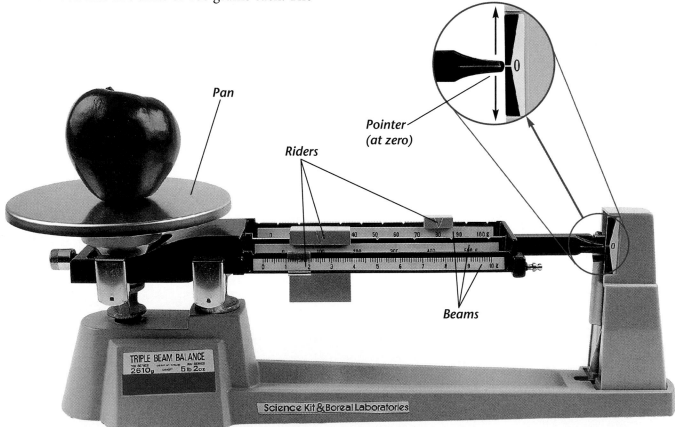

Triple-Beam Balance

List of Chemical Elements

Name	Symbol	Atomic Number	Atomic Mass†
Actinium	Ac	89	(227)
Aluminum	Al	13	26.982
Americium	Am	95	(243)
Antimony	Sb	51	121.75
Argon	Ar	18	39.948
Arsenic	As	33	74.922
Astatine	At	85	(210)
Barium	Ba	56	137.327
Berkelium	Bk	97	(247)
Beryllium	Be	4	9.012
Bismuth	Bi	83	208.980
Bohrium	Bh	107	(264)
Boron	B	5	10.811
Bromine	Br	35	79.904
Cadmium	Cd	48	112.411
Calcium	Ca	20	40.078
Californium	Cf	98	(251)
Carbon	C	6	12.011
Cerium	Ce	58	140.115
Cesium	Cs	55	132.905
Chlorine	Cl	17	35.453
Chromium	Cr	24	51.996
Cobalt	Co	27	58.933
Copper	Cu	29	63.546
Curium	Cm	96	(247)
Dubnium	Db	105	(262)
Dysprosium	Dy	66	162.50
Einsteinium	Es	99	(252)
Erbium	Er	68	167.26
Europium	Eu	63	151.965
Fermium	Fm	100	(257)
Fluorine	F	9	18.998
Francium	Fr	87	(223)
Gadolinium	Gd	64	157.25
Gallium	Ga	31	69.723
Germanium	Ge	32	72.61
Gold	Au	79	196.967
Hafnium	Hf	72	178.49
Hassium	Hs	108	(265)
Helium	He	2	4.003
Holmium	Ho	67	164.930
Hydrogen	H	1	1.008
Indium	In	49	114.818
Iodine	I	53	126.904
Iridium	Ir	77	192.22
Iron	Fe	26	55.847
Krypton	Kr	36	83.80
Lanthanum	La	57	138.906
Lawrencium	Lr	103	(262)
Lead	Pb	82	207.2
Lithium	Li	3	6.941
Lutetium	Lu	71	174.967
Magnesium	Mg	12	24.305
Manganese	Mn	25	54.938
Meitnerium	Mt	109	(268)
Mendelevium	Md	101	(258)
Mercury	Hg	80	200.659
Molybdenum	Mo	42	95.94

Name	Symbol	Atomic Number	Atomic Mass†
Neodymium	Nd	60	144.2
Neon	Ne	10	20.180
Neptunium	Np	93	(237)
Nickel	Ni	28	58.69
Niobium	Nb	41	92.906
Nitrogen	N	7	14.007
Nobelium	No	102	(259)
Osmium	Os	76	190.23
Oxygen	O	8	15.999
Palladium	Pd	46	106.42
Phosphorus	P	15	30.974
Platinum	Pt	78	195.08
Plutonium	Pu	94	(244)
Polonium	Po	84	(209)
Potassium	K	19	39.098
Praseodymium	Pr	59	140.908
Promethium	Pm	61	(145)
Protactinium	Pa	91	231.036
Radium	Ra	88	(226)
Radon	Rn	86	(222)
Rhenium	Re	75	186.207
Rhodium	Rh	45	102.906
Rubidium	Rb	37	85.468
Ruthenium	Ru	44	101.07
Rutherfordium	Rf	104	(261)
Samarium	Sm	62	150.36
Scandium	Sc	21	44.956
Seaborgium	Sg	106	(263)
Selenium	Se	34	78.96
Silicon	Si	14	28.086
Silver	Ag	47	107.868
Sodium	Na	11	22.990
Strontium	Sr	38	87.62
Sulfur	S	16	32.066
Tantalum	Ta	73	180.948
Technetium	Tc	43	(98)
Tellurium	Te	52	127.60
Terbium	Tb	65	158.925
Thallium	Tl	81	204.383
Thorium	Th	90	232.038
Thulium	Tm	69	168.934
Tin	Sn	50	118.710
Titanium	Ti	22	47.88
Tungsten	W	74	183.85
Ununbium	Uub	112	(272)
Ununhexium	Uuh	116	*
Ununnilium	Uun	110	(269)
Unununium	Uuu	111	(272)
Ununoctium	Uuo	118	*
Ununquadium	Uuq	114	*
Uranium	U	92	238.029
Vanadium	V	23	50.942
Xenon	Xe	54	131.29
Ytterbium	Yb	70	173.04
Yttrium	Y	39	88.906
Zinc	Zn	30	65.39
Zirconium	Zr	40	91.224

†Numbers in parentheses give the mass number of the most stable isotope.

*Newly discovered

Periodic Table of the Elements

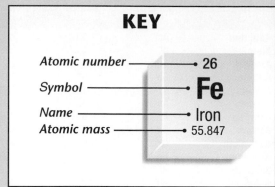

KEY

Atomic number —————→ 26

Symbol —————→ **Fe**

Name —————→ Iron

Atomic mass —————→ 55.847

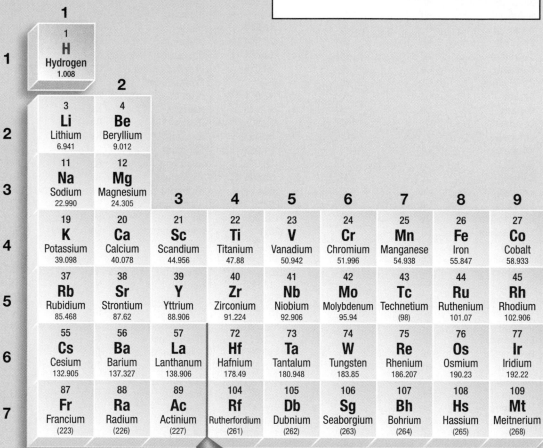

1

1
H
Hydrogen
1.008

1

2

3	4
Li	**Be**
Lithium	Beryllium
6.941	9.012

2

11	12
Na	**Mg**
Sodium	Magnesium
22.990	24.305

3

3 **4** **5** **6** **7** **8** **9**

19	20	21	22	23	24	25	26	27
K	**Ca**	**Sc**	**Ti**	**V**	**Cr**	**Mn**	**Fe**	**Co**
Potassium	Calcium	Scandium	Titanium	Vanadium	Chromium	Manganese	Iron	Cobalt
39.098	40.078	44.956	47.88	50.942	51.996	54.938	55.847	58.933

4

37	38	39	40	41	42	43	44	45
Rb	**Sr**	**Y**	**Zr**	**Nb**	**Mo**	**Tc**	**Ru**	**Rh**
Rubidium	Strontium	Yttrium	Zirconium	Niobium	Molybdenum	Technetium	Ruthenium	Rhodium
85.468	87.62	88.906	91.224	92.906	95.94	(98)	101.07	102.906

5

55	56	57	72	73	74	75	76	77
Cs	**Ba**	**La**	**Hf**	**Ta**	**W**	**Re**	**Os**	**Ir**
Cesium	Barium	Lanthanum	Hafnium	Tantalum	Tungsten	Rhenium	Osmium	Iridium
132.905	137.327	138.906	178.49	180.948	183.85	186.207	190.23	192.22

6

87	88	89	104	105	106	107	108	109
Fr	**Ra**	**Ac**	**Rf**	**Db**	**Sg**	**Bh**	**Hs**	**Mt**
Francium	Radium	Actinium	Rutherfordium	Dubnium	Seaborgium	Bohrium	Hassium	Meitnerium
(223)	(226)	(227)	(261)	(262)	(263)	(264)	(265)	(268)

7

Lanthanide Series

58	59	60	61	62
Ce	**Pr**	**Nd**	**Pm**	**Sm**
Cerium	Praseodymium	Neodymium	Promethium	Samarium
140.115	140.908	144.24	(145)	150.36

Actinide Series

90	91	92	93	94
Th	**Pa**	**U**	**Np**	**Pu**
Thorium	Protactinium	Uranium	Neptunium	Plutonium
232.038	231.036	238.029	(237)	(244)

C	Solid	Br	Liquid	H	Gas

	Metal		Metalloid		Nonmetal		Discovered recently

The symbols shown for elements 110–118 are being used temporarily until names for these elements can be agreed upon.

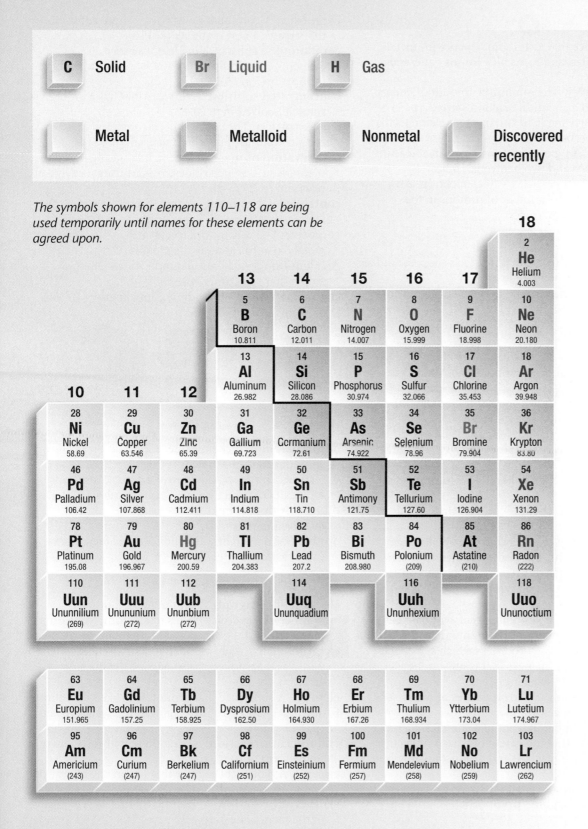

Mass numbers in parentheses are those of the most stable or common isotope.

 A

acid A substance that tastes sour, reacts with metals and carbonates, and turns blue litmus paper red. (p. 90)

activation energy The minimum amount of energy needed to get a chemical reaction started. (p. 33)

alloy A substance made of two or more elements that has the properties of metal. (p. 123)

alpha particle A type of nuclear radiation consisting of two protons and two neutrons. (p. 135)

atom The smallest particle of an element. (p. 20)

atomic number The number of protons in the nucleus of an atom. (p. 55)

B

base A substance that tastes bitter, feels slippery, and turns red litmus paper blue. (p. 95)

beta particle An electron that is given off as nuclear radiation. (p. 135)

C

catalyst A material that increases the rate of a chemical reaction by lowering the activation energy. (p. 36)

cellulose A flexible but strong natural polymer that gives shape to plant cells. (p. 114)

ceramic A hard, crystalline solid made by heating clay and other mineral materials to high temperatures. (p. 128)

chemical bond The force that holds atoms together. (p. 21)

chemical change A change in matter that produces a new substance. (p. 17)

chemical digestion The process that breaks large food molecules into smaller molecules. (p. 104)

chemical equation A short, easy way to show a chemical reaction, using symbols instead of words. (p. 24)

chemical formula A combination of symbols that represent the elements in a compound. (p. 25)

chemical reaction The process in which substances undergo chemical changes that results in the formation of new substances. (p. 17)

chemistry The study of the properties of matter and how matter changes. (p. 14)

coefficient A number in front of a chemical formula in an equation that indicates how many molecules or atoms of each reactant and product are involved in a reaction. (p. 28)

combustion A rapid reaction between oxygen and fuel that results in fire. (p. 40)

composite A combination of two or more substances that creates a new material. (p. 116)

compound A substance made of two or more elements chemically combined in a specific ratio, or proportion. (p. 16)

concentrated solution A mixture that has a lot of solute dissolved in it. (p. 83)

concentration The amount of one material in a certain volume of another material. (p. 35)

conservation of mass The principle stating that matter is not created or destroyed during a chemical reaction. (p. 27)

controlled experiment An experiment in which all factors except one are kept constant. (p. 155)

corrosive The way in which acids react with some metals so as to eat away the metal. (p. 91)

covalent bond A chemical bond formed when two atoms share electrons. (p. 65)

crystal An orderly, three-dimensional pattern of ions or atoms in a solid. (p. 63)

 D

decomposition A chemical reaction that breaks down compounds into simpler products. (p. 30)

digestion The process that breaks down complex molecules of food into smaller molecules. (p. 104)

dilute solution A mixture that has little solute dissolved in it. (p. 83)

double bond A chemical bond formed when atoms share two pairs of electrons. (p. 66)

 **E**

electron dot diagram A representation of the number of valence electrons in an atom, using dots placed around the symbol of an element. (p. 54)

electrons Tiny, negatively charged, high-energy particles that move around outside the nucleus of an atom. (p. 51)

element A substance that cannot be broken down into any other substances by chemical or physical means. (p. 15)

endothermic reaction A reaction that absorbs energy in the form of heat. (p. 33)

enzyme A biological catalyst that lowers the activation energy of reactions in cells. (p. 37)

exothermic reaction A reaction that releases energy in the form of heat. (p. 33)

family Elements in the same vertical column of the periodic table. Also called group. (p. 56)

fuel A material that releases energy when it burns. (p. 40)

gamma radiation A type of nuclear radiation made of high-energy waves. (p. 135)

glass A clear, solid material with no crystal structure, created by heating sand to a very high temperature. (p. 130)

group Elements in the same vertical column of the periodic table. Also called family. (p. 56)

half-life The length of time needed for half of the atoms of a radioactive isotope to decay. (p. 136)

halogen An element belonging to Group 17 of the periodic table. (p. 57)

hydrogen ion A positively charged ion (H^+) formed of a hydrogen atom that has lost its electron. (p. 96)

hydroxide ion A negatively charged ion made of oxygen and hydrogen, OH^-. (p. 97)

hypothesis A possible explanation for a set of observations or answer to a scientific question; must be testable. (p. 154)

indicator A compound that changes color in the presence of an acid or a base. (p. 92)

inhibitor A material that decreases the rate of a reaction. (p. 37)

ion An atom or group of atoms that has become electrically charged. (p. 60)

ionic bond The attraction between oppositely charged ions. (p. 60)

isotope An atom with the same number of protons and different number of neutrons from other atoms of the same element. (p. 134)

manipulated variable The one factor that a scientist changes during an experiment. (p. 155)

mass number The sum of the protons and neutrons in the nucleus of an atom. (p. 134)

matter Anything that has mass and occupies space. (p. 14)

mechanical digestion The physical process that tears, grinds, and mashes large food particles into smaller ones. (p. 104)

mineral A naturally occurring solid that has a crystal structure and a definite chemical composition. (p. 72)

mixture Two or more substances that are mixed together but not chemically combined. (p. 16)

molecular compound A compound consisting of molecules of covalently bonded atoms. (p. 66)

molecule A particle made of two or more atoms bonded together. (p. 20)

monomer Small, carbon-based molecules from which polymers are built. (p. 113)

neutralization A reaction of an acid with a base, yielding a solution that is not as acidic or basic as the starting solutions were. (p. 100)

neutrons Small uncharged particles that are found in the nucleus of an atom. (p. 51)

nonpolar The description of a covalent bond in which electrons are shared equally, or of a molecule containing nonpolar bonds, or polar bonds that cancel out. (p. 68)

nuclear radiation Particles and energy released from a radioactive nucleus. (p. 135)

nuclear reaction A reaction involving the particles in the nucleus of an atom that can change one element into another element. (p. 134)

nucleus The central core of the atom, containing protons and usually neutrons. (p. 51)

operational definition A statement that describes how a particular variable is to be measured or a term is to be defined. (p. 155)

optical fiber A threadlike piece of glass (or plastic) that can be used for transmitting messages in the form of light. (p. 131)

period Elements in the same horizontal row of the periodic table. (p. 56)

pH scale A range of numbers used to express the concentration of hydrogen ions in a solution. (p. 98)

physical change A change that alters the form or appearance of a material but does not make the material into another substance. (p. 17)

plastic A synthetic polymer that can be molded or shaped. (p. 115)

polar The description of a covalent bond in which electrons are shared unequally, or of a molecule containing polar bonds that do not cancel out. (p. 67)

polyatomic ion An ion that is made of more than one atom. (p. 62)

polymer A large, complex, carbon-based molecule built from smaller molecules joined together. (p. 113)

precipitate A solid that forms from a solution during a chemical reaction. (p. 18)

product A substance formed as a result of a chemical reaction. (p. 26)

protons Small positively charged particles that are found in the nucleus of an atom. (p. 51)

radiation therapy A process in which radioactive elements are used to destroy unhealthy cells. (p. 138)

radioactive dating The process of determining the age of an object using the half-life of one or more radioactive isotopes. (p. 136)

radioactive decay The process in which the atomic nuclei of unstable isotopes release fast-moving particles and energy. (p. 134)

reactant A substance that enters into a chemical reaction. (p. 26)

replacement A reaction in which one element replaces another in a compound; or when two elements in different compounds trade places. (p. 31)

responding variable The factor that changes as a result of changes to the manipulated variable in an experiment. (p. 155)

salt An ionic compound made from the neutralization of an acid with a base. (p. 101)

saturated solution A mixture that has so much solute in it that no more will dissolve. (p. 84)

solubility A measure of how well a solute can dissolve in a solvent at a given temperature. (p. 84)

solute The part of a solution present in a lesser amount and that is dissolved by the solvent. (p. 81)

solution A well-mixed mixture. (p. 16)

solvent The part of a solution present in the largest amount and that dissolves other substances. (p. 81)

subscript A number in a chemical formula that tells the number of atoms in a molecule or the ratio of elements in a compound. (p. 25)

suspension A mixture in which particles can be seen and easily separated by settling or filtration. (p. 80)

symbol A one- or two-letter set of characters that is used to identify an element. (p. 25)

synthesis A chemical reaction in which two or more simple substances combine to form a new, more complex substance. (p. 29)

tracer A radioactive isotope that can be followed through the steps of a chemical reaction or industrial process. (p. 137)

unsaturated solution A mixture in which more solute can be dissolved. (p. 84)

valence electrons The electrons that are farthest away from the nucleus of an atom and are involved in chemical reactions. (p. 53)

variable Any factor that can change in an experiment. (p. 155)

Index

electricity 64, 70
electron(s) 51–54
 valence 53–54, 56–57 59–61, 65, 66
electron dot diagrams 54, 65, 66, 68
electron sharing 65–66
 unequal 67–68
electron transfer 59–61
element 15
 comparing families of 56–57
 defined 15
 list of 167
 organizing 55–56
 periodic table of 55–58, 168–169
 radioactive 133–140
 symbols for 25
endothermic reaction 33
energy
 activation 33–34
 in chemical reactions 33
enzymes 37, 38–39
 digestive 105, 106
equations, chemical. *See* chemical equations.
etching 91
evidence, for chemical reactions 18, 19, 22–23
exothermic reaction 33
experiments. *See* scientific investigations.

families, in periodic table 56–57
fiberglass 117, 118
fire(s) 40–43
 baking soda and 40, 42–43
 controlling 41–42
 fighting 42–43
 necessary ingredients of 41
 prevention of 43
 sources of 42
fire extinguishers 43
fire-safe house 43
fire safety 42–43
fire triangle 41
flowcharts 159
fluorine 65, 68
forming operational definitions 155
formulas. *See* chemical formulas.
fossils 136, 137
freezing points, of solutions 86
fuel 40

gamma decay 135
gamma radiation 135, 137–138
gamma rays 135, 137–138
gas production 19
generalizations, skill of making 157
glass 130–131
 in optical fibers 131–132
gluten 147
gold, in aircraft 125
gold alloys 124
Goodyear, Charles 116
graphs 160–162
grocery bags 122
groups, in periodic table 56–57

half-life 136, 137, 140
halite, bonding in 73–74

halite crystal 63
halogen family 57
hazardous chemicals, transporting 44
Hazardous Materials Transportation Act 44
heat
 for fire 41
 and rate of chemical reaction 36
high-density polyethylene (HDPE) 115
Hindenburg 34
home fire safety 42–43
hydrogen ions, in solution 97, 98–99
hydroxide ion 97, 98
hypothesis 154

illustrations, skill of interpreting 156
indicators 79, 92, 95, 99
inert (noble) gases 57
inferring, skill of 150
inhibitors, of chemical reactions 37
interpreting data, skill of 155
interpreting illustrations, skill of 156
ion(s) 60
 polyatomic 62
 positive and negative 60–64
ionic bonds 59–64
 defined 60
 exploring 61
 forming 60
ionic compounds
 crystal shape of 63
 electrical conductivity of 64
 formation of 60–61
 melting points of 64
 naming 62
 properties of 63–64
ionic crystal 63, 73–74
ionic solids, in water 82
ion implantation 124
iron alloys 126
 in aircraft 125
isotopes 134
 using 136–138

judgments, skill of making 157

Kevlar 117
Knickerbocker, Janet 148–149

laboratory balance 166
laboratory safety 163–165
leavening agent 144, 146
length, measuring 152
light-emitting polymers (LEPs) 117
lignin 117
litmus paper 90, 92, 95
low-density polyethylene (LDPE) 115

making generalizations, skill of 157
making judgments, skill of 157
making models, skill of 151
manipulated variable 155
mass
 conservation of 26–27
 measuring 153

mass number 134
matter
 building blocks of 15–16
 changes in 17–18
 conservation of 27
measuring, skill of 152–153
mechanical digestion 104
melting points
 of ionic compounds 64
 of molecular compounds 66–67
metal(s)
 in aircraft 125
 properties of 123
 reactions of acids with 91
 reactive 57
 Wood's 126
metal etching 91
mica 73
mineral(s)
 defined 72
 properties of 72–73
mineral crystals, bonding in 73–74
mixtures 16
models
 of atoms 52–53
 skill of making 151
molecular compounds 66–67
molecular solids, in water 83
molecules 20–21
 attractions between 68–69
 nonpolar 68
 polar 68–69
Molina, Mario 8–11
monomers 113
mouth, pH of 105

Nagaoka, Hantara 52
natural composites 117
natural polymers 114
negative ions 60, 62, 63
neutralization 100, 101
neutral solution 100
neutrons 51, 53, 134
nickel alloys, in aircraft 125
nitroglycerin 37
Nobel, Alfred 37
noble (inert) gases 57
nonmetals, reactive 57
nonpolar bond 68
nonpolar molecules 68, 69
nonpolar solvents 85
nuclear power 138
nuclear reactions 134
nucleus 51, 134
nylon 115, 117

observing, skill of 150
operational definitions 155
optical fibers 131–132
oxygen 66
 for fire 41
 in covalent bonds 66, 68–69
ozone 9
ozone hole 10, 11
ozone layer 8–11

Index

Acknowledgments

Staff Credits

The people who made up the **Science Explorer** team—representing design services, editorial, editorial services, electronic publishing technology, manufacturing & inventory planning, marketing, marketing services, market research, online services & multimedia development, production services, product planning, project office, and publishing processes—are listed below.

Carolyn Belanger, Barbara A. Bertell, Suzanne Biron, Peggy Bliss, Peter W. Brooks, Christopher R. Brown, Greg Cantone, Jonathan Cheney, Todd Christy, Lisa J. Clark, Patrick Finbarr Connolly, Edward Cordero, Robert Craton, Patricia Cully, Patricia M. Dambry, Kathleen J. Dempsey, Judy Elgin, Gayle Connolly Fedele, Frederick Fellows, Barbara Foster, Paula Foye, Loree Franz, Patricia Fromkin, Donald P. Gagnon Jr., Paul J. Gagnon, Joel Gendler, Elizabeth Good, Robert M. Graham, Kerri Hoar, Joanne Hudson, Linda D. Johnson, Anne Jones, Toby Klang, Carolyn Langley, Russ Lappa, Carolyn Lock, Cheryl Mahan, Dotti Marshall, Meredith Mascola, Jeanne Y. Maurand, Karen McHugh, Eve Melnechuk, Natania Mlawer, Paul W. Murphy, Cindy A. Noftle, Julia F. Osborne, Judi Pinkham, Caroline M. Power, Robin L. Santel, Suzanne J. Schineller, Emily Soltanoff, Kira Thaler-Marbit, Mark Tricca, Diane Walsh, Pearl Weinstein, Merce Wilczek, Helen Young.

Illustration

John Edwards & Associates: 52bl, 99
Andrea Golden: 6, 62b, 144, 147
Jared Lee: 34, 60, 87
Martucci Design: 47, 54, 57, 61, 65, 66, 68, 77, 143, 160, 161, 162
Matt Mayerchak: 45, 75, 105t, 107, 113, 158, 159
Fran Milner: 105br
Morgan Cain & Associates: 7, 9, 21, 24, 28, 33, 36, 37, 41, 43, 51, 52t, 52br, 53, 56, 63, 69t, 73, 82, 86, 98, 109, 134, 143, 152, 153, 156, 168–169
Scott Sawyer: 148, 149
Nancy Smith: 22, 38, 58, 70, 88, 102, 120, 140
J/B Woolsey Associates: 109, 135, 137, 211

Photography

Photo Research: Sue McDermott
Cover Image: Brian Sytnyk/Masterfile

Nature of Science
Page 8t, Joe Towers/The Stock Market; **8b,** Bourg/Liaison International; **9,** Leonard Lessin/Peter Arnold; **10–11 both,** NASA.

Chapter 1
Pages 12–13, Kunio Owaki/The Stock Market; **14,** Reinstein, The Image Works; **15l,** Cathlyn Melloan/TSI; **15m,** Bernard Roussel/The Image Bank; **15r,** Bob Firth/International Stock; **16,** Russ Lappa; **17,** Bob Firth/International Stock; **18,** Steve Elmore/The Stock Market; **19t,** Charles D. Winters/Photo Researchers; **19bl,** Russ Lappa; **19ml,** Wood Sabold/International Stock; **19mr,** Ken O'Donaghue; **19br,** Steven Needham/Envision; **20l,** Russ Lappa; **20r,** J. Sulley/The Image Works; **21,** Ken Eward/Science Source/Photo Researchers; **23,** Richard Haynes; **24, 26 all,** Russ Lappa; **27,** John D. Cummingham/Visuals Unlimited; **29,** Koitsu Hirota/The Image Bank; **30,** Paul Sisul/TSI; **31t,** Russ Lappa; **31b,** Charles D. Winters/Photo Researchers; **32t,** Richard Haynes; **32b,** Simon Norfolk/TSI; **33,** Michael Newman/PhotoEdit; **35tl & tr,** Richard Megna/Fundamental Photographs; **35b,** AP/Wide World Photos; **36, 38,** Russ Lappa; **39, 40t,** Richard Haynes; **40b,** Patrick Donehue/Photo Researchers; **41,** Dorothy Littell/Stock Boston; **42 all,** Russ Lappa; **44,** Dede Gilman/Photo Network; **45l,** Steven Needham/Envision; **45r,** Richard Megna/Fundamental Photographs.

Chapter 2
Pages 48–49, Ken Eward/Science Source/Photo Researchers; **50, 51 both, 52tl,tr, 53t,** Russ Lappa; **53b,** Frank Cezus/FPG International; **55,** Richard Megna/Fundamental Photographs; **59t,** Russ Lappa; **59b,** Arthur Gurmankin & Mary Morina/Visuals Unlimited; **61tl,** Lawrence Migdale/Photo Researchers; **61tr,** Richard Megna/Fundamental Photographs; **61b, 62,** Russ Lappa; **63,** M. Claye/Jacana/Photo Researchers; **64,** Richard Megna/ Fundamental Photograhs; **65,** Russ Lappa; **67,** George Disario/The Stock Market; **70, 71,** Richard Haynes; **72l,** Gary Retherford/Photo Researchers; **72r, 73l, m,** Paul Silverman/Fundamental Photographs; **73r,** Ken Lucas/Visuals Unlimited; **74t,** Breck P. Kent/Earth Scenes; **74b,** Russ Lappa.

Chapter 3
Pages 78–79, Minolta Corp.; **80,** Michael Newman/PhotoEdit; **81t, m,** Russ Lappa; **81b,** Leonard Lessin/Peter Arnold; **83,** Russ Lappa; **84,** Tony Freeman/PhotoEdit; **85, 88,** Russ Lappa; **89,** Richard Haynes; **90t,** Russ Lappa; **90b,** Lawrence Migdale/Photo Researchers; **91 both,** Russ Lappa; **92,** Bob Krist/The Stock Market; **93tl,** Russ Lappa; **93tr,** David Young-Wolfe/PhotoEdit; **93bl,** Mark C. Burnett/Stock Boston; **93m, br,** Russ Lappa; **94br,** B. Daemmrich/The Image Works; **94 all others,** Russ Lappa; **95,** P. Aprahamian/ Science Photo Library/Photo Researchers; **96,** Russ Lappa; **97t,** L.S. Stepanowicz/Visuals Unlimited; **97b,** Tom Pantages; **99,** Richard Haynes; **100t,** Jenny Hager/The Image Works; **100b,** Russ Lappa; **101,** George Ranalli/Photo Researchers; **102,** Russ Lappa; **103,** Richard Haynes; **104,** Cleo Photography/Photo Researchers; **106,** Russ Lappa; **107,** Lawrence Migdale/Photo Researchers.

Chapter 4
Pages 110–111, Larry Ulrich/DRK Photo; **112,** John Terence Turner/FPG International; **113,** Russ Lappa; **114l,** Tom Tracey/The Stock Market; **114r,** Inga Spence/Visuals Unlimted; **114b,** William Whitehurst/The Stock Market; **116t,** Leonard Lessin/Peter Arnold; **116l,** Corbis-Bettmann; **116r,** Terry Wild Studio/Uniphoto; **117l,** David Young-Wolfe/PhotoEdit; **117r,** Nick Colaneri/Uniax Corporation; **117b,** Jeffry W. Myers/The Stock Market; **118l,** Bob Torrez/TSI; **118r,** David J. Sams/TSI; **119l,** Dennis O'Clair/TSI; **119r,** Richard Hutchings/Photo Researchers; **120,** Daemmrich/Uniphoto; **121,** Richard Haynes; **122,** Tom Smith/Photo Researchers; **123t,** Russ Lappa; **123b,** Bachmann/PhotoEdit; **124l,** Richard Haynes; **124r,** Diana Calder/The Stock Market; **125t,** AP Photo/Boeing handout/Wide World; **125m,** Peter Gridley/FPG International; **125bl,** De Malglaive E./Liaison International; **125br,** Pratt & Whitney/Liaison International; **127l,** William Hopkins; **127r,** Marc Pokempner/TSI; **128t,** Russ Lappa; **128b,** M. Borchi White Star/Photo Researchers; **129t,** Daniel Aubry/The Stock Market; **129bl,** Mark Richards/PhotoEdit; **129br,** Dan McCoy/Rainbow; **130 both,** James L. Amos/Peter Arnold; **131,** D. Young-Wolff MR/PhotoEdit; **132,** Ted Horowitz/The Stock Market; **133,** Jan Van Der Straet/Granger Collection, NY; **136,** T.A. Wiewandt/DRK Photo; **138l,** Jean-Perrin/CNRI/Science Photo Library/Photo Researchers; **138r,** Alfred Pasieka/Science Photo Library/Photo Researchers; **139 both,** Pat Cunningham/Liaison International.

Interdisciplinary Exploration
Page 144t, Peter Johansky/Envision; **144b,** Scott J. Witte/Index Stock Imagery; **145t,** Russ Lappa; **145m,** Bill Aron/TSI; **145b,** Steven Needham/Envision; **146t,** Tony Freeman/Photo Edit; **146–147,** Paul Chesley/TSI; **147,** Russ Lappa.

Skills Handbook
Page 150, Mike Moreland/Photo Network; **151t,** Foodpix; **151m,** Richard Haynes; **151b,** Russ Lappa; **154,** Richard Haynes; **156,** Ron Kimball; **157,** Renee Lynn/Photo Researchers.